THE

Student's

ANTHOLOGY

THE Student's ANTHOLOGY

Alvin Granowsky
John Dawkins
Eden Force Eskin

GLOBE FEARON
Pearson Learning Group

Alvin Granowsky received his B.A. in English Literature from Colgate University, his M.A.T. in English Education from Harvard University, and his Ed.D. in Reading and Curriculum and Instruction from the University of Pennsylvania.

Dr. Granowsky has written many books that are widely used in schools. He was a teacher of English in New York State junior and senior high schools and served as Director of Reading/Language Arts in the public schools of Greensboro, North Carolina, and Dallas, Texas.

John Dawkins is an author of various textbooks on reading and language arts. He also writes professional articles on language structure and the teaching of reading and English. Mr. Dawkins has an A.M. degree in English from the University of Chicago, where he has done extensive graduate work in linguistics and literature.

Eden Force Eskin is an author and editor who specializes in language arts and social studies textbooks and workbooks. She has served as managing editor of a school dictionary and has been a contributing editor to dictionaries for all levels. In addition, she has contributed articles to reference books on subjects that include vocabulary development, English usage and style, and research and reference skills.

Special thanks to Dorothy Smith, recently retired language arts teacher for the Dallas Independent School District, Dallas, Texas. Mrs. Smith was a consulting author on this text.

Consultants

Ronald N. Kar, Ph.D., Middle School Supervisor, Detroit Public Schools, Detroit, Michigan

Deborah McGriff, Director of Junior High School Program Development, Community School District 13, Brooklyn, New York

Penny Hirschman, Curriculum Coordinator, San Bernardino County, California

Cover: Majory Dressler
Cover photo: Majory Dressler

ISBN 0-835-90044-4
Printed in the United States of America

10 11 12 13 14 15   05 04

1-800-321-3106
www.pearsonlearning.com

CONTENTS

Introduction ....*x*

UNIT 1: BECOMING SOMEBODY

	Introduction to the Unit..1
fiction	The Cub / LOIS DYKEMAN KLEIHAUER 2
fable	The Donkey Who Did Not Want to Be Himself / AESOP.............9
poetry	You / NIKKI GIOVANNI 12
autobiography	The End of My Long Night / HELEN KELLER.............................13
	Vocabulary and Skill Review 23
song	Cat's in the Cradle / HARRY CHAPIN / SANDY CHAPIN..................24
fiction	The Speckled Hen's Egg / NATALIE SAVAGE CARLSON 26
profile	Maya Angelou...35
autobiography	A Taste of Life / MAYA ANGELOU....................................36
poetry	Thumbprint / EVE MERRIAM...44
poetry	Phizzog / CARL SANDBURG 45
	Vocabulary and Skill Review 46
fiction	Gold-Mounted Guns / F. R. BUCKLEY 48
profile	Marjorie Kinnan Rawlings 59
fiction	A Mother in Mannville / MARJORIE KINNAN RAWLINGS.................60
poetry	Advice to Travelers / WALKER GIBSON 69
	Vocabulary and Skill Review 70
	UNIT REVIEW 72
	SPEAKING UP: This Day Is Over / CALVIN O'JOHN 72
	WRITING YOUR OWN DESCRIPTION..............................73

UNIT 2: IT'S ALL IN THE GAME

	Introduction to the Unit...75	
fiction	The Horse of the Sword / MANUEL BUAKEN 76	
fiction	The Comeback / ELIZABETH VAN STEENWYK 86	
biography	The Greatest Woman Athlete / JOHN DEVANEY 94	
poetry	The Base Stealer / ROBERT FRANCIS.......................................102	
poetry	A Football Game / ALICE VAN ECK 103	
	Vocabulary and Skill Review 105	
fiction	The Bear Hunt (excerpt) / LEO TOLSTOY.................................106	
fiction	Racing a Champion / MICHAEL BAUGHMAN 107	
profile	Mildred D. Taylor 113	
fiction	The Emerald-Blue / MILDRED D. TAYLOR.................................114	
poetry	Come Skating / SHEL SILVERSTEIN 122	
poetry	The Acrobats / SHEL SILVERSTEIN 122	
biography	The Courageous Dodger / MARTIN LADER 124	
fiction	One Throw / W. C. HEINZ 131	
	Vocabulary and Skill Review 140	
myth	Atalanta / EDEN FORCE ESKIN 141	
profile	Mark Twain..147	
fiction	The Glorious Whitewasher / MARK TWAIN 148	
	Vocabulary and Skill Review 155	
	UNIT REVIEW 156	
	SPEAKING UP: Boo on Hockey Fights / WARNER WOLF........157	
	WRITING YOUR OWN PLOT...159	

UNIT 3: THE COMIC SPIRIT

	Introduction to the Unit...161	
folktale	The King and His Counselors / AESOP 162	
folktale	Bouki Rents a Horse / HAROLD COURLANDER 167	
folktale	Clever Manka / ETHEL JOHNSTON PHELPS.................................172	

	Vocabulary and Skill Review	179
tall tale	Tall-Tale Sampler	180
poetry	Adventures of Isabel / OGDEN NASH	182
tall tale	Pecos Bill / EDWARD O'REILLY	184
tall tale	Three Strong Women / CLAUS STAMM	192
profile	William Saroyan	201
fiction	One of Our Future Poets, You Might Say / WILLIAM SAROYAN	202
	Vocabulary and Skill Review	207
poetry	Matilda / HILAIRE BELLOC	208
fiction	Put Your Brains in Your Pocket / ARTHUR W. HOPPE	210
fiction	The Black Pearl of Kowloon / WALTER DEAN MYERS	214
nonfiction	Word Play / ANONYMOUS	222
poetry	Arithmetic / CARL SANDBURG	223
fiction	Alice in Wonderland (excerpt) / LEWIS CARROLL	224
	Vocabulary and Skill Review	233
poetry	Looking at Limericks / CAROLYN WELLS / ANONYMOUS / MYRA COHN LIVINGSTON	234
	UNIT REVIEW	236
	SPEAKING UP: IZZY-WUZZY	237
	WRITING YOUR OWN SETTING	239

UNIT 4: GOING BEYOND

	Introduction to the Unit	241
poetry	The Hatch / NORMA FARBER	242
legend	La Llorona / ANONYMOUS	244
myth	The Thunders / ALICE MARRIOTT / MALINDA PEACOCK	249
myth	Echo and Narcissus / ANNE TERRY WHITE	256
	Vocabulary and Skill Review	261
poetry	House Fear / ROBERT FROST	262
poetry	Not Me / SHEL SILVERSTEIN	262
autobiography	Ninth Street Bridge / BILL COSBY	263
fiction	Playmate / LESLIE CROUTCH	268
profile	Isaac Asimov	277
fiction	The Fun They Had / ISAAC ASIMOV	278

	Vocabulary and Skill Review	284
nonfiction	Stars and Planets / FRANK STILLEY..	285
drama	The Different Ones / ROD SERLING...	289
	Vocabulary and Skill Review	303
profile	H. G. Wells...	304
fiction	The Magic Shop (A Bonus Selection) / H. G. WELLS................	305
	UNIT REVIEW	316
	SPEAKING UP: Is There Life on Other Planets? / MARION LANE	317
	WRITING YOUR OWN SKETCH...	319

UNIT 5: STANDING TALL

	Introduction to the Unit..	321
nonfiction	Lifeboat in Space / GURNEY WILLIAMS III	322
poetry	A Nation's Strength / RALPH WALDO EMERSON	330
poetry	Lineage / MARGARET WALKER	331
nonfiction	No Medals for Mary / EVE POWNALL	332
poetry	Winter / NIKKI GIOVANNI	337
	Vocabulary and Skill Review	338
profile	Matsuo Basho	339
poetry	Three Haiku / MATSUO BASHO	340
drama	Wings of Summer / RAY BRADBURY	341
poetry	Canis Major / ROBERT FROST	349
fiction	Say It with Flowers / TOSHIO MORI...	350
	Vocabulary and Skill Review	359
fiction	The Princess and the Nightingale / W. SOMERSET MAUGHAM	360
poetry	If I Can Stop One Heart from Breaking / EMILY DICKINSON......	370
fiction	The Fifty-First Dragon / HEYWOOD BROUN...............................	371
	Vocabulary and Skill Review	381
legend	The Knights of the Silver Shield (A Bonus Selection) / RAYMOND MACDONALD ALDEN...	382
	UNIT REVIEW	391
	SPEAKING UP: In Time of Silver Rain / LANGSTON HUGHES	392
	WRITING YOUR OWN STORY...	393

SKILL DEVELOPMENT

BUILDING FROM DETAILS

The Five W's....................................22
Visualizing From Details.................68
Visualizing Actions 101
The Five Senses 104
Inference...121
Drawing Conclusions 221
Making Predictions.........................255
Paragraph Structure.......................288
    Topic sentence 288
    Supporting details 288

RELATIONSHIPS

Sequence..112
Flashback 130
Cause and Effect...................165, 213

VOCABULARY AND SENTENCE MEANING

Antonyms 11
Multiple Meanings 138
Context Clues 154
Dialogue..171
Figurative Language 248
    Metaphor 248
    Simile..248
Pronoun Reference 283

ORAL INTERPRETATION

Reading Poetry................................46
Telling a Punch Line 123
Reading in Character 166
Performing a Monologue..............267

LITERARY SKILLS

Characters, Plot, Setting, and
    Theme 7
Understanding Characters..34, 43, 58
Understanding Plot.........................85
Conflict 93
Biography (definition) 94
Rising Action 112
Fiction and Nonfiction....................139
Conclusion......................................146
Understanding Setting....................178
Tall Tales (definition) 180
Visualizing the Setting....................191
Kinds of Settings 200
Point of View..................................206
Fantasy 232
Myths (definition) 243
Legends (definition) 243
Topic and Theme............................260
Author's Purpose 276
Recognizing Theme....................302

COMPOSITION

UNIT 1 ....7, 11, 22, 35, 43, 58, 69,
       73
UNIT 2 ....85, 93, 101, 104, 113,121,
       130, 138, 146, 154, 159
UNIT 3 ....166, 171, 178, 191, 200,
       206, 213, 221, 232, 239
UNIT 4 ....248, 255, 260, 267, 276,
       284, 288, 302, 319
UNIT 5 ....329, 336, 348, 358, 369,
       380, 393

INTRODUCTION

Welcome to a new world of literature and reading. Sit back, relax, and get ready to enjoy the selections in every unit.

You will meet many new people in these pages. Some of them are authors. Others are characters in stories, plays, myths, legends, or poems. By getting to know these people through their statements and actions, you may also learn about yourself. You will like some of the people in this book as soon as you meet them. Others will become your friends only with time. A few may remain strangers, but that is all right. The important thing is that you experience the world of ideas and literature, of which these people are a part.

This book is divided into five units. Each unit looks at an important theme in literature and life. In the first unit, for example, the focus is on the experience of growing up.

As you read, you will learn new words. Words that may be unfamiliar to you are defined at the bottom of the page on which they appear. The words in bold type are most important. They are reviewed and appear in a helpful glossary at the back of the book.

While you read, and after you read, take the time to respond and react. The questions in "All Things Considered" will help you check your understanding. Then, in "Thinking It Through," you will have a chance to say, "This is the way I see it, and here is why." Your own thoughts and experiences can be part of the discussion.

Poetry is approached differently, as it should be. Each poem is followed by questions that help you appreciate the poem. Remember that thinking and feeling are both "Ways of Knowing."

Lessons on literature, reading, and thinking follow the selections. New terms are defined and made clear by examples. As you learn, you will be encouraged to apply your new knowledge. A short composition activity wraps things up.

As you come to the end of each unit, you will find opportunities to review and extend your experiences with literature. Participate by "Speaking Up" and "Writing Your Own" description or story. You will be guided in reading aloud to capture the thought and feeling of the printed word. Eye-catching photographs will be the source of ideas for writing.

We have put you, the student, in the title of this book. We welcome you with excitement to the world of reading and literature in The Student's Anthology.

BECOMING SOMEBODY

Everyday you change, you grow, you become somebody. Becoming somebody is a personal adventure. It is a journey of self discovery. It is a way of answering the question, "Who am I?"

In this unit you will meet characters who, like you, face the challenge of becoming somebody. Their stories will make you think, let you dream, and help you understand yourself and others better.

Remember, reading is a way of growing, too. Turn the page and begin the adventure.

THE CUB

by Lois Dykeman Kleihauer

▶ Bill hopes someday to beat his dad in wrestling. Do you think he'll ever do it? If he does, how do you think he will feel?

One of the boy's first memories was of his father bending down from a great height to sweep him into the air. Up the boy went, laughing with delight. He could look down on his mother's upturned face as she watched, laughing, and at his father's thick brown hair and white teeth.

Then down he came, shrieking happily. He was never afraid, not with his father's hands holding him. No one in the world was as strong, or as wise, as his father.

He remembered a time when his father moved the piano across the room for his mother. He watched while she guided it into its new position. He saw the difference in his parents' hands as they rested side by side upon the gleaming wood. His mother's hands were small and slim and delicate, his father's large and square and strong.

As he grew, he learned to play bear. When it was time for his father to come home at night, he would hide behind the kitchen door. When he heard the closing of the garage doors, he would hold his breath and squeeze himself further into the crack behind the door. Then he would be quiet.

It was always the same. His father would open the door and stand there, the backs of his long legs close enough to touch. "Where's the boy?" his father would ask loudly.

The boy would glance at the knowing smile on his mother's face. Then he would leap out and grab his father about the knees. His father would look down and shout, "Hey, what's this? A bear—a young cub!"

Then, no matter how tightly the boy tried to cling, he was lifted up and placed upon his father's shoulder. They would march past his mother, and together they would duck beneath the doorways.

• **delicate** (DEL uh kit) small and fine

Then the boy went to school. On the playground, he learned how to wrestle and shout, how to hold back tears, how to get a hold on anyone who tried to take his football away from him. He came home at night and practiced his new wisdom on his father. Straining and puffing, he tried to pull his father off the big chair. His father kept on reading the paper, only glancing up now and then to ask, "What are you trying to do, boy?"

He would stand and look at his father. "Gee whiz, Dad!" he'd say. Then he would realize that his father was teasing him. He would crawl up on his father's lap and pound on him in loving frustration.

The boy grew—taller, slimmer, stronger. He was like a young buck, with tiny new horns. He wanted to test them in combat with any other young buck's. He measured his biceps with his mother's tape measure. Proudly, he thrust his arm in front of his father. "Feel that!" he said. "How's that for muscle?"

His father put his great thumb into the flexed muscle and pressed. The boy pulled back, protesting, laughing: "Ouch!"

Sometimes they wrestled on the floor together. His mother would move the chairs back and warn, "Be careful, Charles—don't hurt him."

After a while his father would push him aside and sit in the big chair, his long legs stretched out. Then the boy would scramble to his feet, half resentful, half pleased over the ease with which his father mastered him.

"Doggone it, Dad, someday—" he would say.

The boy went out for football and track in high school. He surprised even himself now, there was so much more of him. He could look down on his mother. "Little one," he called her, or "Small fry."

The boy and his father still wrestled occasionally, but it worried his mother. She stood by nervously, unable to understand the need

- frustration (fruh STRAY shun) **feeling of being stopped from reaching a goal**
- combat (KOM bat) **battle**
- flexed (FLEKST) **tightened so that arm is bent and muscle is bulging**
- **resentful** (ri ZENT ful) **annoyed; angry**
- master (MAS tur) **gain control over**
- occasionally (uh KAY zhun ul lee) **now and then**

3

for their struggling. It always ended the same way, with the boy upon his back, and his father grinning down at him. "Give?" the father would ask. "Give," the boy would answer.

"I wish you wouldn't wrestle," his mother would say, unsmiling. "There's no point in it. You'll hurt yourselves—don't do it anymore."

So for nearly a year they had not wrestled, but the boy thought about it one night at dinner. He looked at his father closely. It was strange, but his father didn't look nearly as tall or broad-shouldered as he used to. He could even look his father straight in the eyes.

"How much do you weigh, Dad?" he asked.

His father threw him a mild glance. "About the same; about a hundred and ninety. Why?"

The boy grinned. "Just wondering," he said.

But after a while he went over to his father where he sat reading the paper and took it out of his hands. His father glanced up, his eyes at first questioning and then narrowing to meet the challenge in his son's. "So," he said softly.

"Come on, Dad."

His father took off his coat and began to unbutton his shirt. "You asked for it," he said.

His mother came in from the kitchen, alarmed. "Oh, Charles! Bill! Don't—you'll hurt yourselves!" But they paid no attention to her. They were standing now, their shirts off. They watched each other carefully. The boy's teeth gleamed. They circled for a moment, and then their hands closed upon each other's arms.

They strained against each other. Then the boy went down, taking his father with him. They twisted and turned in silence, seeking an advantage, pressing on to a conclusion. There was the sound of their bodies upon the rug and of the quick intake of breath. The boy sometimes showed his teeth in pain. His mother stood at one side, both hands against her ears. Occasionally her lips moved, but she did not make a sound.

After a while the boy pinned his father on his back. "Give!" he demanded.

His father said "Heck, no!" And with a great effort he pushed the boy off, and the struggle began again.

> • advantage (ad VAN tij) **stronger position**

But at the end his father lay on his back. A look of bewilderment came into his eyes. He struggled against his son's restraining hands. Finally he lay quiet, only his chest heaving, his breath coming loudly.

The boy said, "Give!"

The man frowned, shaking his head.

Still the boy knelt on him, pinning him down.

"Give!" he said, and tightened his grip. "Give!"

All at once his father began to laugh silently, his shoulders shaking. The boy felt his mother's fingers tugging at his shoulder. "Let him up," she said. "Let him up!"

The boy looked down at his father. "Give up?"

His father stopped laughing, his eyes wet. "Okay," he said. "I give."

The boy stood up and reached a hand to his father to help him up. But his mother was before him, putting an arm about his father's shoulders, helping him to rise. They stood together and looked at the boy, his father grinning, his mother with puzzled pain in her eyes.

The boy started to laugh. "I guess I—" He stopped. "Gosh, Dad, I didn't hurt you, did I?"

"Heck, no, I'm all right. Next time . . ."

"Yeah, maybe next time . . ."

- bewilderment (bi WIL dur munt) **confusion**
- restraining (ri STRAYN ing) **holding back; keeping under control**
- heaving (HEEV ing) **rising and falling**

5

His mother did not disagree with what they said. She knew as well as they did that there would never be a next time.

For a moment the three of them stood looking at one another. Then, suddenly, the boy turned. Blindly, he ran through the door under which he had ducked so many times when he had ridden on his father's shoulders. He went out the kitchen door, behind which he had hidden, waiting to leap out and grab his father's legs.

It was dark outside. He stood on the steps, feeling the air cool against his sweaty body. He stood with lifted head, looking at the stars. Then he could not see them because tears burned his eyes and ran down his cheeks.

ALL THINGS CONSIDERED

1. When the story begins, the boy is about (a) two years old. (b) ten years old. (c) eighteen years old.

2. When the story ends, the boy is about (a) two years old. (b) ten years old. (c) eighteen years old.

3. At first, the father calls the boy a (a) monster. (b) big bear. (c) young cub.

4. After school the boy wants to (a) play football with his father. (b) read the paper with his father. (c) wrestle with his father.

5. The boy wants to show off his (a) muscles. (b) good grades. (c) athletic ability.

6. The boy's mother (a) enjoys the wrestling. (b) is disturbed by the wrestling. (c) joins in the wrestling.

7. One of the important lines in the story is (a) "Doggone it, Dad, someday—" (b) "How much do you weigh, Dad?" (c) "Be careful, Charles—don't hurt him."

8. When the father gets the boy down, the father always says, (a) "Someday." (b) "Ouch!" (c) "Give?"

9. When the boy finally beats the father, the father (a) is puzzled. (b) is angry. (c) grins.

10. At the end of the story, the boy is (a) completely happy. (b) somewhat sad. (c) very angry.

THINKING IT THROUGH

1. Why do you think the boy and his father like to wrestle?

2. At the end of the story, why does the boy have tears in his eyes?

3. How would you describe the relationship between the boy and his father?

Literary Skills

Characters, Plot, Setting, and Theme

There are four important elements in most stories—characters, plot, setting, and theme.

Characters are the *people* in a story—those who do things and have things happen to them. Some characters are more important to a story than others. They are the **main characters.** In "The Cub," the boy and his father are the main characters.

Plot is *what happens* in a story. In "The Cub," the plot is that a boy grows up and finally beats his father in a wrestling match.

Setting tells *where* and *when* a story happens. "The Cub" happens in a typical home at the present time.

Theme is the *basic meaning* of a story. Good stories have a theme, or message, that helps you better understand life or see it in a new way. What do you think "The Cub" says about growing up?

For the following activity, use a separate piece of paper. Read each sentence. If it tells about characters, write C. If it tells about plot, write P. If it tells about setting, write S.

1. It was dark outside.
2. Then the boy went to school.
3. His mother's hands were small and slim and delicate, . . .
4. He measured his biceps with his mother's tape measure.
5. He was like a young buck with tiny new horns.

Composition

Follow your teacher's instructions before completing *one* of these writing assignments.

1. The story describes a few of the father's physical features. List as many as you can find.
2. What thoughts do you suppose went through the boy's mind as he stood on the steps? Write what you would hear if he were thinking aloud.

THE BACKGROUND

Fables are stories that are special in three ways:

- They are usually very short.
- The characters are usually animals.
- They teach a moral (or lesson) that is acted out in the story and clearly restated at the end.

You may have read the popular fable "The Tortoise and the Hare." This fable tells of a race between a tortoise (turtle) and a hare (rabbit). The hare is so sure it can win that it takes a nap in the middle of the race. When the hare wakes up, it finds that the slow tortoise is going to cross the finish line first. The fable ends by stating the moral: Slow and steady wins the race.

Aesop (EE sop), a Greek slave, was one of the first and the most popular teller of fables. He lived around 600 B.C. La Fontaine (1621–1695), a French poet, also wrote many well-known fables.

THE DONKEY WHO DID NOT WANT TO BE HIMSELF

adapted from Aesop

▶ The following is a modern version of an Aesop fable. Its moral may be serious, but the story isn't. So enjoy it.

There once was a donkey who led a tough life. His work never ended. His food was nothing but old hay. He slept on the hard ground, and the only blanket he ever had was the snow on a winter night. Only this and not even a "thank you" from his owner.

Then one day the donkey noticed how happy Fido the dog was. "Fido has an easy life," the donkey thought. "His work never even begins! His food is meat, corn-on-the-cob, fresh cookies, everything! He lives inside the house and has a soft bed and wool blanket with 'Fido' embroidered on a corner. He even naps on our owner's lap."

The donkey's eyes grew wider and wider as his thoughts went on and on. "Our owner seems to favor Fido. She's always hugging and petting him. She lets him in the house. She bought him a pretty collar just to show her affection." The more the donkey thought, the more he realized how lucky Fido was. Yes indeed! A dog's life would be good enough for him!

So the donkey studied Fido's ways. Fido barked for joy when their owner came home. He licked her face. He sat up and begged for food. He rolled over. He shook hands to get a bite of cookie. And the owner loved it all.

"Maybe I can't bark," the donkey thought, "but I can sure bray! So that's what I'll do. I'll bray when she comes home, just like that dog barks." The donkey was sure he had hit on a grand idea. "Why didn't I think of this a long time ago? If I want to lead a dog's life, I should act like a dog."

So the donkey did. When their owner came home, the donkey sat down and held out his hoof to shake hands, all the time braying a loud "Hello!" Then he rolled over and waved his legs in the air. "Just like a dog," he told himself. He

- embroidered (em BROI durd) **decorated with fancy needlework**
- **favor** (FAY vur) **give special treatment**
- affection (uh FEK shun) **caring; love**
- bray (BRAY) **make the sound a donkey makes**

9

brayed joyfully, trying to say, "Pat me. Put a collar on me. Call me cute names, if you want."

But his owner didn't understand. "What's gotten into you, you dumb donkey?" she asked. "Have you lost your mind? Who do you think you are?"

This made the donkey try harder. He put his front feet on her shoulders and licked her face.

"Fool!" she screamed. "What do you think you are—a dog? Stop it! Shoo! Get away from me!" She picked up a stick and chased the poor donkey out of the yard and into the barn. Then she locked him in.

All night the donkey tried hard to understand. He was sure his tricks were as good as Fido's. Why didn't their owner like him the way she liked Fido? Back at work the next day, he thought about it and thought about it. Gradually, an idea crossed his mind: *Be yourself or you will be nobody.*

ALL THINGS CONSIDERED

1. This fable is about a donkey who (a) is afraid of dogs. (b) doesn't want to be himself. (c) sleeps on his owner's lap.
2. The donkey's problem is that he (a) doesn't like the life he leads. (b) thinks he's a dog. (c) wants a new owner.
3. The donkey tries to (a) run away from home. (b) work harder than ever. (c) act like a dog.
4. The owner thinks the donkey is (a) lazy. (b) crazy. (c) funny.
5. The moral of this fable is (a) it's better to be a dog than a donkey. (b) be yourself or you will be nobody. (c) a donkey leads a tough life.

THINKING IT THROUGH

1. The last line of the fable is, "Be yourself or you will be nobody." In your own words, what does this statement mean? Do you agree with its message?
2. Are a donkey and a dog good characters for this fable? Would other animals work as well in the story? For example, could a cat and a dog have been used instead? Why?

Vocabulary and Sentence Meaning

Antonyms

Antonyms are words with nearly opposite meanings, such as

young—old   good—bad   love—hate.

Antonyms are often used to describe the differences between things. Reread the first two paragraphs of the fable. Notice the antonyms: The donkey has a *tough* life; the dog has an *easy* life. The donkey's work never *ends;* the dog's work never *begins.*

Below is a list of antonyms followed by four sentences with blank spaces for words. Fill in the blanks with the antonyms that express the meaning of the fable. Do your work on a separate piece of paper.

warm—cold   old—fresh
inside—outside   hard—soft

1. One ate _____ hay; the other ate _____ cookies.
2. One slept on the _____ ground; the other slept on a _____ bed.
3. One had a _____ blanket of wool; the other had a _____ blanket of snow.
4. One lived _____ the house; the other lived _____.

Composition

Follow your teacher's instructions before completing *one* of these writing assignments.

1. Write one sentence for each pair of antonyms below. For example, to use *small—big* in one sentence, you might write this: The *small* boy grew up to be a *big* man.

hard—easy   neat—sloppy
beautiful—ugly   gentle—gruff

2. *Be yourself or you will be nobody.* Use this moral as your opening sentence to a paragraph. Add two or more sentences that explain why this moral is important to remember.

YOU

by Nikki Giovanni

▶ Read the following poem slowly and picture someone saying the words to you. What is the thought expressed by the poem?

I came to the crowd seeking friends
I came to the crowd seeking love
I came to the crowd for understanding

I found you

I came to the crowd to weep
I came to the crowd to laugh

You dried my tears
You shared my happiness

I went from the crowd seeking you
I went from the crowd seeking me
I went from the crowd forever

You came, too

WAYS OF KNOWING

1. Is the speaker of this poem a man or a woman? How would you describe the way the speaker feels?
2. Name three things that the speaker hoped to gain from the crowd.
3. "An individual loses his or her identity in a crowd." Do you think this statement is true? Give reasons to support your answer.
4. The poem seems to be saying that a person can find his or her identity through finding another person. Do you agree? Why?

THE END OF MY LONG NIGHT

by Helen Keller

▶ It will take imagination to do it, but put yourself in the place of a very small child who cannot see, hear, or talk. How will you learn to understand others? How will you learn to express your needs? How will you learn about those things that make life meaningful—like love?

Deaf and Blind

I do not remember what happened during the first months of my illness. I only know that I sat in my mother's lap or held on to her dress as she went about the house. My hands felt every object and noted every motion, and in this way I learned to know many things.

Soon I felt the need of some communication with others and began to make crude signs. A shake of the head meant "No." A nod meant "Yes." A pull meant "Come" and a push, "Go." Was it bread that I wanted? Then I would imitate the acts of cutting the slices and buttering them. My mother made me understand a good deal. I always knew when she wished me to bring her something, and I would run upstairs or anywhere else she indicated. Indeed, I owe to her loving wisdom all that was bright and good in my long night.

I do not remember when I first realized that I was different from other people. I had noticed that my mother and my friends did not use signs, but talked with their mouths. Sometimes I stood between two persons who were talking and touched their lips. I could not understand, and was puzzled.

Meanwhile the desire to express myself grew. The few signs I used became less and less adequate. Soon my failures to make myself understood were followed by outbursts of passion. I felt as if invisible hands were holding me, and I struggled. But it did no good. I generally broke down in tears, exhausted. If my mother happened to be near, I crept into her arms, too miserable even to remember

- crude (KROOD) **rough; badly formed**
- **adequate** (AD uh kwit) **enough; able to be used**
- **passion** (PASH un) **strong feeling**

13

the cause of my outburst. After awhile some means of communication became so necessary that these outbursts came daily, sometimes hourly.

My parents were deeply grieved and puzzled. We lived a long way from any school for the blind or the deaf, and how could anyone come to such an out-of-the-way place as Tuscumbia to teach a child who was both deaf and blind? Indeed, my friends and relatives sometimes doubted whether I could be taught.

Teacher

When I was about six years old, my father heard of an eye doctor in Baltimore who had successfully helped many blind people. My parents at once decided to take me to see him.

The journey was very pleasant. I made friends with many people on the train. One lady gave me a box of shells. My father made holes in these so I could string them, and for a long time they kept me happy and content. The conductor, too, was kind. When he went his rounds, I hung on his coattails while he collected and punched the tickets. His punch, with which he let me play, was a delightful toy. Curled up in a corner of the seat I amused myself for hours making funny little holes in bits of cardboard.

My aunt made me a big doll out of towels. It was a comical, shapeless thing, with no nose, mouth, ears or eyes—nothing that even the imagination of a child could turn into a face. Curiously enough, the absence of eyes struck me more than all the other defects put together. I pointed this out to everybody, but no one seemed able to provide the doll with eyes. Then a bright idea shot into my mind. I tumbled off the seat and searched under it until I found my aunt's cape, which was trimmed with large beads. I pulled two beads off and indicated to her that I wanted her to sew them on my doll. She raised my hand to her eyes in a questioning way, and I nodded excitedly. The beads were sewed in the right place and I could not control my joy.

In Baltimore we were received kindly, but the doctor could do nothing. He said, however, that I could be educated, and advised my

- grieved (GREEVD) **saddened**
- curiously (KYOOR ee us lee) **oddly**
- **defect** (DEE fekt) **fault; imperfection**

father to see Dr. Alexander Graham Bell* of Washington. He would be able to give us information about schools and teachers of deaf or blind children. Immediately we went to Washington to see Dr. Bell. I at once felt the tenderness and sympathy which made Dr. Bell loved by so many. He held me on his knee while I examined his watch, and he made it strike for me. He understood my signs, and I knew it and loved him at once. But I did not dream that the interview would be the door through which I should pass from darkness into light, from isolation to friendship, companionship, knowledge, love.

Dr. Bell advised my father to write to Mr. Anagnos, director of the Perkins Institution for the Blind in Boston, and ask him if he had a teacher who could undertake my education. This my father did at once, and in a few weeks there came a kind letter from Mr. Anagnos. A teacher had been found.

Words

The most important day in all my life is the one on which my teacher, Anne Mansfield Sullivan, came to me. It was the third of March, 1887, three months before I was seven years old.

• isolation (eye suh LAY shun) **being alone**

*Alexander Graham Bell (1847–1922), best known for inventing the telephone in 1876, was also a leading authority on the education of the deaf.

On the afternoon of that eventful day, I stood on the porch, dumb, expectant. I guessed vaguely from my mother's signs and from the hurrying to and fro in the house that something unusual was about to happen, so I went to the door and waited on the steps. I did not know what the future held of marvel or surprise for me. Anger and bitterness had weighed on my mind for weeks followed by a numbing of my senses.

Have you ever been at sea in a dense fog, when it seemed as if a wall of darkness shut you in? When the great ship, guided only by a compass, inched its way toward the shore, and you waited with beating heart for something to happen? I was like that ship before my education began. I had no way of knowing how near the harbor was. "Light! Give me light!" was the wordless cry of my soul, and the light of love shone on me in that very hour.

I felt approaching footsteps. I stretched out my hand, thinking it was my mother. Someone took it. I was caught up and held close in the arms of her who had come to reveal all things to me. It was Annie Sullivan who, more than anything else, had come to love me.

The morning after my teacher came she led me into her room and gave me a doll. The little blind children at the Perkins Institution had sent it. When I had played with it a little while, Miss Sullivan slowly spelled into my hand the word "d-o-l-l." I was at once interested in this finger play and tried to imitate it. When I finally succeeded in making the letters, I was filled with childish pleasure and pride. Running downstairs to my mother I held up my hand and made the letters for doll.

I did not know that I was spelling a word or even that words existed. I was simply making my fingers go in monkey-like imitation. In the days that followed I learned to spell in this uncomprehending way a great many words, among them *pin, hat, cup* and a

- dumb (DUM) **unable to speak**
- expectant (ik SPEK tunt) **waiting for something to happen**
- **vaguely** (VAYG lee) **not clearly**
- bitterness (BIT ur nes) **hurt feelings**
- numbing (NUM ing) **making numb; causing a loss of feeling**
- dense (DENS) **thick**
- reveal (ri VEEL) **show; make known**
- uncomprehending (un kom pree HEND ing) **not understanding**

16

few verbs like *sit, stand,* and *walk.* But my teacher had been with me several weeks before I understood that everything has a name.

One day, while I was playing with my new doll, Miss Sullivan put my big rag doll into my lap also and spelled "d-o-l-l." She was trying to make me understand that "d-o-l-l" stood for both. Earlier in the day we had had a problem with the words "m-u-g" and "w-a-t-e-r." Miss Sullivan had tried to show me that "m-u-g" is *mug* and that "w-a-t-e-r" is *water,* but I continued to confuse the two. She had dropped the subject for the time, only to take it up again at this opportunity. I was angered by this and, picking up the new doll, crashed it to the floor. I was delighted when I felt the pieces of the broken doll at my feet. I felt neither sorrow nor regret. In the still, dark world in which I lived, there was no strong caring or tenderness. I felt my teacher sweep the pieces to one side. I was satisfied that the cause of my discomfort was no longer there. She brought me my hat, and I knew I was going out into the warm sunshine. This thought, if a wordless feeling may be called a thought, made me hop and skip with pleasure.

We walked down the path to the well-house. Someone was drawing water and my teacher placed my hand under the spout. As the cool stream gushed over one hand she spelled into the other the word *water,* first slowly, then rapidly. I stood still, my whole attention fixed upon the motions of her fingers. Suddenly I felt a misty consciousness as of something forgotten—a thrill of returning thought. Somehow the mystery of language was revealed to me. I knew then that "w-a-t-e-r" meant the wonderful cool something that was flowing over my hand. That living word awakened my soul. I knew light, hope, joy. I was a soul set free!

I left the well-house eager to learn. Everything had a name, and each name gave birth to a new thought. As we returned to the house every object which I touched seemed to breathe with life. That was because I saw everything with the strange, new sight that had come to me. On entering the door I remembered the doll I had broken. I felt my way to the hearth and picked up the pieces. I tried vainly to

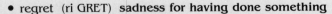

- regret (ri GRET) **sadness for having done something**
- gush (GUSH) **flow freely**
- **consciousness** (KON shus nus) **awareness; knowledge**
- vainly (VAYN lee) **without success**

put them together. Then my eyes filled with tears, for I realized what I had done. For the first time I felt regret and sorrow.

I learned a great many new words that day. *Mother, father, sister, teacher* were among them—words that were to make the world blossom for me. It would have been difficult to find a happier child than I was as I lay in my bed at the close of that eventful day and lived over the joys it had brought me. For the first time I longed for a new day to come.

Love

I had now the key to all language, and I was eager to learn to use it. Children who hear learn language without effort. The words that fall from others' lips are caught by children on the wing, as it were, delightedly. The deaf child, on the other hand, must catch them by a slow and often painful process. Whatever the process, the result is wonderful, as I then knew.

At first, when my teacher told me about a new thing I asked very few questions. My ideas were vague. My vocabulary was inadequate. But as my knowledge of things grew, and as I learned more and more words, my curiosity broadened, and I returned again and again to the same subject, eager for further information.

I remember the morning that I first asked the meaning of the word, "love." This was before I knew many words. I had found a few early violets in the garden and brought them to my teacher. She tried to kiss me, but at that time I did not like anyone to kiss me except my mother. Miss Sullivan put her arm gently around me and spelled into my hand, "I love Helen."

"What is love?" I asked.

She drew me closer to her. "It is here," she said, pointing to my heart, whose beats I was conscious of for the first time. Her words puzzled me very much because I did not then understand anything unless I touched it.

I smelt the violets in her hand and asked, half in words, half in signs, a question which meant, "Is love the sweetness of flowers?"

- eventful (ee VENT ful) **having important results**
- **process** (PRAS es) **way of doing something**
- inadequate (in AD uh kwit) **not enough**
- conscious (KON shus) **aware of**

"No," said my teacher.

Again I thought. The warm sun was shining on us.

"Is this not love?" I asked, pointing in the direction from which the heat came. "Is this not love?"

It seemed to me that there could be nothing more beautiful than the sun, whose warmth makes all things grow. But Miss Sullivan shook her head, and I was greatly puzzled and disappointed. I thought it strange that my teacher could not show me love.

A day or two afterward I was stringing beads of different sizes in regular order—two large beads followed by three small ones, and so on. I had made many mistakes. Miss Sullivan had pointed them out again and again with gentle patience. Finally I noticed an error in the order and for an instant I gave all my attention to the lesson, trying to think how I should have ordered the beads. At this moment, Miss Sullivan touched my forehead and spelled "Think."

In a flash I knew that the word was the name for what was going on in my head. This was my first conscious understanding of an abstract idea.

For a long time I was still. I was not thinking of the beads in my lap. In the light of the new idea, I was trying to find a meaning for "love."

The sun had been under a cloud all day, and there had been brief showers. Then, suddenly, the sun broke forth in all its southern splendor. Again I asked my teacher, "Is this not love?"

"Love is something like the clouds that were in the sky before the sun came out," she answered. Then, in simpler words than these, which at that time I could not have understood, she explained: "You cannot touch the clouds. But you feel the rain and you know how glad the flowers and the thirsty earth are to have it after a hot day. You cannot touch love either. But you feel the sweetness that it pours into everything. Without love you would not be happy. You would not want to play."

The beautiful truth burst upon my mind. I felt suddenly that there were invisible lines stretched between my spirit and the spirit of others.

- **abstract** (ab STRAKT) **not knowable through any of the senses; on the level of ideas**
- splendor (SPLEN dur) **brightness; showiness; glory**

ALL THINGS CONSIDERED

1. Helen Keller's illness left her (a) deaf. (b) blind. (c) deaf and blind.

2. Deafness prevented young Helen from learning to (a) smile. (b) speak. (c) walk.

3. To communicate with others, Helen (a) made gestures with her hands and body. (b) wrote messages. (c) had help from her aunt.

4. Alexander Graham Bell (a) taught Helen to speak. (b) told Helen's father where to go for help. (c) tested Helen to see if she could be educated.

5. Unable to see or hear, Helen felt like a (a) student without a teacher. (b) baby animal without a parent. (c) boat in the fog without a light.

6. Annie Sullivan came as a teacher when Helen was (a) three years old. (b) six years old. (c) ten years old.

7. Helen's first great learning experience was that (a) things have names. (b) words can be spelled. (c) love is a feeling.

8. Helen found that knowing words (a) was useless. (b) gave her light, hope, and joy. (c) made her angry and frustrated.

9. At first, Helen could not understand the meaning of abstract words, such as (a) *water.* (b) *doll.* (c) *love.*

10. When she finally understood the meaning of *love,* she felt (a) a bond with others. (b) numb. (c) very much alone.

THINKING IT THROUGH

1. It has been said that language is what truly sets humans apart from other creatures. How did language change Helen Keller's life? (Give examples.) How would Helen respond to the above statement about the importance of language?

2. Why are abstract words like *think* and *love* harder to understand than concrete words like *book* and *chair?* Why were abstract words so important to Helen?

3. Helen said that the more her knowledge of things grew, the more questions she asked. Why do you think this happened?

Building From Details

The Five W's

The five w's are important question words. They ask the basic questions you must answer in order to understand a story. Remember these five words: *who, what, when, where,* and *why.*

For example, notice how these words ask the basic questions about "The Donkey Who Did Not Want to Be Himself."

- Who is the fable mainly about? (A donkey)
- What happens? (A donkey tries to act like a dog, but his owner thinks he is crazy and chases him into the barn.)
- When do the events happen? (The time is not told.)
- Where do the events happen? (On a farm)
- Why does the donkey try to act like a dog? (So he can lead an easy life)

You should ask yourself the five w's with any story you read. Here are the same questions for "The End of My Long Night." Write the answers on a separate piece of paper.

1. Who is the selection mainly about?
2. What happens?
3. When do most of the events happen?
4. Where do most of the events happen?
5. Why? (Why can be many things. Why is Annie Sullivan able to help Helen? Why is learning language important to Helen? Why does Helen write this selection? Answer *one* of these questions.)

Composition

Follow your teacher's instructions before completing *one* of these writing assignments.

1. What words do you think describe Annie Sullivan? Helen mentioned that she was patient. List three other words to describe her. For each word, write a sentence explaining why you chose it.
2. What is the very first thing you remember? Tell about it in a short paragraph.

VOCABULARY AND SKILL REVIEW

Before completing the exercises that follow, you may wish to review the **bold-faced** words on pages 2–20.

I. On a separate sheet of paper, write the *italicized* word that best fills the blank in each sentence. Use each word only once.

> *abstract*   *process*   *vaguely*
> *adequate*   *resentful*   *favor*
> *consciousness*   *delicate*
> *defect*   *passion*

1. The glass animal was so _____, I feared I might break it.
2. She _____ understood the meaning of the difficult words.
3. Without speech, there seemed to be no _____ way to communicate.
4. Children may sometimes be _____ of others who have more toys.
5. Love and hate are _____ ideas.
6. A good jeweler can easily notice a _____ in a diamond or other gem.
7. Her father had to go through the _____ of finding her a teacher.
8. I picked the red scarf rather than the blue because I _____ red.
9. Her _____ of other people's feelings stopped her from making rude remarks.
10. His outbursts of _____ usually took the form of yelling and foot-stamping.

II. On your paper, mark each statement *true* or *false*. If a statement is *false*, explain what is wrong.

1. "The Cub" is a fable.
2. Most characters in fables are animals.
3. The five w's are *who, what, when, where,* and *which.*
4. The setting of a story is *what happens.*
5. The *who* question asks about characters in a story.

CAT'S IN THE CRADLE

by Harry and Sandy Chapin

▶ When you hear a song, do you think of its words as poetry
set to music? The words of this song are spoken by a father
, who was just too busy to spend time with his son. What sort
of person does the son become?

My child arrived just the other day.
He came to the world in the usual way.
But there were planes to catch and bills to pay.
He learned to walk while I was away.
And he was talkin' 'fore I knew it, and as he grew
He'd say, "I'm gonna be like you, Dad.
You know I'm gonna be like you."

And the cat's in the cradle and the silver spoon
Little Boy Blue and the man in the moon.
"When you comin' home, Dad?"
"I don't know when, but we'll get together then.
You know we'll have a good time then."

My son turned ten just the other day.
He said, "Thanks for the ball, Dad, come on let's play.
Can you teach me to throw?" I said, "Not today.
I got a lot to do." He said, "That's O.K."
And he walked away. But his smile never dimmed.
It said, "I'm gonna be like him, yeah.
You know I'm gonna be like him."

And the cat's in the cradle and the silver spoon
Little Boy Blue and the man in the moon.
"When you comin' home, Dad?"
"I don't know when, but we'll get together then.
You know we'll have a good time then."

Well, he came from college just the other day,
So much like a man I just had to say,
"Son, I'm proud of you. Can you sit for awhile?"
He shook his head and he said with a smile,
"What I'd really like, Dad, is to borrow the car keys.
See you later. Can I have them, please?"

And the cat's in the cradle and the silver spoon
Little Boy Blue and the man in the moon.
"When you comin' home, Son?"
"I don't know when, but we'll get together then.
You know we'll have a good time then."

I've long since retired. My son's moved away.
I called him up just the other day.
I said, "I'd like to see you, if you don't mind."
He said, "I'd love to, Dad, if I can find the time.
You see my new job's a hassle and the kids have the flu,
But it's sure nice talkin' to you, Dad.
It's been sure nice talkin' to you."

And as I hung up the phone it occurred to me—
He'd grown up just like me.
My boy was just like me.

And the cat's in the cradle and the silver spoon
Little Boy Blue and the man in the moon.
"When you comin' home, Son?"
"I don't know when, but we'll get together then, Dad.
We're gonna have a good time then."

WAYS OF KNOWING

1. About how old is the father at the beginning of this song? About how old is he at the end?
2. What did the son want most from his father? What was the father's response?
3. When the son grew up, what did the father want most from him? What was the son's response?
4. How would you describe the feelings the father and son have for each other?

THE SPECKLED HEN'S EGG

by Natalie Savage Carlson

▶ In this story, Madame Roberge tries to become somebody *extra* special. What does she learn?

Once in another time, a very strange thing happened to Madame Roberge.

Madame took very good care of her chickens. They produced many eggs, and she sold their eggs at the store for a good price.

She was miserly with her egg money and hoarded it in the closet in a silver bowl. The bowl was shaped something like a fan, and it was said to have been brought from Quebec in the long ago by her great-grandfather, Lazare Proutte.

Madame was very proud of the bowl. She was also proud of all the coins that her eggs made for her. So it was fitting that the coins should be saved in the silver bowl.

- **miserly** (MY zur lee) **stingy**
- hoarded (HORD id) **saved; stored up**

26

One day when Madame went out to her henhouse to gather the eggs, the scrawny old speckled hen was on the nest. Madame shooed her with her lips and a swing of her skirts. The hen jumped off the nest and ran away, flapping her wings and cackling.

Madame was displeased to see that there was only one egg in the nest.

"That worthless creature!" said Madame Roberge. This is the first egg she has laid in a week. She is no longer worth her feed. I will put her in my stewpot on Sunday."

Madame was about to drop the egg into her apron when she noticed a strange thing about it. There was a picture on the egg, just as surely as if it had been painted there. She studied it carefully. Yes, the picture on the egg was certainly of something. But what?

The next time Madame went to the store in the village with her eggs, she took the unusual one with her.

"This one is not for sale," Madame told Henri Dupuis, the store-keeper. "It is a very strange egg laid by my old speckled hen. See, there is a picture on it. What would you say it is?"

Henri Dupuis looked at the egg closely. Others who were in the store gathered around.

"Perhaps you aren't feeding your hens the right food," said Henri. "Now I have a new kind of chicken feed that—"

But André Drouillard, who had taken the egg in his own hands, interrupted.

"It is surely some omen," he said. "See these long lines that curve like feathers—like an Indian war bonnet?"

"Perhaps there will be an Indian uprising," cried Angéline Meloche in terror.

But the pop-eyed Eusible Latrop had to have his say.

"You are all wrong," he said. "This is a crown on the egg. See! A royal crown. Perhaps it means that Madame Roberge has noble blood in her veins and does not know it."

Madame immediately believed this explanation because it sounded closer to the truth.

- scrawny (SKRAW nee) **thin; skinny**
- omen (OH mun) **sign of what is to come**
- noble (NOH bul) **related to royalty**

27

"My great-grandfather, Lazare Proutte, was a rich man," she remembered, "but everyone thought it strange that he had nothing to say of his life before he came here. Perhaps he was a *compte* or a *duc* in disguise. No doubt the King was displeased with him over some matter and he had to hide in the New World. Yes, I am sure of it. One said he always seemed a little uneasy when strangers were around."

Madame proudly went home and put the wonderful egg in a prominent place on her parlor table. Instead of stewing the speckled hen, she made a special pet of her and built her a runway all for herself. She planted flowers in it and saw that the water dish and feed bowl were always full.

Then a great change came over Madame. She no longer sold eggs at the store because she said that was quite beneath a noblewoman. She took in an orphan girl to do her work so that she would have more time for her embroidery, which was a pastime of the rich. She even began to call herself Madame *de* Roberge, which had a more aristocratic sound, even though the crown on the egg had nothing to do with her husband's family.

She took to walking about with the wart on her nose so high she no longer could see many of her old friends. She walked about with a la-la-de-da air and carried her handkerchief, so!

Sometimes her needle would snag in the fancy handkerchief she was embroidering and her eyes would have a faraway look.

"Perhaps I am really a *comtesse* or a *marquise* or even a *princesse*," she would dream to herself. "If only Great-grandpère Proutte had not made such a secret of his life before he came here!"

She began to wonder why the egg with the crown had been laid on that certain day—no sooner, no later. It was an omen all right. But what did it mean?

- compte (KUMPT) **the French word for count (a nobleman)**
- duc (DUHK) **the French word for duke (highest ranking nobleman)**
- prominent (PRAM uh nunt) **standing out; easy to see**
- aristocratic (uh ris tuh KRAT ik) **belonging to the upper classes**
- snag (SNAG) **catch on something**
- comtesse (KUM tes) **the French word for countess (a noblewoman)**
- marquise (mahr KEEZ) **a noblewoman ranking just below a duchess or countess**

Omens often had to do with death. Perhaps the death of some important person back in old France. Death in noble families meant money and castles and titles changing hands.

Perhaps—could it be—was it possible? Yes, that was it! Some high and rich relative in France had died. The crown on the egg meant that it was time for her to claim her inheritance.

She puzzled over this for a few days. Then she made up her mind. She would take her egg money and make the long trip to the big church in Quebec where the old priest kept the documents and records of the past. She would learn the secret of her noble blood.

She hitched Coquin, the wheezy horse, to the two-wheeled cart and set forth on the trip to Quebec. She would go to the old priest and have him look up the family record of the Prouttes. Her egg money would be spent for food and lodging along the way.

Madame de Roberge set off in high spirit. She sat straight on the edge of the hard seat, with the reins in her hands and her wart in the air, so!

It was as if the two-wheeled cart pulled by the wheezy Coquin had become a fine coach drawn by four spirited white horses. And Madame the Marquise rode forth in silks and brocades and jewels.

- title (TYT ul) **paper showing ownership**
- **inheritance** (in HER uh tuns) **money and belongings that are passed down from parent to child**
- wheezy (HWEE zee) **breathing with difficulty**
- brocades (broh KAIDZ) **clothing made of expensive cloth with pretty raised designs**

From time to time, she passed people on the road. To them she gave a stiff little bow of the head and half a smile, as if saluting her humble peasants.

At night Madame sought shelter in farmhouses, where the owners were overcome with awe and hospitality when they learned that their guest was a distinguished noblewoman riding to Quebec to claim an inheritance across the sea. They would not even accept payment for food and lodging, so honored were they. And the Marquise still had enough of the peasant left in her to be glad that she could hold fast to her egg money.

When Madame drove Coquin down the cobbled streets of Quebec to the big church, she had no feeling of the country bumpkin come to the city. Rather she sat proudly erect, with her la-la-de-da air and her wart high in the air, so!

She twirled her embroidered handkerchief daintily as she told the priest that she had come to seek records of the noble Proutte family so that she could rightfully claim an inheritance in France.

The priest led her into a cellar beneath the church where all the old papers and records were kept. He pulled out drawers, fussed through yellow papers and adjusted his spectacles. So old were most of the documents that fine, dry dust blew from the drawers and Madame from time to time had to use her fancy handkerchief with a vigor that was not so la-la-de-da.

"Proutte, Proutte, Proutte," chanted the priest. "Ah, here we have him. Guillaume Proutte, who came to the New World with Champlain."

"Yes, yes," cried Madame impatiently, "that must be the one. Was he a *duc* or a *marquis*?"

The priest pinched his eyebrows together and popped the tip of his tongue out of his lips. He studied the fine handwriting. He shook his head sadly.

"Alas!" he said. "This Guillaume Proutte was released from a

- awe (AW) **respect and admiration**
- cobbled (KOB uld) **paved with rounded stones**
- bumpkin (BUMP kin) **awkward, simple person**
- embroidered (em BROI durd) **decorated with fancy needlework**
- documents (DOK yuh munts) **important papers**
- New World—**North and South America**

Paris prison on condition that he sail to the New World and turn over a new leaf."

Madame hastily leaned over his shoulder and strained her own eyes on the handwriting.

"Tut! Tut!" said the priest. "It seems that Guillaume did not turn his leaf over, for he was up before the council three times for stealing skins. And you must know, my daughter, that skins were the coin of the country in those days."

"How disgusting!" exclaimed Madame. "That must be some other family of Prouttes. Look further, my father. What about Lazare Proutte?"

The priest dug through some more documents.

"Here is another Proutte," he said. "Yes, it is your Lazare."

"That's the one!" exclaimed Madame. "He was my great-grandfather."

The priest slowly and laboriously read the document. He mumbled from time to time. Certain phrases crawled into Madame's ears like stinging ants.

"Baptized but never confirmed. Apprenticed to Marc Nadie, the silversmith. Disappeared from Quebec at the same time as the silver bowl of the Sieur de Mare, which had been left with the smith for polishing."

"But—but there must be some mistake," Madame stammered.

Then she told the priest about the wonderful egg with the crown on it which her speckled hen had laid.

"I have it here in my bag," she said, "wrapped in a piece of musquash fur."

She carefully took it out of the fur and held it up.

"See," she said, "a distinct crown. It must mean something."

The priest pinched his brows together again and pushed his glasses higher on his nose.

"But Madame is looking at it upside down," he said. "Turn it around—like this! Now what does it look like to you?"

- laboriously (luh BOR ee us lee) **with great effort**
- confirmed (kun FURMD) **made a full member of a church or synagogue**
- apprenticed (uh PREN tist) **taken on to learn a job**
- musquash (MUS kwawsh) **North-American Indian word for** *muskrat*
- **distinct** (dis TINKT) **clear; unmistakable**

"It—it looks like the silver bowl my great-grandfather, Lazare—er—ah—the bowl I keep my egg money in."

"There, you have it, my daughter," said the priest with a twinkle in his eye. "The sign on the egg is a warning that one of Proutte blood should never let money get too strong a hold on her."

So when Madame drove back to her village, the two-wheeled cart was no longer a coach and Coquin no longer divided himself into four prancing white steeds. And Madame the Marquise had been left behind in the dusty church cellar. The return trip dug quite deeply into the egg money, too. For while it is a rare privilege to entertain a *marquise,* it is nothing but a nuisance to have ordinary persons turning in from the road to crowd one's table and beds.

Madame Roberge's wart came down, her la-la-de-da manner was gone and her handkerchief had been left where it fell in the cellar of the big church in Quebec. She found a husband for the orphan girl and went back to her own scrubbing and cooking.

She began to sell eggs at the store again, and spoke in a friendly manner to everyone. The priest noticed that she became a bit more generous with her Sunday offerings, and she no longer took pleasure in hoarding money. Perhaps this was because she no longer had a fine bowl to save it in, since the silver one was turned into a water pan for the chickens. And the old speckled hen disappeared from the fancy runway only to find herself in the stewpot one Sunday.

So you see, my friends, it is not a good thing to hold one's nose high and go about with a la-la-de-da air, for a turn of the egg can easily change a crown into a stolen bowl.

- prancing (PRANS ing) **moving with a light step**
- privilege (PRIV uh lij) **special right**
- **nuisance** (NOO suns) **bother**

ALL THINGS CONSIDERED

1. This story takes place in the (a) present. (b) future. (c) past.
2. Madame Roberge makes money by (a) selling eggs. (b) cleaning houses. (c) doing embroidery.
3. Madame Roberge keeps the money she makes (a) in the bank. (b) under her bed. (c) in a silver bowl.
4. A picture on an egg causes Madame Roberge to think (a) she is from a noble family. (b) she will soon die. (c) someone is playing a trick on her.
5. Soon after finding the egg, Madame Roberge (a) takes in an orphan girl to do her housework. (b) moves to a larger house. (c) buys a fine coach.
6. Madame Roberge travels to Quebec to (a) visit her grandfather. (b) trace the records of her family. (c) trade her old horse for a new one.
7. It appears from church records that Madame Roberge's great-grandfather, Lazare Proutte, (a) stole a silver bowl. (b) was a very wealthy man. (c) stole valuable skins.
8. When the egg is turned around, the picture suddenly looks like a (a) hen. (b) crown. (c) bowl.
9. The meaning of the picture on the egg is finally explained by (a) Guillaume Proutte. (b) the orphan girl. (c) the priest.
10. Upon returning home, Madame Roberge (a) drops her fancy airs and becomes more generous. (b) continues to pretend she is a noblewoman. (c) adopts the orphan girl.

THINKING IT THROUGH

1. Three explanations of the picture on the egg are given to Madame Roberge by the people in the store. Which explanation does Madame Roberge decide is true? What does this tell about her?
2. Using your own words or words from the story, describe how Madame Roberge felt before she found the egg, after she found the egg, and after she visited the priest.
3. Reread the next to last paragraph of the story. How do you think Madame Roberge feels at the end of the story?

Literary Skills

Understanding Characters

Understanding the characters is probably the most important thing to do when reading a story. A character has **character traits.** These describe the character. For example, one character may be smart, energetic, and curious. Another may be helpful, friendly, and hard-working. A character's likes and dislikes can also be considered traits.

There are several ways to learn about characters. One way is to *note what the author tells you about them.* Rather than say that a character is selfish, for example, the author may describe how the character has little concern for others. A good writer lets the reader identify character traits.

In "The Speckled Hen's Egg," the author tells you these things about Madame Roberge:

> Madame took very good care of her chickens. They produced many eggs, and she sold their eggs at the store for a good price.
>
> She was miserly with her egg money and hoarded it in the closet in a silver bowl.

Just these few sentences tell you that she was good at business, and that she loved money.

On a separate sheet of paper, match each of Madame Roberge's character traits listed below with the sentence which shows that trait.

curious	proud
impatient	puts on airs

1. "Madame proudly went home and put the wonderful egg in a prominent place on her parlor table."
2. "She walked about with a la-la-de-da air and carried her handkerchief, so!"
3. "She began to wonder why the egg with the crown had been laid on that certain day—no sooner, no later."
4. "'Yes, yes,' cried Madame impatiently, 'that must be the one.'"

Composition

Follow your teacher's instructions before completing *one* of these writing assignments.

1. In "The Speckled Hen's Egg," a single picture is seen as many things. Write three things the picture was thought to illustrate.
2. Choose a character from any of the stories or poems you have read in this unit. List that character's traits and write a sentence for each trait explaining why you chose it.

Maya Angelou (Born 1928)

Maya Angelou was born Marguerite Johnson in St. Louis, Missouri. As a child, she lived with her grandparents in Stamps, Arkansas. Later she moved to San Francisco, where she lived with her mother and went to high school.

Angelou's love for literature and language has led her to careers in writing and the theater. As the lead in the opera Porgy and Bess, she toured Europe and Africa. While in Africa, she wrote for newspapers in Ghana and Egypt. At home, she took part in the "Black Heritage" television series, which featured artists from various fields. As a writer, Angelou is probably best known for her poems, plays, and three-volume autobiography.

An **autobiography** (aw toh by AHG ruh fee) is like a story in many ways. It tells what happens to certain people in a given place and time. It usually has a theme. But an autobiography is not a work of fiction. It is the true story of a person's life, and it is written by that person.

35

A TASTE OF LIFE

by Maya Angelou

▶ Can a person enter your life and change it forever? It happened to Maya Angelou. She tells how in the following selection from *I Know Why the Caged Bird Sings*, the first volume of her autobiography. At the time, she is nine and her brother Bailey is ten. They are living with their grandparents in the small town of Stamps, Arkansas. Their grandparents own a store, and Maya (or Marguerite) calls her grandmother "Momma."

For nearly a year, I sopped around the house, the Store, the school and the church, like an old biscuit. . . . Then I met, or rather got to know, the lady who threw me my first life line.

Mrs. Bertha Flowers was the aristocrat of Black Stamps. She had the grace of control to appear warm in the coldest weather, and on the Arkansas summer days it seemed she had a private breeze which swirled around, cooling her. She was our side's answer to the richest white woman in town.

Her skin was a rich black that would have peeled like a plum if snagged, but then no one would have thought of getting close enough to Mrs. Flowers to ruffle her dress, let alone snag her skin. She didn't encourage familiarity. She wore gloves too.

I don't think I ever saw Mrs. Flowers laugh, but she smiled often. A slow widening of her thin black lips to show even, small white teeth, then the slow effortless closing. When she chose to smile on me, I always wanted to thank her. . . .

She was one of the few gentlewomen I have ever known, and has remained throughout my life the measure of what a human being can be.

Momma had a strange relationship with her. Most often when she passed on the road in front of the Store, she spoke to Momma in that soft yet carrying voice, "Good day, Mrs. Henderson." Momma responded with "How you, Sister Flowers?"

Mrs. Flowers didn't belong to our church, nor was she Momma's familiar.

- **aristocrat** (uh RIS tuh krat) **upper-class person**
- snag (SNAG) **catch on something**
- ruffle (RUF ul) **to bother; to disturb**
- familiar (fuh MIL yur) **close friend**

Why on earth did she insist on calling her Sister Flowers? Shame made me want to hide my face. Mrs. Flowers deserved better than to be called Sister. Then, Momma left out the verb. Why not ask, "How *are* you, *Mrs.* Flowers?" With the unbalanced passion of the young, I hated her for showing her ignorance to Mrs. Flowers. It didn't occur to me for many years that they were as alike as sisters, separated only by formal education.

Although I was upset, neither of the women was in the least shaken by what I thought an unceremonious greeting. Mrs. Flowers would continue her easy gait up the hill to her little bungalow, and Momma kept on shelling peas or doing whatever had brought her to the front porch.

Occasionally, though, Mrs. Flowers would drift off the road and down to the Store and Momma would say to me, "Sister, you go on and play." As I left I would hear the beginning of an intimate conversation. Momma persistently using the wrong verb, or none at all.

"Brother and Sister Wilcox is sho'ly the meanest—" "Is," Momma? "Is"? Oh, please, not "is," Momma, for two or more. But they talked, and from the side of the building where I waited for the ground to open up and swallow me, I heard the soft-voiced Mrs. Flowers and the textured voice of my grandmother merging and melting. They were interrupted from time to time by giggles that must have come from Mrs. Flowers (Momma never giggled in her life). Then she was gone. . . .

- ignorance (IG nur uns) **lack of knowledge**
- unceremonious (un ser uh MOHN ee us) **without proper manners**
- gait (GAYT) **way of walking**
- bungalow (BUNG uh low) **one-story house**
- intimate (IN tuh mut) **close; friendly**
- persistently (pur SIS tunt lee) **continuing to do**
- textured (TEKS churd) **having a rich quality**
- **merging** (MURJ ing) **blending; combining**

She acted just as refined as whitefolks in the movies and books and she was more beautiful, for none of them could have come near that warm color without looking gray by comparison. . . .

One summer afternoon, sweet-milk fresh in my memory, she stopped at the Store to buy provisions. Another Negro woman of her health and age would have been expected to carry the paper sacks home in one hand, but Momma said, "Sister Flowers, I'll send Bailey up to your house with these things."

She smiled that slow dragging smile, "Thank you, Mrs. Henderson. I'd prefer Marguerite, though." My name was beautiful when she said it. "I've been meaning to talk to her, anyway." They gave each other age-group looks.

Momma said, "Well, that's all right then. Sister, go and change your dress. You going to Sister Flowers's."

. . . What on earth did one put on to go to Mrs. Flowers's house? I knew I shouldn't put on a Sunday dress. It might be sacrilegious. Certainly not a house dress, since I was already wearing a fresh one. I chose a school dress, naturally. It was formal without suggesting that going to Mrs. Flowers's house was equivalent to attending church.

I trusted myself back into the Store.

"Now, don't you look nice." I had chosen the right thing, for once.

"Mrs. Henderson, you make most of the children's clothes, don't you?"

"Yes, ma'am. Sure do. Store-bought clothes ain't hardly worth the thread it take to stitch them."

"I'll say you do a lovely job, though, so neat. That dress looks professional."

Momma was enjoying the seldom-received compliments. Since everyone we knew (except Mrs. Flowers, of course) could sew competently, praise was rarely handed out for the commonly practiced craft.

"I try, with the help of the Lord, Sister Flowers, to finish the inside just like I does the outside. Come here, Sister."

I had buttoned up the collar and tied the belt, apronlike, in back. Momma told me to turn around. With one hand she pulled the strings and the belt fell free at both sides of my waist. Then her large hands were at my neck, opening the button loops. I was terrified. What was happening?

"Take it off, Sister." She had her hands on the hem of the dress.

"I don't need to see the inside, Mrs. Henderson, I can tell. . . ." But the dress was over my head and my arms were

---

- refined (ri FYND) **well mannered**
- **provisions** (pruh VIZH unz) **food and other items**
- sacrilegious (sak rih LIJ us) **insulting to what is sacred**
- formal (FOR mul) **proper; correct**
- equivalent (i KWIV uh lunt) **equal to**
- competently (KOM puh tunt lee) **ably; with enough skill**

stuck in the sleeves. Momma said, "That'll do. See here, Sister Flowers, I French-seams around the armholes." Through the cloth film, I saw the shadow approach. "That makes it last longer. Children these days would bust out of sheet-metal clothes. They so rough."

"That is a very good job, Mrs. Henderson. You should be proud. You can put your dress back on, Marguerite."

"No ma'am. Pride is a sin. And 'cording to the Good Book, it goeth before a fall."

"That's right. So the Bible says. It's a good thing to keep in mind."

I wouldn't look at either of them. Momma hadn't thought that taking off my dress in front of Mrs. Flowers would kill me stone dead. If I had refused, she would have thought I was trying to be "womanish.". . . Mrs. Flowers had known that I would be embarrassed and that was even worse. I picked up the groceries and went out to wait in the hot sunshine. It would be fitting if I got a sunstroke and died before they came outside. Just dropped dead on the slanting porch.

There was a little path beside the rocky road, and Mrs. Flowers walked in front swinging her arms and picking her way over the stones.

She said, without turning her head, to me, "I hear you're doing very good school work, Marguerite, but that it's all written. The teachers report that they have trouble getting you to talk in class." We passed the triangular farm on our left and the path widened to allow us to walk together. I hung back in the separate unasked and unanswerable questions.

"Come and walk along with me, Marguerite." I couldn't have refused even if I wanted to. She pronounced my name so nicely. Or more correctly, she spoke each word with such clarity that I was certain a foreigner who didn't understand English could have understood her.

"Now no one is going to make you talk—possibly no one can. But bear in mind, language is man's way of communicating with his fellow man and it is language alone which separates him from the lower animals." That was a totally new idea to me, and I would need time to think about it.

"Your grandmother says you read a lot. Every chance you get. That's good, but not good enough. Words mean more than what is set down on paper. It takes the human voice to infuse them with the shades of deeper meaning."

I memorized the part about the human voice infusing words. It seemed so valid and poetic.

- French-seam (french SEEM) sew in a special way that finishes the edge
- **clarity** (KLAR i tee) clearness
- infuse (in FYOOZ) fill; pour into
- valid (VAL id) true; correct; justified

She said she was going to give me some books and that I not only must read them, I must read them aloud. She suggested that I try to make a sentence sound in as many different ways as possible.

"I'll accept no excuse if you return a book to me that has been badly handled." My imagination boggled at the punishment I would deserve if in fact I did abuse a book of Mrs. Flowers's. Death would be too kind and brief.

The odors in the house surprised me. Somehow I had never connected Mrs. Flowers with food or eating or any other common experience of common people. There must have been an outhouse, too, but my mind never recorded it.

The sweet scent of vanilla had met us as she opened the door.

"I made tea cookies this morning. You see, I had planned to invite you for cookies and lemonade so we could have this little chat. The lemonade is in the icebox."

It followed that Mrs. Flowers would have ice on an ordinary day, when most families in our town bought ice late on Saturdays only a few times during the summer to be used in the wooden ice-cream freezers.

She took the bags from me and disappeared through the kitchen door. I looked around the room that I had never in my wildest fantasies imagined I would see. Browned photographs leered or threatened from the walls and the white, freshly done curtains pushed against themselves and against the wind. I wanted to gobble up the room entire and take it to Bailey, who would help me analyze and enjoy it.

"Have a seat, Marguerite. Over there by the table." She carried a platter covered with a tea towel. Although she warned that she hadn't tried her hand at baking sweets for some time, I was certain that like everything else about her the cookies would be perfect.

They were flat round wafers, slightly browned on the edges and butter-yellow in the center. With the cold lemonade they were sufficient for childhood's life-long diet. Remembering my manners, I took nice little lady-like bites off the edges. She said she had made them expressly for me and that she had a few in the kitchen that I could take home to my brother. So I jammed one whole cake in my mouth and the rough crumbs scratched the insides of my jaws, and if I hadn't had to swallow, it would have been a dream come true.

- boggle (BOG ul) **hesitate; become uncertain**
- outhouse (OUT hous) **a shed used as an outdoor toilet**
- **fantasy** (FAN tuh see) **daydream; imaginary happening**
- leer (LEER) **look with a sly, almost evil expression**
- analyze (AN uh lyz) **study in detail**
- sufficient (suh FISH unt) **enough**

As I ate she began the first of what we later called "my lessons in living." She said that I must always be intolerant of ignorance but understanding of illiteracy. That some people, unable to go to school, were more educated and even more intelligent than college professors. She encouraged me to listen carefully to what country people called mother wit. That in those homely sayings was couched the collective wisdom of generations.

When I finished the cookies she brushed off the table and brought a thick, small book from the bookcase. I had read *A Tale of Two Cities* and found it up to my standards as a romantic novel. She opened the first page and I heard poetry for the first time in my life.

"It was the best of times and the worst of times. . . ." Her voice slid in and curved down through and over the words. She was nearly singing. I wanted to look at the pages. Were they the same that I had read? Or were there notes, music, lined on the pages, as in a hymn book? Her sounds began cascading gently. I knew from listening to a thousand preachers that she was nearing the end of her reading, and I hadn't really heard, heard to understand, a single word.

"How do you like that?"

It occurred to me that she expected a response. The sweet vanilla flavor was still on my tongue and her reading was a wonder in my ears. I had to speak.

I said, "Yes, ma'am." It was the least I could do, but it was the most also.

- intolerant (in TOL ur unt) **not willing to put up with**
- **illiteracy** (il LIT ur uh see) **lack of ability to read or write**
- homely (HOHM lee) **common and simple**
- couch (COUCH) **put into words**
- collective (kuh LEK tiv) **shared by all members of a group**
- romantic (roh MAN tik) **imaginative; exciting**
- cascading (kas KAYD ing) **falling quickly**

"There's one more thing. Take this book of poems and memorize one for me. Next time you pay me a visit, I want you to recite.". . .

On that first day, I ran down the hill and into the road (few cars ever came along it) and had the good sense to stop running before I reached the Store.

I was liked, and what a difference it made. I was respected not as Mrs. Henderson's grandchild or Bailey's sister but for just being Marguerite Johnson. . . .

ALL THINGS CONSIDERED

1. Marguerite thinks Mrs. Flowers is (a) a perfect person. (b) a deeply religious person. (c) the richest woman in town.

2. A good word to describe Mrs. Flowers is (a) funny. (b) sorrowful. (c) refined.

3. Marguerite is embarrassed by (a) her own ignorance. (b) Mrs. Flowers's strange behavior. (c) her grandmother's "bad" grammar and use of words.

4. Marguerite's grandmother is (a) unfriendly to Mrs. Flowers. (b) serious about her sewing. (c) embarrassed by Marguerite's behavior.

5. Mrs. Flowers believes that words have more meaning when (a) spoken aloud. (b) put to music. (c) read silently.

6. Marguerite calls her visits with Mrs. Flowers (a) adventures. (b) history lessons. (c) lessons in living.

7. Mrs. Flowers encourages Marguerite to (a) write a letter every day. (b) help her brother learn to read. (c) respect poor people who have no formal education.

8. Mrs. Flowers tells Marguerite to (a) write to the President. (b) memorize a poem. (c) buy new books to read.

9. When Mrs. Flowers reads aloud, the words sound to Marguerite like (a) meaningless chatter. (b) poetry. (c) thunder.

10. Marguerite is happy that she is liked for being (a) the granddaughter of the store owner. (b) Bailey's sister. (c) herself.

THINKING IT THROUGH

1. In your own words, explain what Mrs. Flowers meant to Marguerite. Do you think Mrs. Flowers changed the course of Marguerite's life? Explain.

2. Marguerite is pleased because she is liked for being herself. Why is being liked for being yourself important?

3. Why do you think Maya (or Marguerite) chose to write about her life? How can writing about your own experiences help you?

Literary Skills

Understanding Characters

One way to learn about characters in a story is to note what the author tells you about them. You read about this on page 34.

Another way to learn about characters is to *listen to what the characters say.* In "A Taste of Life," Mrs. Flowers speaks several times. What she says helps us understand the kind of person she is.

The first thing that Mrs. Flowers says is "Good day, Mrs. Henderson." Those few words tell us two important things about her: she has good manners and she is educated. We know these two things about Mrs. Flowers because she does not say "Hi, there" or "What's up?" or "How you, Sister?"

Later on, Mrs. Flowers strengthens these ideas about her character by saying things such as:

"I'd prefer Marguerite. . . ." (She does not say "How about Marguerite?")

"I'll say you do a lovely job. . . . That dress looks professional." (She does not say "That looks good. . . . That dress is professional.")

We become certain that Mrs. Flowers is educated when Marguerite visits her. Find some of Mrs. Flowers's statements that show her education. Write three or four of these sentences on your paper.

Composition

Follow your teacher's instructions before completing *one* of these writing assignments.

1. Write an autobiographical sentence. Make it true and interesting. You might begin your sentence like this: "When I was ___ years old, I. . . ."

2. Write a paragraph that describes a person you admire. Tell who this person is in your opening sentence. Then explain why you admire this person in two or more sentences that follow.

43

▶ Some poems tell a story. Other poems, called **lyric poems,** simply express an idea or feeling. As you read the two lyric poems that follow, ask yourself these questions: Who is speaking? What is the speaker's main idea? In what way is the language in the poem special?

THUMBPRINT

by Eve Merriam

In the heel of my thumb
are whorls, whirls, wheels
in a unique design:
mine alone.
What a treasure to own!
My own flesh, my own feelings.
No other, however grand or base,
can ever attain the same.
My signature,
thumbing the pages of my time.
My universe key,
my singularity.
Impress, implant,
I am myself,
of all my atom parts I am the sum.
And out of my blood and my brain
I make my own interior weather,
my own sun and rain.
Imprint my mark upon the world,
whatever I shall become.

- whorl (WORL) a circle, as made by petals around the center of a flower or by the turns of a shell
- unique (yoo NEEK) one of a kind
- base (BAYS) of low value
- attain (uh TAYN) reach; gain
- singularity (sing yoo LAR uh tee) oneness; singleness
- impress (IM pres) mark; stamp
- implant (IM plant) something deeply planted
- imprint (im PRINT) make a mark

PHIZZOG

by Carl Sandburg

This face you got,
This here phizzog you carry around,
You never picked it out for yourself, at all, at all—did you?
This here phizzog—somebody handed it to you—am I right?
Somebody said, "Here's yours, now go see what you can do with
    it."
Somebody slipped it to you and it was like a package marked:
"No goods exchanged after being taken away"—
This face you got.

WAYS OF KNOWING

1. Compare "Thumbprint" and "Phizzog." Which poem is more concerned with what you look like? Which poem is more concerned with the kind of person you are?

2. The speaker in "Thumbprint" is "I." Who is "I"?

3. Both poems are concerned with the uniqueness of every person—only you are "you" and only I am "I." Which poem leaves you with a better feeling about yourself?

4. Compare the language in the left column with the language in the right column. Why did Sandburg choose to use the language in the left column?

This face you got . . .	This face you have got . . .
This here phizzog . . .	This phizzog . . .
You never picked it out for yourself at all, at all— did you?	You didn't choose it for yourself, did you?

5. The language in "Thumbprint" is special in at least two ways. Some of the lines end with rhyming words (words whose endings sound alike). How many rhyming words can you find? Other lines contain words that sound alike at the beginning. Find two lines with words like these.

• phizzog (fi ZOG) face

Oral Interpretation

Most poems should be read aloud. It is important to hear how they sound.

Practice reading "Thumbprint" or "Phizzog." First, read silently, trying to hear in your mind how the poem should sound. Then read aloud, slowly. Follow these suggestions:

- For "Thumbprint," follow the punctuation carefully. For example, pause briefly at each of the commas.
- For "Phizzog," read the questions so they sound like questions. Pause just before the last line of the poem.

VOCABULARY AND SKILL REVIEW

Before completing the exercises that follow, you may wish to review the **bold-faced** words on pages 26–41.

I. On your paper, mark each sentence *correct* or *incorrect*. If it is *incorrect*, rewrite the sentence to make it correct.

1. Mrs. Flowers firmly believed that reading would help spread *illiteracy*.
2. To Marguerite Johnson, the graceful and proper Mrs. Flowers was an *aristocrat*.
3. The *merging* voices of the two women sounded like one voice.
4. Milk, eggs, and soap were the only *provisions* she bought at the store that day.
5. The people felt it was a *nuisance* to have a noblewoman at their table so they welcomed her.
6. Being *miserly* with her money, Madame Roberge had none left when she needed groceries.
7. The beautiful words created in her mind *fantasies* of far-off places.
8. If Madame Roberge had received a big *inheritance*, she would have had to work longer and harder.
9. She spoke with such *clarity* that her words could be understood by everyone.
10. The picture of the crown was so *distinct* that no one could recognize it.

II. The following paragraphs are from "A Taste of Life." Mrs. Flowers is the speaker in the second paragraph. Use what you have learned in this unit about understanding characters to answer the questions below.

Mrs. Bertha Flowers was the aristocrat of Black Stamps. She had the grace of control to appear warm in the coldest weather, and on the Arkansas summer days it seemed she had a private breeze which swirled around, cooling her. . . .

"Your grandmother says you read a lot. Every chance you get. That's good, but not good enough. Words mean more than what is set down on paper. It takes the human voice to infuse them with the shades of deeper meaning."

1. We know that Mrs. Flowers is an aristocrat in Marguerite's eyes because (a) Mrs. Flowers herself tells us. (b) the author tells us. (c) Mrs. Flowers has lots of money.

2. The way that Mrs. Flowers is described shows that the author (a) thinks highly of her. (b) feels sorry for her. (c) knows nothing about her.

3. We know that Mrs. Flowers thinks spoken language is important because (a) Mrs. Flowers herself tells us. (b) the author tells us. (c) Mrs. Flowers talks a great deal.

4. Three character traits of Mrs. Flowers are (a) awkward, silly, and illiterate. (b) earthy, noisy, and comic. (c) graceful, cool, and intelligent.

GOLD-MOUNTED GUNS

by F. R. Buckley

▶ Stories set in the Old West usually have a "good guy" and a "bad guy." Can you find the good guy and bad guy in this story?

Evening had fallen on Longhorn City. To the south a lone star twinkled in the velvet sky. Soon a hard-faced man ambled down the main street and chose a pony from the dozen hitched beside Tim Geogehan's general store. The town was lit only by weak lights from the one store and one saloon, so it was from the dark shadows that a voice came. It was calling to the hard-faced man.

"Tommy!" the voice softly called.

The hard-faced man made a slight movement—a bare flick of the hand at the gun belt, but it was a movement perfectly understood by the figure in the shadows.

"Wait a minute!" the voice pleaded.

A moment later, his hands upraised, the figure of a young man moved into the zone of light that shone bravely out through Tim Geogehan's back window.

"Don't shoot," he said, trying to control the nervousness caused by the weapon pointing steadily at him. "I'm—a friend."

For perhaps fifteen seconds the newcomer and the hard-faced man studied each other with the steady eyes of those who take chances of life and death. The young man noted the sinister droop of a gray mustache over a hidden mouth, and shivered a little as his gaze met that of a pair of steel-blue eyes. The lean man with the gun saw before him a boyish yet rather handsome face marked now by a certain desperation.

- **lone** (LOHN) **single**
- **amble** (AM bul) **walk at a slow, easy pace**
- **sinister** (SIN is tur) **suggesting evil**
- **desperation** (des puh RAY shun) **feeling of hopelessness**

48

"What do you want?" he asked, sharply.

"Can I put my hands down?" countered the boy.

The lean man considered.

"All things bein' equal," he said, "I think I'd rather you'd first tell me how you got round to callin' me Tommy. Been askin' people in the street?"

"No," said the boy. "I only got into town this afternoon, an' I ain't a fool anyway. I seen you ride in this afternoon, and the way folks backed away from you made me wonder who you was. Then I seen them gold-mounted guns of yourn, an' of course I knew. Nobody ever had guns like them but Pecos Tommy. I could ha' shot you while you was gettin' your horse, if I'd been that way inclined."

The lean man bit his mustache.

"Put 'em down. What do you want?"

"I want to join you."

"You want to *what?*"

"Yeah, I know it sounds foolish to you, mebbe," said the young man. "But, listen—your side-kicker's in jail down in Rosewell. I figured I could take his place—anyway, till he got out. I know I ain't got any record, but I can ride, an' I can shoot the pips out of a ten-spot at ten paces. I also got a little job to bring into the firm, to start with."

The lean man's gaze narrowed.

"Have, eh?" he asked, softly.

* inclined (in KLYND) **tending to do**

49

"It ain't anythin' like you go in for as a rule," said the boy, apologetically, "but it's a roll of cash an'—I guess it'll show you I'm straight. I only got on to it this afternoon. Kind of timely I should meet you right now."

The lean man chewed his mustache. His eyes did not move.

"Yeah," he said, slowly. "What you quittin' punchin' for?"

"Sick of it."

"Figurin' robbin' trains is easier money?"

"No," said the young man, "I ain't. But I like a little fun in life. They ain't none in punchin'."

"Got a girl?" asked the lean man.

The boy shook his head. The hard-faced man nodded reflectively.

"Well, what's the job?" he asked.

The light from Geogehan's window was suddenly cut off by the body of a man. Someone was cupping his hands about his eyes, staring out into the night to locate the buzz of voices at the back of the store.

"If you're goin' to take me on," said the young man, "I can tell you while we're ridin' toward it. If you ain't—why, there's no need to go no further."

The lean man slipped back into its holster the gold-mounted gun he had drawn. He glanced once at the figure in the window and again, piercingly, at the boy whose face now showed white in the light of the rising moon. Then he turned his pony and mounted.

"Come on," he commanded.

Five minutes later the two had passed the limits of the town. They were heading for the low range of hills to the south. By this time, Will Arblaster had given the details of his job to the unemotional man at his side.

"How do you know the old guy's got the money?" came a level question.

"I saw him come out of the bank this afternoon, grinnin' all over his face an' stuffin' it into his pants-pocket," said the boy. "An' when

- **apologetically** (uh pol uh JET ik lee) in a manner that asks to be excused or forgiven
- punchin'—short for being a cowpuncher, or cowboy
- reflectively (ri FLEK tiv lee) thoughtfully
- **unemotional** (un ih MOH shun ul) without feeling
- level (LEV ul) honest

he was gone, I kind of inquired who he was. His name's Sanderson. He lives in this yer cabin right ahead a mile. Looked kind of a soft old geezer—kind that'd give up without any trouble. Must ha' been quite some cash there, judgin' by the size of the roll. But I guess when *you* ask him for it, he won't mind lettin' it go."

"I ain't goin' to ask him," said the lean man. "This is your job."

The boy hesitated.

"Well, if I do it right," he asked, with a trace of tremor in his voice, "will you take me along with you sure?"

"Yeah—I'll take you along."

The two riders rounded a shoulder of the hill. There, in the moonlight, they saw the dark shape of a cabin, its windows un-lighted. The lean man chuckled.

"He's out."

Will Arblaster swung off his horse.

"Maybe," he said, "but likely the money ain't. He started off home. If he's had to go out again, likely he's hid the money some-place. Folks know *you're* about. I'm goin' to see."

Stealthily he crept toward the house. The moon went behind a cloud-bank, and the darkness swallowed him. The lean man, mo-tionless on his horse, heard the rap of knuckles on the door—then a pause, and the rattle of the latch. A moment later came the heavy thud of a shoulder against wood—a cracking sound, and a crash as the door went down. The lean man's lips tightened. From within the cabin came the noise of the boy stumbling over furniture. Then the fitful fire of a match lit the windows. The man on the horse, twenty yards away, could hear the clumping of the other's boots on the rough board floor, and every rustle of the papers that he fumbled in

- trace (TRAYS) **small amount**
- stealthily (STEL thuh lee) **quietly; secretively**

51

his search. Another match scratched and sputtered, and then came a sudden cry of triumph. Running feet padded across the short grass and Will Arblaster drew up, panting.

"Got it!" he gasped. "The old fool! Put it in a tea-canister right on the mantelshelf. Enough to choke a horse! Feel it!"

The lean man, unemotional as ever, reached down and took the roll of money.

"Got another match?" he asked.

Willie struck one, and watched, panting, while his companion flipped through the bills.

"Fifty tens," said the lean man. "Five hundred dollars. Guess I'll carry it."

His cold blue eyes turned downward, and focused again on the younger man's upturned face. The bills were stowed in a pocket of the belt beside one of those gold-mounted guns. For a moment, the lean man's hand seemed to hesitate over its butt; then, as Willie smiled and nodded, it moved away. The match burned out.

"Let's get out of here," Willie urged. The hand which had hovered over the gun-butt grasped the boy's shoulder.

"No, not yet," the man said quietly. "Not just yet. Get on your hawss, an' set still awhile."

The young man mounted. "What's the idea?"

"Why!" said the level voice. "This is a kind of novelty to me. Robbin' trains, you ain't got any chance to see results, but this here's different. Figure this old guy'll be back pretty soon. I'd like to see what he does when he finds his roll's gone. Ought to be amusin'!"

The boy tried to laugh. "Ain't he liable to——"

"He can't see us," said the lean man with a certain new cheerfulness in his voice. "An' besides, he'll think we'd naturally be miles away. An' besides that, we're mounted, all ready."

"What's that?" whispered the boy, laying a hand on the man's arm.

They listened.

"Probably him," the lean man said. "Now stay still."

There were two riders—by their voices, a man and a girl. They were laughing as they rode up to a broken-down old stable at the rear of the house. They put up the horses, then came round to the

---

- stow (STOH) **put away**
- novelty (NOV ul tee) **something new or unusual**

front. Walking to the door, their words came clearer to the ears of the listeners.

"I feel mean about it, anyhow," said the girl's voice. "You going on living here, Daddy, while——"

"Tut-tut-tut!" said the old man. "What's five hundred to me? I ain't never had that much in a lump, an' shouldn't know what to do with it if I had. 'Sides, your Aunt Elviry didn't give it you for nothin'. 'If she wants to go to college,' says she, 'let her prove it by workin'. I'll pay half, but she's got to pay t'other half.' Well, you worked, an'—— Where on earth did I put that key?"

There was a silence, broken by the grunts of the old man as he searched his pockets. Then the girl spoke, and the tone of her voice was the more terrible for the restraint she was putting on it.

"Daddy—the—the—did you leave the money in the house?"

"Yes. What is it?" cried the old man.

"Daddy—the door's broken down, and——"

There was a hoarse cry. Boot-heels stumbled across the boards, and again a match flared. Its pale light showed a girl standing in the doorway of the cabin, her hands clasped. Beyond the wreckage of the door a bent figure with silver hair tottered away from the mantelshelf. In one hand Pa Sanderson held the flickering match, in the other a tin box.

"Gone!" he cried in his cracked voice. "Gone!"

Willie Arblaster drew a breath through his teeth and moved uneasily in his saddle. Instantly a lean, strong hand, with a grip like steel, fell on his wrist and grasped it. The man behind the hand chuckled.

"Listen!" he said.

"Daddy—Daddy—don't take on so—please don't," came the girl's voice, itself trembling with held-back tears. There was a scrape of chair-legs on the floor as she forced the old man into his seat by the fireplace. He hunched there, his face in his hands. She struck a match and laid the flame to the wick of the lamp on the table. As it burned up, she went back to her father, knelt by him, and threw her arms about his neck.

"Now, now, now!" she pleaded. "Now, Daddy, it's all right. Don't take on so. It's all right."

- restraint (ri STRAYNT) **holding back; keeping in check**
- totter (TOT ur) **walk unsteadily**

But he would not be comforted.

"I can't replace it!" cried Pa Sanderson, dropping trembling hands from his face. "It's gone! Two years you've been away from me. Two years you've slaved in a store. And now I've——"

"Hush, hush!" the girl begged. "Now, Daddy—it's all right. I can go on working, and——"

With great effort, the old man got to his feet. "Two years more slavery, while some skunk drinks your money, gambles it—throws it away!" he cried. "Curse him! Whoever it is, curse him! What's a man goin' to believe when years of scrapin' like your aunt done, an' years of slavin' like yours, an' all our happiness today can be wiped out by a low sneakin' thief in a minute?"

The girl put her hand over her father's mouth.

"Don't, Daddy," she choked. "It only makes it worse. Come and lie down on your bed. I'll make you some coffee. Don't cry, Daddy darling. Please."

Gently, like a mother with a little child, she led the heartbroken old man out of the watchers' line of vision, out of the circle of lamplight. More faintly, but still with heartbreaking distinctness, the listeners could hear the sounds of weeping.

The lean man chuckled, and pulled his bridle.

"Some circus!" he said appreciatively. "C'mon, boy."

His horse moved a few paces, but Will Arblaster's did not. The lean man turned in his saddle.

"Ain't you comin'?" he asked.

For ten seconds, perhaps, the boy made no answer. Then he urged his pony forward until it stood side by side with the man's.

"No," he said. "An'—an' I ain't goin' to take that money, neither."

"Huh?"

The voice was slow and meditative.

"Don't know as ever I figured what this game meant," he said. "Always seemed to me that all the hardships was on the stick-up man's side—gettin' shot at an' chased and so on. Kind of fun, at that. Never thought 'bout—old men cryin'."

"That ain't my fault," said the lean man.

"No," said Will Arblaster, still very slowly. "But I'm goin' to take

- distinctness (dis TINKT nes) **clearness**
- meditative (MED i tay tiv) **thoughtful**

54

that money back. You didn't have no trouble gettin' it, so you don't lose nothin'."

"Suppose I say I won't let go of it?" suggested the lean man with a sneer.

"Then," snarled Arblaster, "I'll blow your head off an' take it! Don't you move, you! I've got you covered. I'll take the money out myself."

His revolver muzzle under the man's nose, he snapped open the pocket of the belt and pulled out the roll of bills. Then, regardless of a possible shot in the back, he swung off his horse and with steady, determined steps, walked to the lighted doorway of the cabin.

The lean man, unemotional as ever, sat perfectly still, listening. Soon there came a burst of voices from the cabin, sounding their surprise, their joy.

● sneer (SNEER) **scornful tone**

It was a full ten minutes before Will Arblaster reappeared in the doorway, alone. His figure outlined against the light, he made a quick movement of his hand across his eyes, then stumbled forward through the darkness toward his horse. Still the lean man did not move.

"I'm sorry," said the boy as he mounted. "But——"

"I ain't," said the lean man quietly. "What do you think I made you stay an' watch for, you young fool?"

The boy made no reply. Suddenly the hair prickled on the back of his neck and his jaw fell.

"Say," he demanded hoarsely at last. "Ain't you Pecos Tommy?"

The lean man's answer was a short laugh.

"But you got his guns, an' the people in Longhorn all kind of fell back!" the boy cried. "If you ain't him, who are you?"

The moon had drifted from behind a cloud and flung a ray of light across the face of the lean man as he turned it, narrow-eyed, toward Arblaster. The pale light picked out the grim lines of that face, emphasizing the cluster of sun-wrinkles about the deep eyes and underscoring with black lines the long sweep of the fighting jaw.

"Why," said the lean man dryly, "I'm the sheriff that killed him yesterday. Let's be ridin' back."

- prickle (PRIK ul) **give an odd feeling of tiny pinpricks on the skin**
- grim (GRIM) **determined; hard; stern**

ALL THINGS CONSIDERED _____

1. Will Arblaster thinks the hard-faced man is Pecos Tommy because (a) he looks like Pecos Tommy. (b) he has gold-mounted guns. (c) Tim Geogehan calls him Tommy.

2. Will wants to be accepted as a (a) robber. (b) sheriff's assistant. (c) sharpshooter.

3. Will has in mind to rob (a) a bank. (b) a train. (c) an old man.

4. The hard-faced man makes Will (a) do the robbery by himself. (b) wait outside while he steals the money. (c) fool the old man and his daughter into leaving the house.

5. After Will gets the money, the hard-faced man wants to (a) leave immediately. (b) give the money back. (c) stay and watch.

6. The money was meant to be used for (a) the girl's wedding. (b) the girl's college education. (c) buying a ranch.

7. When he discovers the money is gone, the old man is (a) heartbroken. (b) happy his daughter won't be leaving. (c) scared that Pecos Tommy will be back.

8. Will returns to the house with the money because (a) he feels sorry for the father and daughter. (b) he is afraid of getting caught. (c) the lean man tells him to.

9. Will shows he is brave by (a) breaking down the door and taking the money. (b) catching Pecos Tommy. (c) risking being shot as he returns to the house.

10. The lean man turns out to be (a) Pecos Tommy. (b) Will's father. (c) the sheriff.

THINKING IT THROUGH _____

1. Why does the lean man make Will wait to see how the old man and his daughter react? How would the story have been different if they had left when Will wanted to?

2. Will seems to have a great change of mind. He steals some money; a few minutes later, he returns it. What is the reason for this change of mind? Could such a big change in such a short time happen in real life?

3. The character we think is Pecos Tommy suddenly turns out to be someone else. What changes—the character or our knowledge of him?

4. The story ends when the lean man tells who he is. What do you think will happen next?

Literary Skills

Understanding Characters

You now know two ways to learn about characters in a story:

- Note what the author tells you about them (page 34).
- Listen to what the characters say (page 43).

A third way to learn about characters is to *think about what the characters do.* Will Arblaster in "Gold-Mounted Guns" does a number of things that show the kind of person he is. First, although he is nervous, he still approaches the man he thinks is Pecos Tommy, a very dangerous criminal. This shows that Will has nerve, maybe even courage.

What does Will do that shows he is probably pretty smart? For one thing, when he and the lean man get to the cabin and find no one at home, Will still looks for the money. He explains that folks know Pecos Tommy is around, so they are likely to hide their money at home.

What does Will do at the end of the story that shows his bravery? Write two or three sentences in your own words describing one of his brave actions.

What does Will do that shows he is kind? Write two or three sentences describing something he does that shows his kindness.

Composition

Follow your teacher's instructions before completing *one* of these writing assignments.

1. Write at least five words or phrases from the story that tell you it is nighttime.
2. What kind of person do you think Pa Sanderson's daughter is? Write at least three things she says or does that support your answer.

Marjorie Kinnan Rawlings (1896-1953)

Marjorie Kinnan Rawlings was born in Washington, D.C., and was educated at the University of Wisconsin. She worked for newspapers in Kentucky and New York while writing short stories.

Her newspaper career was successful, but her short stories were not. Finally, in 1928, she left her newspaper job and moved to the backwoods of Florida. There she found a place and people that moved her to write with understanding and deep sympathy. Her stories began to be accepted for publication. In 1938 her novel *The Yearling* appeared. It won a Pulitzer Prize and was made into a movie. The novel's main character has been called "one of the most appealing boy characters since Huckleberry Finn."

In the story that follows, you will meet another appealing Rawlings character.

A MOTHER IN MANNVILLE

by Marjorie Kinnan Rawlings

▶ We all have to struggle to become somebody. But some of us have a harder time than others. Do you blame Jerry for wanting to be loved?

The orphanage is high in the Carolina mountains. Sometimes in winter the snowdrifts are so deep that the school and living quarters are cut off from the village below, from all the world. Fog hides the mountain peaks. The snow swirls down the valleys. And a wind blows so bitterly that the orphanage boys who take the milk twice daily to the baby cottage reach the door with fingers stiff in an agony of numbness.

"Or when we carry trays from the cookhouse for the ones that are sick," Jerry said, "we get our faces frostbit, because we can't put our hands over them. I have gloves," he added. "Some of the boys don't have any."

He liked the late spring, he said. The rhododendron was in bloom, a carpet of color, across the mountainsides, soft as the May winds. He called it laurel.

"It's pretty when the laurel blooms," he said. "Some of it's pink and some of it's white."

I was there in autumn. I wanted quiet, isolation, to do some troublesome writing. I was homesick, too, for the flaming of maples in October, and for corn shocks and pumpkins and black-walnut trees and the lift of hills. I found them all, living in a cabin that belonged to the orphanage, half a mile beyond the orphanage farm. When I took the cabin, I asked for a boy or man to come and chop wood for the fireplace. The first few days were warm. I found what wood I needed about the cabin. No one came, and I forgot the order.

- **agony** (AG uh nee) great pain
- **isolation** (eye suh LAY shun) being alone; away from others

I looked up from my typewriter one late afternoon, a little startled. A boy stood at the door, and my pointer dog, my companion, was at his side and had not barked to warn me. The boy was probably twelve years old, but under-sized. He wore overalls and a torn shirt, and was barefooted.

He said, "I can chop some wood today."

I said, "But I have a boy coming from the orphanage."

"I'm the boy."

"You? But you're small."

"Size don't matter, chopping wood," he said. "Some of the big boys don't chop good. I've been chopping wood at the orphanage a long time."

I pictured a small pile of mangled branches for my fires. I was well into my work and not interested in conversation. I was a little plain spoken.

"Very well. There's the ax. Go ahead and see what you can do."

I went back to work, closing the door. At first the sound of the boy drag-ging brush annoyed me. Then he began to chop. The blows were rhythmic and steady. Shortly I had forgotten him, the sound no more of an interruption than a steady rain. I suppose an hour and a half passed, for when I stopped and stretched, and heard the boy's steps on the cabin stoop, the sun was dropping behind the farthest mountain.

The boy said, "I have to go to supper now. I can come again tomorrow eve-ning."

I said, "I'll pay you now for what you've done," thinking I should probably have to insist on an older boy. "Ten cents an hour?"

"Anything is all right."

We went together back of the cabin. An astonishing amount of solid wood had been cut. There were cherry logs and heavy roots of rhododendron, and blocks from the waste pine and oak left from the building of the cabin.

"But you've done as much as a man," I said. "This is a splendid pile."

I looked at him, actually, for the first time. His hair was the color of the corn shocks, and his eyes, very direct, were like the mountain sky when rain is pend-ing—gray, with a showing of that miracu-lous blue. As I spoke a light came over him, as though the setting sun had touched him with the same overspread-ing glory with which it touched the moun-tains. I gave him a quarter.

• mangled (MANG guld) twisted

"You may come tomorrow," I said, "and thank you very much."

He looked at me, and at the coin, and seemed to want to speak, but could not, and turned away.

"I'll split the kindling tomorrow," he said over his thin ragged shoulder. "You'll need kindling and medium wood and logs and backlogs."

At daylight I was half awakened by the sound of chopping. Again it was so even in texture that I went back to sleep. When I left my bed in the cool morning, the boy had come and gone, and a stack of kindling was neat against the cabin wall. He came again after school in the afternoon and worked until time to return to the orphanage. His name was Jerry; he was twelve years old, and he had been at the orphanage since he was four. I could picture him at four, with the same grave gray-blue eyes and the same—independence? No, the word that comes to me is "integrity."

The word means something very special to me, and the quality for which I use it is a rare one. My father had it—but almost no one I know has it with the clarity, the purity, the simplicity of a mountain stream. But the boy Jerry had it. It is bedded on courage, but it is more than brave. It is honest, but it is more than honesty. The ax handle broke one day.

Jerry said the woodshop at the orphanage would repair it. I brought money to pay for the job and he refused it.

"I'll pay for it," he said. "I broke it. I brought the ax down careless."

"But no one hits accurately every time," I told him. "The fault was in the wood of the handle. I'll see the man from whom I bought it."

It was only then that he would take the money. He was standing back of his own carelessness. He was a free-will agent and he chose to do careful work, and if he failed, he took the responsibility for it.

And he did for me the unnecessary thing, the kind and thoughtful thing, that we find done only by the great of heart. Things no training can teach, for they are done on the instant, and not based on experience. He found a cubby-hole beside the fireplace that I had not noticed. There, of his own accord, he put kindling and "medium" wood, so that I might always have dry fire material ready in case of sudden wet weather. A stone was loose in the rough walk to the cabin. He dug a deeper hole and steadied it, although he came, himself, by a shortcut over the bank. I found that when I tried to return his thoughtfulness with such things as candy and apples, he was wordless. "Thank you" was, perhaps, an ex-

---

- kindling (KIND ling) **small pieces of wood for starting a fire**
- **integrity** (in TEG ri tee) **honesty; uprightness; wholeness of being**
- clarity (KLAR i tee) **clearness**
- accurately (AK yur it lee) **perfectly on target**

pression for which he had had no use, for his courtesy was natural. He only looked at the gift and then at me, and a curtain lifted, so that I saw deep into the clear well of his eyes. Gratitude was there, and affection, soft over the firm rock of his character.

He made simple excuses to come and sit with me. I could no more have turned him away than if he had been physically hungry. I suggested once that the best time for us to visit was just before supper, when I left off my writing. After that, he waited always until my typewriter had been quiet for some time. One day I worked until nearly dark. I went outside the cabin, having forgotten him. I saw him going up over the hill in the twilight toward the orphanage. When I sat down on my stoop, a place was warm from his body where he had been sitting.

He became close, of course, with my pointer, Pat. There is a strange understanding between a boy and a dog. Perhaps they possess the same singleness of spirit, the same kind of wisdom. It is difficult to explain, but it exists. When I went across the state for a weekend, I left the dog in Jerry's charge. I gave him the dog whistle and the key to the cabin, and left enough food. He was to come two or three times a day and let out the dog, and feed and exercise him. I should return Sunday night, and Jerry would take out the dog for the last time Sunday af-

ternoon and then leave the key under an agreed hiding place.

My return was delayed and fog filled the mountain passes so that I dared not drive at night. The fog held the next morning, and it was Monday noon before I reached the cabin. The dog had been fed and cared for that morning. Jerry came early in the afternoon, anxious.

"The superintendent said nobody would drive in the fog," he said. "I came just before bedtime last night and you hadn't come. So I brought Pat some of my breakfast this morning. I wouldn't have let anything happen to him."

"I was sure of that. I didn't worry."

"When I heard about the fog, I thought you'd know."

He was needed for work at the orphanage and he had to return at once. I gave him a dollar in payment, and he looked at it and went away. But that night he came in the darkness and knocked at the door.

"Come in, Jerry," I said, "if you're allowed to be away this late."

"I told maybe a story," he said. "I told them I thought you would want to see me."

"That's true," I assured him, and I saw his relief. "I want to hear about how you managed with the dog."

He sat by the fire with me, with no other light, and told me of their two days together. The dog lay close to him, and found a comfort there that I did not have

---

- gratitude (GRAT i tood) **thankfulness**
- **possess** (puh ZES) **have**

for him. And it seemed to me that being with my dog, and caring for him, had brought the boy and me, too, together, so that he felt that he belonged to me as well as to the animal.

"He stayed right with me," he told me, "except when he ran in the laurel. He likes the laurel. I took him up over the hill and we both ran fast. There was a place where the grass was high and I lay down in it and hid. I could hear Pat hunting for me. He found my trail and he barked. When he finally found me, he acted crazy, and he ran around and around me, in circles."

We watched the flames.

"That's an apple log," he said. "It burns the prettiest of any wood."

We were very close.

He suddenly needed to speak of things he had not spoken of before, nor had I cared to ask him.

"You look a little bit like my mother," he said, "Especially in the dark, by the fire."

"But you were only four, Jerry, when you came here. You have remembered how she looked, all these years?"

"My mother lives in Mannville," he said.

For a moment, finding that he had a mother shocked me as greatly as anything in my life has ever done. I did not know why it disturbed me. Then I understood my distress. I was filled with a passionate resentment that any woman should go away and leave her son. A fresh anger added itself. A son like this one. . . . The orphanage was a wholesome place, the officials were kind, good people, the food was more than adequate, the boys were healthy, a ragged shirt was no hardship, nor the doing of clean labor. Granted, perhaps, that the

- **passionate** (PASH un it) **full of strong feeling**
- **resentment** (ri ZENT munt) **feeling of being insulted or treated unfairly**
- **adequate** (AD uh kwit) **enough**

64

boy felt no lack, what about the mother? At four he would have looked the same as now. Nothing, I thought, nothing in life could change those eyes. His quality must be apparent to an idiot, a fool. I burned with questions I could not ask. In any of them, I was afraid, there would be pain.

"Have you seen her, Jerry—lately?"

"I see her every summer. She sends for me."

I wanted to cry out. "Why are you not with her? How can she let you go away again?"

He said, "She comes up here from Mannville whenever she can. She doesn't have a job now."

His face shone in the firelight.

"She wanted to give me a puppy, but they can't let any one boy keep a puppy. You remember the suit I had on last Sunday?" He was plainly proud. "She sent me that for Christmas. The Christmas before that"—he drew a long breath, enjoying the memory—"she sent me a pair of skates."

"Roller skates?"

My mind was busy, making pictures of her, trying to understand her. She had not, then, entirely deserted or forgotten him. But why, then. . . . I thought, "But I must not condemn her without knowing more."

"Roller skates. I let the other boys use them. They're always borrowing them. But they're careful of them."

What fact other than poverty. . . .

"I'm going to take the dollar you gave me for taking care of Pat," he said, "and buy her a pair of gloves."

I could only say, "That will be nice. Do you know her size?"

"I think it's eight and a half," he said. He looked at my hands.

"Do you wear eight and a half?" he asked.

"No. I wear a smaller size, a six."

"Oh! Then I guess her hands are bigger than yours."

I hated her. Poverty or no, there was other food than bread, and the soul could starve as quickly as the body. He was taking his dollar to buy gloves for her big stupid hands, and she lived away from him, in Mannville, perfectly content with sending him skates.

"She likes white gloves," he said. "Do you think I can get them for a dollar?"

"I think so," I said.

I decided that I should not leave the mountains without seeing her and knowing for myself why she had done this thing.

The human mind scatters its interests as though made of thistledown, and every wind stirs and moves it. I finished my work. It did not please me, and I gave my thoughts to another field. I should need some Mexican material.

I made arrangements to close my Florida place. Mexico immediately, and doing the writing there. Then, Alaska with my brother. After that, heaven knew what or where.

• **condemn** (kun DEM) consider guilty

I did not take time to go to Mannville to see Jerry's mother, nor even to talk with the orphanage officials about her. My mind was busy with my work and my plans. And after my first fury at her—we did not speak of her again—his having a mother not far away, in Mannville, relieved me of the ache I had had about him. He did not question the odd relation. He was not lonely. It was none of my concern.

He came every day and cut my wood and did small helpful favors and stayed to talk. The days had become cold, and often I let him come inside the cabin. He would lie on the floor in front of the fire, with one arm across the pointer, and they would both doze and wait quietly for me. Other days they ran with a common ecstasy through the laurel, and since the asters were now gone, he brought me back red maple leaves, and chestnut boughs dripping with a grand yellow. I was ready to go.

I said to him, "You have been my good friend, Jerry. I shall often think of you and miss you. Pat will miss you too. I am leaving tomorrow."

He did not answer. When he went away, I remember that a new moon hung over the mountains, and I watched him go in silence up the hill. I expected him the next day, but he did not come. The details of packing my personal belongings, loading my car, arranging the bed over the seat, where the dog would ride, occupied me until late in the day. I closed the cabin and started the car, noticing that the sun was in the west and I should do well to be out of the mountains by nightfall. I stopped by the orphanage and left the cabin key and money for my light bill with Miss Clark.

"And will you call Jerry for me to say good-by to him?"

"I don't know where he is," she said. "I'm afraid he's not well. He didn't eat his dinner this noon. One of the boys saw him going over the hill into the laurel. He was supposed to fire the boiler this afternoon. It's not like him; he's unusually reliable."

I was almost relieved, for I knew I should never see him again, and it would be easier not to say good-by to him.

I said, "I wanted to talk with you about his mother—why he's here—but I'm in more of a hurry than I expected to be. It's out of the question for me to see her now. But here's some money I'd like to leave with you to buy things for him at Christmas and on his birthday. It will be better than for me to try to send him things. I could so easily duplicate—skates, for instance."

She blinked her honest eyes.

"There's not much use for skates here," she said.

Her stupidity annoyed me.

"What I mean," I said, "is that I don't want to duplicate things his mother sends him. I might have chosen skates if I didn't know she had already given them to him."

"I don't understand," she said. "He has no mother. He has no skates."

• **duplicate** (DOO pli kayt) repeat; do the same thing

ALL THINGS CONSIDERED ──────────────

1. The narrator (person who tells the story) is a (a) teacher. (b) writer. (c) skater.

2. She hires a boy from a nearby orphanage to (a) chop wood. (b) run errands. (c) sweep the cabin.

3. The boy who arrives is (a) older than she expected. (b) smaller than she expected. (c) her own son.

4. Jerry surprises her by (a) chopping a fine pile of wood. (b) breaking the ax handle. (c) calling her Mother.

5. For the narrator, the quality that Jerry has is (a) happiness. (b) intelligence. (c) integrity.

6. Jerry waits for the narrator to finish work each day in order to (a) be given dinner. (b) sit and talk. (c) receive his pay.

7. At one point, Jerry tells the narrator that (a) she is his mother. (b) she reminds him of his mother. (c) he has no mother.

8. The narrator is outraged that anyone would (a) want to be Jerry's mother. (b) lie to her. (c) leave a son like Jerry.

9. When the narrator tells Jerry she is leaving, he (a) walks away silently. (b) asks her to stay. (c) asks to go with her.

10. At the end of the story, the narrator is surprised to learn that (a) Jerry stole her dog, Pat. (b) Jerry has a mother *and* a father. (c) Jerry has no mother.

THINKING IT THROUGH ──────────────

1. We are told that Jerry didn't have much use for the words "Thank you." Does this mean he is lacking in manners? Find the sentence in the story that gives the narrator's view of this.

2. Would you describe Jerry as responsible? Give examples to support your answer.

3. How does the narrator feel when Jerry tells her he has a mother in Mannville?

4. Why does Jerry say he has a mother in Mannville? Why doesn't he mention her at the beginning? How would the story have been different if he never told the narrator that he had a mother?

Building From Details

Visualizing From Details

When you picture what you read, you are **visualizing.** Writers often use descriptive words and details to give a clear mental picture of the characters, setting, and events in a story.

In the following passage from "A Mother in Mannville," which details help you picture Jerry?

> I looked up from my typewriter one late afternoon, a little startled. A boy stood at the door, and my pointer dog, my companion, was at his side. . . . The boy was probably twelve years old, but undersized. He wore overalls and a torn shirt, and was barefooted.

Below are two drawings of Jerry as he is described in the following passage. Which drawing best fits the passage? List four details that helped you decide.

> He would lie on the floor in front of the fire, with one arm across the pointer, and they would both doze and wait quietly for me.

Composition

Follow your teacher's instructions before completing *one* of these writing assignments.

1. The last three sentences in the story are spoken by Miss Clark at the orphanage: "'I don't understand,' she said. 'He has no mother. He has no skates.'" Write one or two sentences that the narrator might have said in response to Miss Clark. Use quotation marks around her exact words.

2. The narrator says of Jerry, "And he did for me the unnecessary thing, the kind and thoughtful thing, that we find done only by the great of heart." Do you know anyone like that? Write a few sentences telling about something that person did.

ADVICE TO TRAVELERS

by Walker Gibson

A burro once, sent by express,
His shipping ticket on his bridle,
Ate up his name and his address,
And in some warehouse, standing idle,
He waited till he like to died.
The moral hardly needs the showing:
Don't keep things locked up deep inside—
Say who you are and where you're going.

WAYS OF KNOWING

1. In the first sentence of this poem, the subject is the burro. What are the verbs—that is, what does the burro do?

2. What is humorous in this poem? What is serious?

3. "Advice to Travelers" seems to be a poem for travelers—people in a bus station or airport, for example. But in what sense are we all travelers? Is the advice in the poem good for all of us? Why?

- burro (BUR oh) a small donkey
- bridle (BRY dul) the part of a horse's harness that fits on its head

69

VOCABULARY AND SKILL REVIEW ⎯⎯⎯⎯⎯⎯⎯⎯

Before completing the exercises that follow, you may wish to review the **bold-faced** words on pages 48–69.

I. Choose the answer that best completes each sentence.

1. If you spoke *apologetically,* you spoke (a) as if you were sorry. (b) as if you were angry. (c) very rapidly.

2. A person with *integrity* is (a) clever. (b) neat. (c) honest.

3. You shouldn't *condemn* people until you are sure they are (a) innocent. (b) guilty. (c) honest.

4. *Passionate* feelings can be of love or hate, but they are always (a) strong. (b) silly. (c) weak.

5. To *possess* something is to (a) want it. (b) fight it. (c) have it.

6. Don't *duplicate* your efforts if you want to (a) waste time. (b) save time. (c) tell time.

7. The *agony* of fingers numb with cold was shown by the boy's (a) smile. (b) shrug. (c) tears.

8. The *unemotional* woman did not like to show that she had (a) intelligence. (b) common sense. (c) feelings.

9. The *lone* star twinkled in a sky that was (a) otherwise empty. (b) full of stars. (c) sprinkled with stars.

10. Some people seek *isolation* because they enjoy being (a) in front of an audience. (b) alone. (c) in a crowd.

II. In your mind, visualize a character from "Gold-Mounted Guns" or "A Mother in Mannville."

1. Picture the character at a specific point in the story. What is the character doing or saying? What is the character wearing? What do you think is the expression on the character's face?

2. Write a short description of the character. Include as many details as you can.

UNIT REVIEW

Each unit review is a chance to review your study of literature. Do it carefully and it will strengthen your learning. Evaluate your right and wrong answers. This will tell you what you know, what you don't know, and what you aren't certain about. It will make future learning easier.

Write all of your answers on a separate sheet of paper.

I.   Match the terms in Column A with their definitions in Column B.

	A		B
1.	theme	a)	story of one's own life
2.	plot	b)	where and when a story happens
3.	characters	c)	who a story is about
4.	setting	d)	what happens in a story
5.	autobiography	e)	basic meaning of a story

II. You have read about the five w's. On your paper, write the w word that belongs in each blank below.

1. _____ characters
2. _____ actions or events
3. _____ place
4. _____ time
5. _____ reason for something

After each Unit Review there is a passage for you to practice reading aloud. Reading aloud helps you develop self-confidence and improve your speaking ability. It can also be fun.

Keep these tips in mind:

1. Before you speak, get comfortable. Relax. Then speak loudly and clearly. Most beginners speak too fast—don't!
2. If you happen to make a mistake, forget it. Go on reading.
3. Pretend that you wrote the words you are speaking. Let your face and tone of voice express the meaning of the words.
4. Read the piece aloud several times. Each time you read it, you will notice different things and get different meanings.

SPEAKING UP

This first unit is almost over. But the chance to reflect on who you are and who you are becoming is yours each day. The following poem expresses that idea in language any one of us might use.

Begin by reading the poem silently. Think about the ideas and feelings expressed. Then, read the poem aloud. (You may want to read it in front of a mirror or to a friend.) Pause at periods and commas, and raise your voice at the end of questions.

THIS DAY IS OVER

by Calvin O'John (Ute-Navajo)

When the day is over,
I think of all I did.
Did I goof off,
Or did I accomplish something?
Did I make a new friend,
Or did I make an enemy?
Was I mad at everybody,
Or was I nice?
Anyway, what I did today is over.
While I sleep,
The world will be shining up
A new day for me to use,
Or goof up,
Or whatever I decide
To do with it.
Tonight, I pick out
"Nice," and
"Friendly," and
"Accomplish something."

WRITING YOUR OWN DESCRIPTION

Did you ever see a stranger and wonder what that person was like? Try doing that with one of the people in this picture. You will be asked to write a description of that person. Your description should make a reader want to find out more about the person.

1. **Prewriting:** First give the person a name. Then list about five words that describe the person. Include words that describe personality as well as looks.
2. **Writing:** Use your prewriting plan to write a paragraph. You might begin like this: Robin is very friendly. Her dark eyes sparkle when she smiles.
3. **Revising:** Reread your paragraph. Do the sentences follow in a natural order? Is your description interesting? Does each sentence have a subject and a verb? Check your punctuation and your capitalization. Make corrections and then rewrite your paragraph neatly.

73

IT'S ALL IN THE GAME

It's easy to cry that you're beaten—and die;
   It's easy to crawfish and crawl;
But to fight and to fight when hope's out of sight—
   Why, that's the best game of them all!

from "The Quitter" by Robert Service

There are many kinds of games—ball games and board games, street games and school-yard games. There are tricks to play on others. There is even the game of life.

As you read each selection in this unit, think about the kind of game being played. Ask yourself how well the players play the game. Do they play by the rules? Do they "fight and fight when hope's out of sight"? Who wins and who loses?

THE HORSE
OF THE SWORD

by Manuel Buaken

▶ This story takes place in the Philippines, an island country in the Pacific. Maning has talked his father into buying the "outlaw" horse. Can he now turn that horse into a winner? How do you develop a winner? Is it with a whip or with kindness and understanding?

"Boy, get rid of that horse," said one of the wise old men from Abra. "That's a bandit's horse. See that sign of evil on him? Something tragic will happen to you if you keep him."

But another one of the old horse traders who had gathered at that auction declared, "That's a good omen. The sword on his shoulder means leadership and power."

As for me, I knew this gray colt was a wonder horse the moment I saw him. These other people were blind. They only saw that this gray shaggy horse bore the marks of many whips, that his ribs almost stuck through his hide, that his great eyes rolled in defiance and fear as the auctioneer approached him. They couldn't see the meaning of that sword he bore—a marking not in the gray color, but in the way that the hair had arranged itself. It was parted to form an outline of a sword that was broad on his neck and tapered to a fine point on his shoulder.

Father, too, was blind against this horse. He argued with me and scolded: "Maning, when I promised you a pony as a reward for good work in high school English, I thought you'd use good judgment in choosing. It is true this horse has good blood. But he has always been worthless. He is bad-tempered and will not allow himself to be bathed and curried. No one has ever been able to ride him. Now, that black pony over there is well trained—"

- **tragic** (TRAJ ik) **very sad or harmful**
- omen (OH mun) **sign of what is to come**
- defiance (di FY uns) **refusal to obey**
- taper (TAY pur) **grow narrower at one end**
- curry (KUR ee) **comb and clean a horse**

76

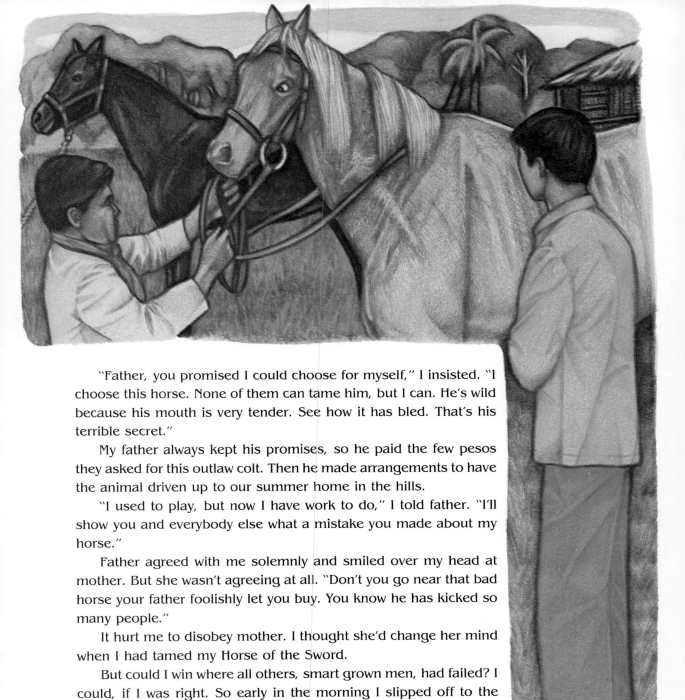

"Father, you promised I could choose for myself," I insisted. "I choose this horse. None of them can tame him, but I can. He's wild because his mouth is very tender. See how it has bled. That's his terrible secret."

My father always kept his promises, so he paid the few pesos they asked for this outlaw colt. Then he made arrangements to have the animal driven up to our summer home in the hills.

"I used to play, but now I have work to do," I told father. "I'll show you and everybody else what a mistake you made about my horse."

Father agreed with me solemnly and smiled over my head at mother. But she wasn't agreeing at all. "Don't you go near that bad horse your father foolishly let you buy. You know he has kicked so many people."

It hurt me to disobey mother. I thought she'd change her mind when I had tamed my Horse of the Sword.

But could I win where all others, smart grown men, had failed? I could, if I was right. So early in the morning I slipped off to the meadow. The Horse of the Sword was alert for any whips. He snorted a warning at me, and backed away as I approached.

- peso (PAY so) **Philippine paper money**
- solemnly (SOL um lee) **in a very serious way**

77

"What a body you have," I said, talking to accustom him to my voice and to assure him of my peaceful intentions. "Wide between the shoulders. That's for strength and endurance. Long legs for speed, and a proud arched neck."

I kept walking slowly toward him and talking softly until he stopped backing away. He neighed defiance at me and his eyes rolled angrily. Those big eyes were so human in their dare and their appeal. He didn't move now as I inched closer, but I could see his muscles twitch. Very softly and gently I put my hand on his shoulder. He jumped away. I spoke softly and again put my hand on his shoulder. This time he stood. I kept my hand on his shaggy shoulder. Then slowly I slipped it up to his head, then down again to his shoulder and down his legs. It was a major victory.

That very day I began grooming him, currying his coat, getting out the collection of insects in his skin. He sometimes jumped away but he never kicked at me. The next day I was able to lead my gray horse across the meadow with my hand on his mane as his only guide. This "untamable outlaw" responded to my light touch. It was the simple truth that his mouth was too tender for a jerking bridle bit. The pain just drove him wild. That's all that had made him an outlaw. Gentle handling, no loud shouts, no jerks on his tender mouth, good food, and a cleaned skin—these spelled health and contentment. Kindness had conquered. In a few weeks the hollows filled out with firm flesh to give the gray horse beauty. Spirit he always had.

Every morning I slipped off to the meadow. Mother was anxious to have the house quiet so father could write. So I had a free hand. It didn't take more than a month to change my horse from a raging outlaw to a glossy miracle. But was his taming complete? Could I ride him? Was he an outlaw at heart?

In the cool of a late afternoon, I mounted to his back. If he threw me I would be alone in my defeat. My fall would be cushioned by the grass. He trembled a little as I leaped to his back. But he stood quiet. He turned his head, his big eyes questioning me. Then, obedient to my "*Kiph*"—"Go"—he trotted slowly away.

- intention (in TEN shun) **something one means to do**
- **endurance** (en DUR uns) **power to keep going**
- contentment (kun TENT munt) **peaceful, happy feeling**

I knew a thrill then, the thrill of mastery and of fleet motion on the back of this steed whose stride was so smooth, so much like flying. He ran about the meadow eagerly, and I turned him into the mountain lane. "I know how a butterfly feels as it skims along," I cried delightedly.

Down the lane we flew. Mother stood beside her flame tree. The Horse of the Sword pranced into the yard. Mother gasped in amazement. "Mother, I disobeyed you," I blurted out quickly. "I'm sorry, but I had to show you. You were wrong, everybody was wrong about this horse."

Mother tried to be severe with me, but soon her smile warmed. She said, "Yes, I was wrong, Maning. What have you named your new horse?"

"A new name. That's a good idea. Mother, you must name him."

Mother's imagination gave her the name at once. "Glory, that's his name. *Moro Glorioso.* Gray Glory." So Moro Glory it was.

Too soon, vacation was over and I had to go back to school. But Moro Glory went with me.

"You take better care of that horse than you do of yourself," father complained. "If you don't stop neglecting your lessons, I'll have the horse taken up to the mountain pasture again."

"Oh, no, Father, you can't do that," I exclaimed. "Moro Glory must be here for his lessons too. Every day I teach him and give him practice. Next spring, at the *feria,* he is going to show all those fine horses they boast about so much."

Father knew what I meant. Those boasts had been mosquito bites in his mind too, for our barrio of Santa Lucia was known to be horse-crazy.

For instance, the priest, Father Anastacio, petted his horse Tango. The presidente had said in public, "My Bandirado Boyo is a

---

- **stride** (STRYD) long step; way of walking
- prance (PRANS) move with a light step, as if dancing
- blurt (BLURT) say suddenly, without meaning to
- severe (suh VEER) very strict
- *feria* (FAY ree uh) Spanish word for a fair
- **boast** (BOHST) brag; claim with pride
- *barrio* (BAH ree oh) Spanish word for neighborhood or area

horse whose bloodlines are known all the way back. These others are mere plow animals." But the horse that really set the tongues wagging in Santa Lucia and in Candon was Allahsan, who belonged to Bishop Aglipay. There were magic wings on his hooves, it was said. Another boaster was the city treasurer, who had recently acquired a silver-white horse, Purao.

The chief of police hung his head in shame now. His Castano had once been the pride of Santa Lucia. He had beaten Katarman—the black satin horse from the nearby barrio of Katarman who had so often humbled Santa Lucia's pride. Much as the horses of Santa Lucia set their owners to boasting against one another, all united against Katarman. Katarman, so the tale went, never faltered till his race was won.

These were the boasts and boasters I had set out to dust with defeat.

Winter was soon gone, the rice harvested, the sugar cane milled, and high school graduation was approaching. At last came the feria day. Excitement was a wild thing in the wind at the feria. News of the challenge of the wonder horse Moro Glory had spread. I could hear many people shouting, "The Horse of the Sword!" These people were glad to see the once-despised outlaw colt turn by magic into the barrio's pride. They were cheering for my horse, but the riders of the other horses weren't cheering. I was a boy, riding an untried yet much feared horse. They didn't want me there, so they raised the entrance fee. But father had fighting blood also. He borrowed the money for the extra fee.

The race was to be a long-distance trial of speed and endurance, run on the Provincial Road for a race track. A mile down to the river, then back to the judge's stand in the plaza.

Moro Glory looked them over, all the big-name horses. I think he measured his speed against them and knew they didn't have

- bloodlines (BLUD lynz) **ancestors; parents, grandparents, and so on**
- boaster (BOHST ur) **person who brags or boasts**
- humble (HUM bul) **make someone feel small or ashamed**
- falter (FAWL tur) **stumble; move in an unsteady way**
- fee (FEE) **charge or payment**
- plaza (PLAH zuh) **public square or market area**

enough. I looked them over too. I was excited. Yet I knew I must be on guard. These riders were experienced. So were their horses. Moro Glory had my teaching only. I had run him this same course many times. Moro Glory must not spend his strength on the first mile. He must save his speed for a sprint. In the high school, I had made the track team. An American coach had taught me, and I held this teaching in my head now.

The starter gave his signal and the race began. Allahsan led out at a furious pace. The other horses set themselves to overtake him. It hurt my pride to eat the dust of all the others all the way out the first mile. I knew it must be done.

"Easy," I commanded, and Moro Glory obeyed me as always. We were last, but Moro Glory ran that mile feather-light on his feet.

At the river's bank all the horses turned quickly to begin the last mile. The flagman said, "Too late, boy," but I knew Moro Glory.

I loosened the grip I held and he spurted ahead in flying leaps. In a few space-eating strides he overtook the tiring Allahsan. The pace-setter was breathing in great gasps. "Where are your magic wings?" I called as we passed.

"*Kiph,*" I urged Moro Glory. I had no whip. I spoke to my horse and knew he would do his best. I saw the other riders lashing their mounts. Only Moro Glory ran as he willed.

Oh, it was a thrill, the way Moro Glory flew, his hooves hardly seeming to touch the ground. The wind whipped at my face and I yelled just for pleasure. Moro Glory thought I was commanding more speed and he gave it. He flattened himself closer to the ground as his long legs reached forward for more and more. Up, and up. Past the strong horses from Abra, past the bright Tango. Bandirado Boyo was next in line. Moro Glory surged past him. Then Purao yielded his place without a struggle.

Now there was only Katarman, the black thunder horse ahead, but several lengths ahead. Could Moro Glory make up this handicap

- course (KORS) **road or path**
- sprint (SPRINT) **short run at top speed**
- flagman (FLAG mun) **person who gives signals**
- spurt (SPURT) **move in a short, quick burst of energy**
- pace-setter (PAYS SET ur) **one who sets the speed**
- handicap (HAN dee cap) **anything that adds to the difficulty of a task**

81

in this short distance? Already we were at the big tree—this was the final quarter.

"Here it is, Moro Glory. This is the big test," I shouted. "Show Katarman how your sword conquers him."

Oh, yes, Moro Glory could do it. And he did. He ran shoulder to shoulder with Katarman.

I saw that Katarman's rider was swinging his whip wide. I saw it come near to Moro Glory's head. I shouted to the man and the wind brought his answering curse at me. I must decide now, decide between Moro Glory's danger and the winning of the race. That whip might blind him. I knew no winning was worth that. I pulled against him, giving up the race.

Moro Glory had always obeyed me. He always responded to my lightest touch. But this time my sharp pull at his bridle brought no response. He had the bit between his teeth. Whip or no whip, he pulled ahead of Katarman.

"Moro Glory—the Horse of the Sword," the crowd cheered as the gray horse swept past the judges, a winner.

I leaped from his back and caught his head. Blood streamed down the side, but his eyes were unharmed. The sword on his shoulder was touched with a few drops of his own blood.

Men also leaped at Katarman, and dragged his rider off before the judges could interfere. The winner's wreath and bright ribbon went to Moro Glory, and we paraded in great glory. I was so proud. The Horse of the Sword had run free, without a whip, without spurs. He had proved his leadership and power. He had proved himself.

Golden days followed for Moro Glorioso. Again and again we raced, and always Moro Glory won.

Then came the day when my father said, "The time has come for you, my son, to prove your sword, as Moro Glory proved his. You must learn to be a leader."

And so I sailed away to America, to let the world know my will. As Moro Glory had proved himself, so must I.

- wreath (REETH) circle of flowers
- spur (SPUR) sharp spike on a rider's boot used to make the horse go faster

ALL THINGS CONSIDERED _____

1. Maning's father promises him a horse as a (a) reward for good schoolwork. (b) way to become famous. (c) pet to keep him company.

2. People think Maning should not buy the gray horse because (a) the boy does not know enough about horses. (b) they are afraid Maning and his horse will win all the races. (c) they think the horse is dangerous.

3. Maning sees that the horse is wild because (a) a bridle and bit bother its tender mouth. (b) it comes from a stable of bad horses. (c) the "sword" on its shoulder has made it evil.

4. The most important thing Maning does to tame the horse is to (a) refuse to feed it unless it obeys. (b) speak gently to it and pat it softly. (c) ride it in the meadow.

5. Once tamed, the horse is named Moro Glory by (a) Maning. (b) Maning's mother. (c) Maning's father.

6. Moro Glory is entered in a race that takes place (a) during the winter. (b) in the spring. (c) while Maning is away at school.

7. Maning learned his ideas about racing from (a) a track coach. (b) the chief of police. (c) books on horse racing.

8. Maning is different from the other riders because he does not (a) care if he wins or loses. (b) use a whip. (c) race his horse hard in the last mile.

9. Maning is afraid to let his horse pass Katarman because (a) the people cheering for Katarman have threatened him. (b) he does not want to race his horse too hard. (c) the other rider's whip might blind Moro Glory.

10. After winning several races with Moro Glory, Maning (a) travels to America. (b) returns to high school. (c) becomes the new presidente.

THINKING IT THROUGH _____

1. If you had to tame a wild horse, how would you go about it? Would you follow the same steps as Maning? Explain.

2. Do you think Maning's decision not to pass Katarman was a good one? Why do you think Moro Glory did not slow down when Maning pulled at the bridle?

3. Before winning the race, Maning had several other victories. What were they? See if you can think of at least three ways that Maning "won" something important.

4. Reread the last two paragraphs of the story. What does Maning's father mean when he says, "The time has come for you, my son, to prove your sword, as Moro Glory proved his"?

84

Literary Skills

Understanding Plot

A series of events or actions takes place in every story. This series of events is called the **plot.** The events that make up the plot are all connected. Together, these connected events tell the story.

The plot of most stories can be told in one sentence. In "The Horse of the Sword" the sentence that tells the plot might be: "A boy gets an 'outlaw' horse, tames it, and wins a race."

Many smaller events in a story are also part of the plot. For example, look at the sentence on page 77. "My father always kept his promises, so he paid the few pesos they asked for this outlaw colt." That sentence tells part of the plot because it explains how the boy got the horse.

A description of the horse would not be part of the plot. A description of the place where something happened would not be part of the plot either. Only events are part of the plot.

Read the sentences below. On a separate sheet of paper, write *P* if a sentence tells about plot or *N* if a sentence does not tell about plot.

1. The sword could be seen in the way the hair was arranged.
2. The boy talked softly to tame the horse.
3. The horse had insects in its coat.
4. The boy rode the horse for the first time.
5. The horse won the race without being whipped.

Composition

Follow your teacher's instructions before completing *one* of these writing assignments.

1. Both Maning and his horse win respect in the story. List some things teenagers can do to win respect from adults.
2. Write a one-paragraph summary of the story. Tell only the plot.

THE COMEBACK

by Elizabeth Van Steenwyk

▶ Laurie wanted very much to win the figure skating finals. Her accident had almost put her out of the skating game. Now she was back. Was winning the most important thing?

Laurie sat in the deserted dressing room that smelled of sweat socks and leftover lunches. She thought about all the times she'd done this before—just sat in a dressing room of an ice rink somewhere and waited for her turn to compete. Today wasn't one of the ordinary times, however. Today marked her comeback in the National Junior figure skating finals.

"If I place in one of the top three positions," she thought, "I'll qualify to move up to Seniors next year and then, after that, world competition and the Olympics. Fantastic!"

If Laurie thought, coming down from her excitement with a thud. That big word *if*. Before the accident, no one could beat her in competition. From that first day, when she was ten and passed the Preliminary test, she'd glided right through the local divisions into National Beginners.

"Hi, Laurie," Kathy said, suddenly bursting through the door. "Welcome back to the competition ranks. We've missed you these last six months."

"I've missed being here," Laurie said.

"How's the knee?" Kathy's face suddenly turned serious. "Is it going to slow you down? I mean, you had such a lot going for you. We really thought you'd be in the Seniors by now and then in the Olympics."

"I guess we'll find out tonight just where I stand," Laurie felt her confidence drain away.

- **compete** (kum PEET) **enter a contest and try to win**
- qualify (KWOL i fy) **show that one has the needed ability**
- competition (kom puh TISH un) **contest; test of skill**
- thud (THUD) **dull sound**
- preliminary (pri LIM uh ner ee) **first; before the main part**
- **confidence** (KON fi dens) **belief in oneself**

"We have some new people this year, Laurie," Kathy said, adjusting her laces. "A girl from Connecticut named Jinny Jordan, who's really strong in everything—schools, freestyle, you name it."

"I saw some of her figures this morning," Laurie said. "They were unbelievable!"

"Wait'll you see her freestyle program tonight," Kathy said. "She does four double axels and a triple toe loop at the end. Can you believe it?"

Laurie thought about this and knew that she'd have to include a triple toe loop, too. She had hoped to leave it out because it put an added strain on her knee, but now there was no choice. "I'll have to try the triple and pray," she thought.

"Is Jinny ahead in the scoring?" Laurie asked.

"She's the one you have to beat this year," Kathy replied as she hurried out, slamming the door behind her.

For a moment Laurie sat quietly, getting used to the feeling. Until the accident, everyone had said Laurie Collins is the one to beat. Now the one to beat was someone she'd never heard of before. "Has everyone written me out of the competition since the accident?" she wondered.

The accident. Who could have predicted it? No one figured on that awful rainy night when she and Mom were driving home after a

- schools (SKOOLZ) particular patterns that a skater must make in competition
- freestyle (FREE styl) choice of any patterns one likes, usually put together in a group of steps
- figure (FIG yur) step, pattern on the ice
- axel (AK sul) jump from one skate followed by a turn and landing on the other skate
- predict (pri DIKT) say something will happen before it happens

practice session. The car in front of them swerved on the slippery road, and they plowed into it. Later, examinations at the hospital revealed that torn cartilage in her right knee would need three months to mend and three more months of therapy and practice if she hoped to regain her position.

She jumped up and drew back as her right knee sent pain signals up and down her leg. The doctor said it would do that for a while. After waiting for the feeling to pass, she moved slowly across the room, then back again, to limber up. She did a few knee bends, holding onto the back of a chair for support.

Suddenly she caught sight of her image in the mirror, then stood up and looked herself right in the eye. "Who are you kidding?" she asked. "And what makes you think you have a chance tonight?" She covered her eyes with her hands, and then said with determination, "I just have to win."

The door swung open and Laurie looked up into the mirror again. Reflected there was a girl about her own age but shorter and more powerfully built. At the moment her arms were overloaded with a skate equipment bag, a thermos, a warm-up jacket, and a pair of skates.

The girl dumped some of her belongings onto a chair. The bag fell to the floor with a thud. "Hi, I'm Jinny Jordan," she said.

"Hi, I'm Laurie Collins." Laurie felt ill at ease.

"So this is the competition," she thought. "Because of her, I may lose tonight."

"This costume was my mom's idea," Jinny began, looking at her red, white, and blue skating dress. "I hope no one expects me to skate to the 'Star Spangled Banner'."

Laurie smiled and then looked down at Jinny's skating bag. "Hey," she said, "some stuff fell out of your bag, Jinny. Guess you didn't have it zipped up all the way."

- reveal (ri VEEL) **show; make known**
- cartilage (KAHR ti lij) **tough tissue that is attached to bones and that often turns into bone**
- therapy (THER uh pee) **medical treatment to help heal an injury or illness**
- limber up (LIM bur UP) **exercise to make the muscles move smoothly**
- determination (di tur mi NAY shun) **strong feeling of having made up one's mind to do something**

Jinny looked at the clothes and equipment that lay scattered on the floor. She started gathering her belongings when the door opened.

"Jinny," Kathy said, poking her head in. "You're supposed to get your music tape out to the sound engineer right away."

"I thought I gave it to him half an hour ago. Tell him it's the dark green box with my initials marked in white in the top right-hand corner."

"Maybe you better remind him. He claims you never gave it to him and he's about ready to explode."

"Then I don't know what I did with it," Jinny said, hurrying out after Kathy.

Laurie laced her boots one more time. "That's funny," she thought. "She has a chance to win tonight and she doesn't even know what she did with her music." Music was nearly as important to the freestyle program as the skating itself. It created mood, rhythm, style. Laurie had worked for months with her coach to select, then tape, her music program. If she lost her tape, she might as well forget about competing. It was that simple.

● rhythm (RITH um) regular sound or movement patterns

She stood up and walked to the chair to try a few more knee bends with her boots relaced. As she came down for the second time, Laurie saw something small and dark green behind the leg of the dressing table. She bent over to pull it out and saw the white initials J.J. in the top right-hand corner.

"Must have rolled out of her bag when she dropped it," Laurie thought. She stood there not moving for what must have been only seconds. Yet it seemed like years while she thought about her next move.

"All I'd have to do is forget that I found this. If Jinny doesn't have her music, she might as well not skate. She would look pretty ridiculous skating with no sound. And then," Laurie thought, "I would win, because she's the only real competition I have."

Laurie shivered slightly at the possibility. "Do I really want to win that much?" she wondered. "Does winning mean so much that I'd be willing to cheat for it?"

The door flew open. "Hey, you're on after Jinny," Kathy said, "and she's in real trouble. She still can't find her music."

Laurie hesitated for only a second. "Tell her I found her tape," she said, heading for the door. "And then would you mind giving it to the sound engineer. I'm already laced up."

Then Laurie made her way to the rink. Moving to the edge of the ice, she watched Jinny skate gracefully to the taped music. Afterward she nervously waited for her cue. When the announcer called her name, Laurie glided quickly to the center of the rink as her music began. She waited until the taped music filled the stadium over the loudspeaker, let the drum beat inside her head to catch the rhythm, then stroked hard into a double toe spin as the drum roll reached its peak. She followed with a strong spiral on her right leg that carried her half way around the edge of the rink.

"Good," she thought, "my knee's holding up!"

She didn't leave one figure out as she felt herself gliding, spinning out of one figure and into another. The audience applauded from time to time, enthusiastically supporting her in her comeback.

- hesitate (HEZ i tayt) **stop for a short time, as if not sure what to do**
- cue (KYOO) **signal to begin to do something**
- spiral (SPY rul) **movement in a circle or coil**

The closing strains of music lifted her into a difficult triple toe loop that made the audience gasp. Finally it was over. The applause blanketed her and she stood for a moment there in the spotlight. Afterward she waved to the crowd and quickly made her way to the exit. Her coach ran over and hugged her.

"You did it Laurie," she said. "You didn't make a single mistake. I think you won."

Laurie said nothing, but smiled as she waited for her marks. When they came, she knew she'd beaten Jinny Jordan and everyone else.

"Laurie, you won! You won!" Kathy screamed, as she rushed up to her.

"Yeah, I guess I did," was all Laurie could manage. Then, as she put on her blade guards and walked back to the dressing room, she thought, "But no one will ever know how close I really came to losing."

• strain (STRAYN) **musical sound or melody**

ALL THINGS CONSIDERED _____

1. Laurie is skating in (a) the Junior figure skating finals. (b) the Senior figure skating finals. (c) the Olympics.

2. Laurie stopped skating for six months because she (a) had lost too many competitions. (b) was in a car accident. (c) needed more time to practice.

3. The person Laurie has to beat is (a) Kathy. (b) Jinny. (c) Colin.

4. Laurie is worried about the triple toe loop because (a) she often does it wrong. (b) it caused her accident. (c) it puts strain on her knee.

5. Before going out to skate, she (a) does some exercises. (b) listens to her tape. (c) talks with her coach.

6. The music tape is important because it (a) sets the mood for the skating. (b) shows the skater can play music, too. (c) keeps others from doing the same steps.

7. Jinny's tape was (a) stolen by Laurie. (b) dropped on the floor. (c) lost by the sound engineer.

8. Laurie knows she will win for sure if (a) her music is better than anyone else's. (b) she does more double axels than anyone else. (c) Jinny does not have her music.

9. The applause Laurie hears as she skates seems to say (a) Kathy is winning. (b) the audience supports Laurie's comeback. (c) Jinny did the best triple toe loop.

10. At the end, Laurie feels glad because (a) she won without cheating. (b) even though she lost, she did her best. (c) she was not nervous.

THINKING IT THROUGH _____

1. Do you think it is harder to win the first time or to make a comeback? Why?

2. What words or phrases would you use to describe Jinny Jordan? Find details in the story to support your answers.

3. How does cheating affect the feeling of being a winner? Which is more important—doing your best or having others think you are the best?

Literary Skills

Conflict

How would you tell the plot of "The Comeback" in one or two sentences? Here is a possible answer. "When Laurie attempts to win a skating competition, she must decide whether to cheat. She does not cheat and wins honestly."

Think about the part that says "she must decide whether to cheat." That part of the story is a conflict. A **conflict** is a kind of fight, contest, or struggle. In this story, Laurie's conflict is with herself. Should she keep silent about Jinny's music tape and give herself a better chance of winning? Should she tell where Jinny's tape is and possibly lose? She must decide what to do.

There are two main kinds of conflict. One kind is the *conflict with oneself.* This is the conflict Laurie has in deciding what to do. The other kind is the *conflict a character has with other characters.* An example of this second kind of conflict is the competition between the skaters. In this story, Laurie's conflict with herself is the more important conflict.

Conflict helps make a story interesting. A plot depends on conflict. If you think about some of your favorite stories, you will probably find that the most exciting parts involve conflict.

Make two lists for the conflict Laurie has with herself. Call one list "Reasons for not helping Jinny." Call the other list "Reasons for helping Jinny." Write at least two reasons under each heading.

Composition

Follow your teacher's instructions before completing *one* of these writing assignments.

1. Imagine that you are a reporter talking to Laurie after the finals. Write five questions you would ask her. Remember, a reporter would not know about Laurie's conflict over Jinny's tape.
2. Do you think a person has the same feeling about winning after cheating as winning fair and square? Write a paragraph telling what you think about the two ways of winning.

THE
BACKGROUND

A **biography** (by AWG ruh fee) is the story of a real person's life. That person is the *subject* of the biography and may or may not be alive today. A biography may tell about the subject's entire life or just an important part of it.

To write a good biography, a writer needs facts and a sense of what the person is or was really like. To gather information, writers often interview the person or the person's family or friends. Facts about the person's life are also found in books, newspapers, magazines, and diaries.

How does a biography differ from an autobiography? Look back to page 35.

THE GREATEST WOMAN ATHLETE

by John Devaney

▶ At a time when most girls did not go out for sports, she was outstanding at every sport she tried. Then when life tested her, she fought like a winner. Here is a short biography of the person considered by many to be the outstanding woman athlete of the twentieth century.

The announcer's voice boomed through Dyche Stadium in Evanston, Illinois: "And now, the one-girl track team from Texas, Babe Didrikson . . . "

The big crowd waited for the start of the 1933 National AAU track-and-field championship. All eyes were on the 19-year-old girl from Texas, who was now marching out onto the track.

- track (TRAK) **sports and contests in running, throwing, and jumping**
- AAU—**initials of the Amateur Athletic Union, which is in charge of amateur athletic contests**

Her name was Mildred Didrikson. But no one called her Mildred. She'd been called Babe since she was 12. She earned the nickname playing baseball and slamming home runs so far that one kid said, "She hits 'em farther than Babe Ruth."

In just two years of competition, Babe Didrikson had already won 92 track-and-field medals. She'd set three American records in less than a year. And she had only begun.

As the greatest woman athlete of her time, she was never shy about her talents. "I knew exactly what I wanted to be when I grew up," she once said. "My goal was to be the greatest athlete who ever lived."

Babe's mother had been a skier in Norway. Mildred inherited her mother's interest in athletics. She and her sister played football, shot basketballs, threw baseballs, even lifted weights.

Surprisingly, all this activity didn't help Babe grow. As a sophomore in high school she was only five feet tall and weighed less than 90 pounds. Her size, though, didn't stop her from trying out for the Beaumont High girls' basketball team. The coach said she was too small. Babe, never one to be discouraged, spent a year practicing. By her junior year she'd only grown to five-foot-two

and 110 pounds, but she could hit baskets with deadly accuracy. The coach put her on the team.

One rainy night, Beaumont went to Houston to play. Watching the game was Colonel M. J. McCombs. The Colonel was a sports fan. He had organized his own basketball team for women, which he called the Cyclones. The team was one of the finest in the country. To keep it among the finest, the Colonel was always looking for new talent.

That night he found talent as he watched a thin girl with short black hair and a hawklike face pop baskets from all over the floor. After the game the Colonel talked to Babe. Would she come to Dallas after she was graduated the following June? The Colonel would pay her $75 a month to be a typist in his company during the day. This would enable her to be a Cyclone basketball player in the evenings and keep an amateur status.

The Babe was delighted. She was a quick typist, and $75 a month was a lot of money in those days. She went to Dallas, typed all day, and shot baskets much of the night. She shot so well that the Cyclones won the National AAU championship that year. Babe was picked to be on the women's All-American team.

To keep his players in condition during the off-season, the Colonel decided

- **goal** (GOHL) something one tries to reach; aim
- sophomore (SOF uh mor) person in the second year of high school or college
- accuracy (AK yuh ruh see) careful and exact way; way that is close to perfectly on target
- colonel (KUR nul) title of honor used in some southern states; also a title for a military officer

She was beating everyone. There was no sport she wouldn't try. Someone once asked her: "At what sport are you best?"

"I'm best at everything," said Babe.

She and the Colonel aimed to prove it at the 1932 Olympics in Los Angeles. To make the United States team, the best men and women track stars gathered at Dyche Stadium for the 1932 AAU championships. There, teams from all over the country would go after two prizes: the AAU championship for their team, and a place on the Olympic squad. Most teams numbered fifteen or twenty. The Colonel sent just one—Babe Didrikson.

The one-woman team marched into the stadium proudly, while the spectators buzzed. How would she do against champions from all over the nation?

In the dressing room the other girls learned quickly what Babe had in mind for them. "I'm gonna whup you all," she said in her slow drawl.

And that she did. During the next two days she took first place in the shot put, first in the javelin throw, first in the broad jump, first in the baseball throw, first in the hurdles, a tie for first in the high jump, and fourth in the discus.

to enter them in track-and-field meets. "What events," he asked Babe, "do you want to try?"

"How many events do they have in a track meet?" asked Babe.

"Oh, eight or nine."

"I'll try 'em all," said Babe.

By the end of the track season she had set new records for women.

- spectator (SPEK tay tur) **person who watches, not a player**
- drawl (DRAWL) **speak in a slow way**
- shot put (SHOT put) **contest in which a heavy metal ball (*shot*) is thrown for the greatest possible distance**
- javelin (JAV uh lin) **light spear that is thrown for the greatest possible distance**
- hurdle (HUR dul) **frame or fence that runners jump over as part of a race called *hurdles***
- discus (DIS kus) **heavy disk that is thrown for the greatest possible distance**

After the final event the judges counted up the team scores. Babe Didrikson was the winner. She was on her way to Los Angeles for the Olympics.

But she was unhappy. The Olympic rules allowed her to enter only three events—the high jump, the hurdles, and the javelin throw. "I'd like to win four first-place medals," she said. "If they let me enter the discus throw I think I can win that, too."

But the night before the Olympics, alone in her hotel room, an attack of nerves struck. There she was, only 18, someone who'd been competing in track-and-field events for only two years. She'd never had any real coaching. What she knew she'd read in track manuals or picked up watching others. Now she was in the Olympics, competing against champions from all over the world. Maybe she'd make a fool of herself. She paced up and down the room much of the night.

The next afternoon, her bony face serious, she walked nervously up to the line. She picked up the javelin, crouched for a few moments, then sprang toward the line, holding the javelin behind her right ear.

All her nervous energy, building throughout the night, suddenly exploded. Out flew the javelin in a high, flawless curve. The big crowd in the Los Angeles Coliseum—some 62,000 people—gasped. When the javelin landed, the crowd burst into applause. The spectators could see that it had landed in an area few of the javelin throwers had reached. Moments later the Coliseum was filled with cheering. The announcer had just read off the distance: 132 feet, 7⅞ inches—a world record for women. Babe had her first gold medal.

Five days later she knelt for the start of the 80-meter hurdles. At the gun, Violet Webb of Great Britain jumped into the lead, with Babe and Marjorie Clark of South Africa a foot behind her at the first hurdle.

Over they went, Violet a stride in front as the three hit the track. As they approached the second hurdle, Babe was closing the gap. She and Violet swept over the second hurdle like twins. But when they hit the ground, Babe was slightly ahead.

Down they charged for the third hurdle. Over they went. Now, with just two hurdles to go, Babe led, and the British runner was fading. But out of the pack on Babe's right, came flying America's Evelyn Hall.

Babe flew over the next-to-last hurdle, but she stumbled when she hit the track, losing a stride. As they headed for the last hurdle Evelyn Hall was only a foot behind.

- nerves (NURVZ) **extreme nervousness; panic**
- manual (MAN yoo ul) **book that explains how to do something**
- **compete** (kum PEET) **enter a contest and try to win**
- flawless (FLAW lis) **perfect; without any faults**

97

The two Americans glided over the last hurdle. As Babe hit the dirt she stumbled slightly again. Now Evelyn Hall and she were shoulder to shoulder as they sprinted, arms pumping, for the finish line.

Down they came, the two girls matching strides. Then, as all champions must, Babe reached down for something extra. In an explosion of energy, she took off to win by the length of a finger. The time was 11.7 seconds, a world record.

Now Babe had two gold medals. She seemed sure to win her third when she broke a world record for the high jump. But Jean Shiley, another American, cleared the bar on her final jump at 5-foot-5¼ inches, tying Babe.

The bar was set at 5-foot-5¾ inches. Both girls missed on their first two tries. On her third try Jean went over cleanly.

Now it was Babe's final turn—a third gold medal was riding on this last jump. She dashed toward the bar and sailed over it. The crowd burst into a roar as Babe jumped up, smiling. But a judge was running toward the bar, his hand high.

Foul! The jump did not count, the event was over. Jean Shiley had won the gold medal. The judge said that Babe had dived over the bar. In those days the jumper's feet had to go over the bar first.

"My feet went over first," Babe yelled. "I've been jumping that way all afternoon."

But the judge was firm. Later, sympathetic reporters gathered around this girl who'd collected two gold and one silver medal. "Is there anything at all you don't play?" asked one.

"Yes," said Babe. "Dolls."

During the next few years, in movie houses across the nation, people burst into applause when the newsreels showed her playing tennis against champion Vinnie Richards, or playing third base for the House of David men's baseball team, or playing basketball with a seven-man, three-woman team of her own. Once, on a dare, she pitched in spring training against the world champion Philadelphia A's.

By 1935 she was talking about a

- sprint (SPRINT) **run a short distance at top speed**
- explosion (eks PLOH zhun) **bursting forth**

career in golf. Oddly, this athlete who could play anything had trouble learning golf. But even when she was struggling, she told people: "I'm going to become the greatest woman golfer."

And she did, after years of practice that often left her hands bleeding and scarred. She hit tee shots 240 yards, longer than most men. In the 1940s and 1950s she was the top money-winner among women golfers.

"In any tournament," one reporter wrote, "there is Babe Didrikson and the rest."

In 1938 she married George Zaharias, a professional wrestler. Later, George gave up wrestling to become her business manager. Together they toured the country, winning golf prizes.

In 1953 Babe was found to have cancer. Three months after a major operation she went to Chicago for a big tournament. "I've just got to find out if I can play tournament golf again," she said. "It's the biggest thing in my life—next to George."

She won that tournament. A little later she won the U.S. Women's Open by 12 strokes. Coming off the 18th green, she shouted to reporters: "This will tell people not to be afraid of cancer."

That winter the sports writers awarded her the Ben Hogan Trophy for the greatest comeback of the year. The trophy went up on a shelf in Babe's home, along with a plaque from the Associated Press. On the plaque were the words: Babe Didrikson, Greatest Woman Athlete of the First 50 Years of the Twentieth Century.

There would be no more trophies. She went back to the hospital in 1956. She didn't have long to live. But when people came to visit her they went away cheered rather than sad. Babe laughed with them, told jokes, and repeated to them what she'd said to George: "Now, honey, don't take on so. While I've been in the hospital I've learned one thing. A moment of happiness is a lifetime, and I have had a lot of happiness. I have had a lot of it."

- **plaque** (PLAK) flat piece of wood or metal with something written on it, usually given to honor someone

ALL THINGS CONSIDERED _____

1. Mildred Didrikson was called Babe because she (a) was very young when she started in sports. (b) was small for her age. (c) hit baseballs like Babe Ruth.

2. In high school she (a) played basketball. (b) was on the track team. (c) played on the boys' football team.

3. She took a job typing because (a) there were no girls' sports teams. (b) she was not sure that she wanted to be an athlete. (c) she did not want to play for money.

4. In 1932, Babe went to the AAU games as (a) part of a Texas track team. (b) a one-woman team. (c) a basketball player.

5. At the 1932 Olympics, she was unhappy because she could not (a) compete against the men. (b) enter four events. (c) get the crowd's attention.

6. At the Olympics, she won (a) two gold medals. (b) three gold medals. (c) four gold medals.

7. One of her high jumps was called foul because she did not go over the bar (a) head first. (b) feet first. (c) without touching it.

8. Didrikson later gained fame in the sport of (a) golf. (b) wrestling. (c) boxing.

9. Her husband, George Zaharias, was a professional (a) golfer. (b) wrestler. (c) boxer.

10. She showed great courage when she learned (a) her husband had died. (b) she had cancer. (c) the sports writers had turned against her.

THINKING IT THROUGH _____

1. Why do some athletes brag about their skills? How may this help them? How may this hurt them?

2. When Babe Didrikson began her career, most girls did not want to be athletes. How can a person like Didrikson change the way people think about women athletes? Do you think that she would have more people to compete against today?

3. "Then, as all champions must, Babe reached down for something extra." What does this statement (page 98) mean? Have you ever had to do the same? If so, how did reaching down for something extra change your game?

4. In what way did Didrikson remain a winner to the end? Why did she think she was lucky? Do you agree with her?

Building From Details

Visualizing Actions

Can you picture the events in a story? You will recall that getting a picture in your mind is called **visualizing.** When you read, try to visualize the actions being described.

Reread the two paragraphs on page 97 that begin "The next afternoon, her bony face serious. . . ." Then look at the following drawings. Find details in each drawing that do *not* match the actions described. On a separate sheet of paper, explain what is wrong with the drawings and tell how to correct them.

Composition

Follow your teacher's instructions before completing *one* of these writing assignments.

1. Has anyone broken Babe Didrikson's records in the javelin throw or the 80-meter hurdles? Use an up-to-date almanac to look up Olympic track-and-field records for women. In complete sentences, tell who holds the current records in these two events.

2. Think of a sport you like to play or watch. What motion or movement is involved? Write a short paragraph to describe that action. Some motions you may want to describe are hitting a baseball, shooting a foul shot in basketball, or signaling to a friend that you have located seats in a crowded stadium. Pretend that the reader has to use your paragraph to copy the action.

101

THE BASE STEALER

by Robert Francis

▶ Did you ever watch someone steal a base in baseball? The runner schemes to gain another base while the pitcher is getting ready to throw. It takes a lot of skill to steal a base.

Poised between going on and back, pulled
Both ways taut like a tightrope-walker,
Fingertips pointing the opposites,
Now bouncing tiptoe like a dropped ball
Or a kid skipping rope, come on, come on,
Running a scattering of steps sidewise,
How he teeters, skitters, tingles, teases,
Taunts them, hovers like an ecstatic bird,
He's only flirting, crowd him, crowd him,
Delicate, delicate, delicate, delicate—now!

WAYS OF KNOWING

1. Timing is very important in stealing a base. How does the poet let you feel the timing?
2. The poet compares the base stealer to a tightrope-walker and then to a kid skipping rope. How is a base stealer like each?
3. What are the action words in the seventh line? What feeling do these words suggest?
4. Read the last line again. Why do you think the poet repeats the word *delicate*? What do you see happening after the last word, *now*?

- **poised** (POYZD) balanced and ready to move
- taut (TAWT) pulled tight
- skitter (SKIT ur) move quickly and lightly
- taunt (TAWNT) make fun of; tease
- hover (HUV ur) stay or wait without moving
- ecstatic (ek STAT ik) full of joy or delight

A FOOTBALL GAME

by Alice Van Eck

▶ When you think about the game of football, what comes to
mind? Here is one poet's idea of a football game.

It's the might, it's the fight
　　Of two teams who won't give in—
It's the roar of the crowd
　　And the "Go, fight, win!"

It's the bands, it's the stands,
　　It's the color everywhere.
It's the whiff, it's the sniff
　　Of the popcorn on the air.

It's a thrill, it's a chill,
　　It's a cheer and then a sigh;
It's that deep, breathless hush
　　When the ball soars high.

Yes, it's more than a score
　　Or a desperate grasp at fame;
Fun is King, win or lose—
　　That's a football game!

WAYS OF KNOWING

1. What are three things the speaker mentions about a football
   game? What is one thing the speaker does not mention? Is the
   speaker most likely a player or a spectator? Explain.

2. Can you read the poem so that it sounds like a cheer? Try it. What
   feeling do you get from the poem now?

3. Look at the first line of each part of the poem. What are the rhyming words?

4. Read the poem again. How does it talk about sounds? How does
   it talk about things you see? How does it talk about smells? Does
   it talk about things you taste or touch?

● **soar** (SAWR) fly upward

103

Building From Details

The Five Senses

Have you ever stopped to think that you get most of your information about the world through your five senses? The five senses are *sight, hearing, smell, taste,* and *touch.* If a writer really wants to get across an idea, a good way is to use words that appeal to the senses. There are many words that tell about sight, sound, smell, taste, and touch.

Look again at the poem "A Football Game." Which sense belongs with each of the following lines? Write your answers on a separate sheet of paper.

1. "It's the roar of the crowd
And the 'Go, fight, win!'"
2. "It's the color everywhere."
3. "It's the whiff, it's the sniff
Of the popcorn on the air."
4. "It's a cheer and then a sigh;
It's that deep, breathless hush"

Now, think of something about a football game that appeals to the sense of touch or taste. Write a sentence about it in the style of lines 1–4 above.

Composition

Follow your teacher's instructions before completing *one* of these writing assignments.

1. Think of a sport or other activity, other than football, that you enjoy. Write five sentences about it that begin: "I like the (sight, sound, and so on) of. . . . " Let each sentence tell about a different sense.
2. Write a short poem that appeals to the senses. In your poem, try to use descriptions that include three of the five senses. Use your own topic or choose a sport, food, place, or season of the year.

VOCABULARY AND SKILL REVIEW

Before completing the exercises that follow, you may wish to review the **bold-faced** words on pages 76–103.

I. On a separate sheet of paper, write the *italicized* word that best fills the blank in each sentence. Each word should be used only once.

boast	*compete*	*confidence*	*endurance*	*goal*
plaque	*poised*	*soar*	*stride*	*tragic*

1. The horse moved with a long _____ and with his head held high.
2. She was allowed to _____ in only three events.
3. You should have heard them _____ about how great they were.
4. Regular exercise helps to build strength and _____ for long races.
5. She gained more and more _____ in herself as she began to win.
6. Several lives were lost in the _____ accident.
7. The team worked hard to reach its _____ of winning the series.
8. We watched a kite _____ through the air like a bird.
9. The diver stood _____, waiting for the right moment to dive.
10. The players gave their manager a _____ as thanks for his help that season.

II. Sometimes it is interesting to watch a plot develop. You can do this by reading the first part of a story and then pausing to think about the direction the story is taking. You might ask yourself questions such as these: What actions are likely to happen in this setting? Have all the characters been introduced? What choices are the characters facing?

On the next page is the first part of a short story by one of Russia's finest writers. Leo Tolstoy was born in 1828 and died in 1910. He wrote many famous works, including *War and Peace*.

As you read, notice details that tell you about the plot. Watch for the beginnings of conflicts. Then answer questions 1–5 on a separate sheet of paper.

from THE BEAR HUNT

by Leo Tolstoy

▶ It's cold. A bear and a hunting party have crossed paths.
Everyone has a different idea of what the next move should
be.

We were out bear hunting. The friend who was with me shot a bear and wounded him, but the bear had gone off.

Our hunting party gathered together there in the forest and began trying to figure out what we should do. Should we go after the bear right away, or wait two or three days until the animal holed up somewhere?

We asked the two peasants who were acting as our guides if it would be possible to overtake the bear right then. One of them, an old man, said, "You can't do it. You'll have to wait until the bear has settled down. In about five days you'll be able to catch up with him. But if you go after him now you'll just scare him, and he won't hole up at all."

But the young guide disagreed with the old man, and said it was possible to overtake the bear right then and there. "In this snow," the guide said, "that bear won't get very far. He's a fat one, and he's probably lying down somewhere already. And if he isn't, I'll catch up with him on my skis."

My friend, though, was against going after the bear now. It was his opinion that we should wait.

So I said, "Let's not argue. You do what you want to. I'll go along with Demyan here, and track him. If we catch up with him, fine. If we don't, it doesn't matter. There's nothing else to do today, and it's still early."

So that's what we did.

1. Where does the action take place?
2. How does the plot begin?
3. What is the conflict between members of the hunting party?
4. Who is in conflict with the bear?
5. What action is about to take place?

RACING A CHAMPION

by Michael Baughman

▶ How important is age in sports? Can a teenager beat a man past 60 even if the man is a "pretty good swimmer"? The teenager in this story thinks he has a good chance.

I once competed in a 200-yard race against one of the greatest swimmers of the century. At the time—the early 1950s—I was a junior high student at Punahou School in Hawaii. I was also a member of the Outrigger Canoe Club on Waikiki Beach. During summer vacations, I often arrived there at 7:30 in the morning. The club was usually empty at that hour. For that matter, so was Waikiki Beach, except for a dozen or so beachboys getting ready for a day of taking tourists surfing and canoeing.

There was one other club member who would turn up early on summer mornings, though. He was a tall, handsome, silver-haired Hawaiian. I could tell that he didn't spend a lot of time at the beach because his face was a darker brown than his body. Occasionally, I saw him swimming with a slow, graceful stroke that carried him effortlessly along at an impressive pace to the beach wall and back again.

One morning when I'd arrived at the club earlier than usual, I was on the beach loading a two-person canoe for a day of spearing fish. He walked past me on his way to the water. Then he stopped.

"Where do you spear?" he asked.

"Usually by the old sunken barge, out past Baby Surf."

"Do you surf, too?" he asked.

"Sure!" I replied.

- beachboys (BEECH boyz) **young men who work at a beach club**
- **tourist** (TOOR ist) **person who travels for enjoyment**
- surf (SURF) **ride waves into the shore**
- occasionally (uh KAY zhun uh lee) **now and then**
- effortlessly (EF urt les lee) **without hard work; with little effort**

107

"How about swimming?"

"I'm a pretty good swimmer," I said.

"You probably go to Punahou School, right?"

"Right," I answered.

"You going to try out for their swim team?"

"I already play football and basketball and run track," I said.
"You're pretty fast. I'll bet you were on a swim team."

"I was once, a long time ago," he told me. "How would you like
to swim against me? Just for fun, I mean."

"Now? Against you?"

"Sure. Just for fun. Down to the beach wall and back." He
pointed in that direction. "It's just about 200 yards." He was smiling
at me.

"Okay," I said.

We waded into the warm water, out through the gentle waves to a
depth of about four or five feet. He smiled again, then said, "Let's
go," and started swimming.

108

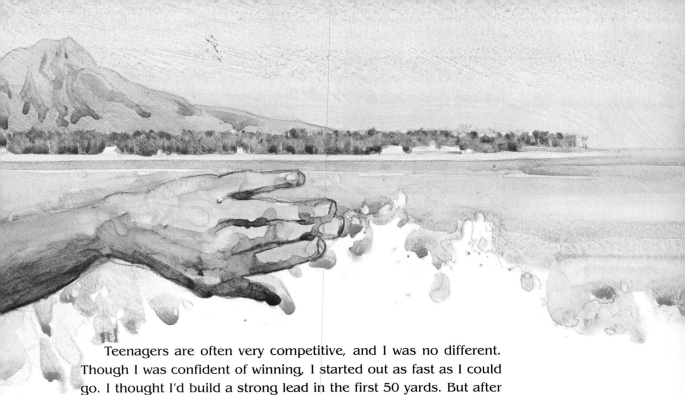

Teenagers are often very competitive, and I was no different. Though I was confident of winning, I started out as fast as I could go. I thought I'd build a strong lead in the first 50 yards. But after those 50 yards, we were even. He won't be able to hold this pace for long, I told myself.

When we reached the beach wall, we were still dead even. I was already about three-quarters exhausted. My legs felt heavy. My shoulders started to burn. As we turned back, he smiled at me.

"What's going on here?" I thought. "He doesn't look tired at all. He must be faking. He's got to be worse off than I am."

I was able to hold my pace for another 40 or 50 yards, at which point we were still swimming side by side. By now, though, I was taking two strokes to my opponent's one. My legs were in knots. My arms and shoulders were numb, and my head was spinning. I wanted very badly to quit and walk the rest of the way. But I struggled and made it, fighting the water, which felt like warm molasses.

"Just about even," he said, when we finally stopped in front of the club.

I was panting for breath. "Guess so," I said, trying not to show it.

"Thanks for the swim," he added.

"Sure."

- competitive (kum PET uh tiv) **eager to win**
- **opponent** (uh POH nunt) **person on the other side; person one is trying to beat**

109

"You're pretty good all right. But you might as well stay with football, basketball, and track," he told me.

"Well . . . sure," I said.

"See you later."

He walked out of the water and up the beach. I stayed where I was, recovering.

Ten minutes later my friend, Sammy Kauua, arrived. I told him *some* of what had happened.

"See that old guy standing by the canoe?" I said. "He's a pretty good swimmer. I swam down to the beach wall and back with him. Who is he, anyway?"

Sammy laughed. "Are you kidding? Where have you been all your life? Wake up! That's Duke Kahanamoku. He won gold medals at the Olympics. I guess he's pretty good for sure!"

That night I looked him up in an almanac. Duke Kahanamoku had won a gold and a silver medal in 1912 and two golds in 1920. He had also won a silver in 1924. He was past 60 when I "raced" against him.

Several days later when I saw Kahanamoku on the beach, I talked to him about his swimming career. What I really wanted to know was how an athlete could become good enough to win in the Olympics.

"How hard did you have to train?" I asked him. "I mean, how many miles a day did you have to swim?"

"Oh, I trained," he said. "But not hard, really. I did most of my swimming at the beach. I swam after my surfboard when a wave washed it in. I swam because I liked it. It was always fun, and I was pretty good at it. We trained all right, but mostly we just swam. It was natural. I always enjoyed doing it."

I was disappointed at the time because there was no easy answer there, no secret formula for success as an athlete. Thinking back on it now, though, I find the answer he gave me very appealing.

The preceding adaptation is reprinted courtesy of SPORTS ILLUS-TRATED. © 1984 Time Inc. First Person by Michael Baughman. "The Author Found He Was in Over His Head When He Took on This Old-timer."

- almanac (AWL muh nak) **book that has records of things that have happened**
- **career** (kuh REER) **work a person has chosen to do**
- formula (FOR myuh luh) **rule for doing things; recipe**

ALL THINGS CONSIDERED _____

1. The teenager is on the beach in the morning because it is (a) before school. (b) summer vacation. (c) a school holiday.

2. The teenager has (a) never seen the older man before. (b) often spoken to the older man. (c) seen the older man swimming before.

3. The two meet because (a) the man speaks to the teenager. (b) a friend introduces them. (c) the teenager speaks to the man.

4. The man asks the teenager to (a) take him canoeing. (b) introduce him to Sammy Kauua. (c) race him to the beach wall and back.

5. At the beginning of the race, the teenager (a) swims very fast. (b) is way ahead of the man. (c) lets the man take the lead.

6. By the time they reach the beach wall (a) the teenager knows he will win. (b) the teenager is almost exhausted. (c) the man has stopped smiling.

7. At the finish, (a) the man wins. (b) the teenager wins. (c) the man and teenager come in about even.

8. The man turns out to be (a) Sammy's uncle. (b) a swimming coach. (c) an Olympic champion.

9. The teenager talks about swimming to the man (a) later that afternoon. (b) the next day. (c) several days later.

10. The teenager is disappointed because the man (a) can't tell him how to become a champion. (b) does not seem to be proud of his swimming record. (c) refuses to race again.

THINKING IT THROUGH _____

1. In the first paragraph, the narrator says that he raced one of the greatest swimmers of the century. Did knowing that fact give away the story? Who did you think was going to win the race? What were your reasons?

2. Sammy told his friend who the older man was. Why do you think the young man looked it up in an almanac? Is Duke Kahanamoku a real person? How could you find out?

3. Do you think Duke Kahanamoku raced as hard as he could? Explain your answer.

Relationships

Sequence

To follow the plot of a story, you need to pay attention to the **sequence,** or order of events. This means knowing what happened first, second, third, and so on.

One way to follow the sequence of a story is to notice words or groups of words that tell *when.* Here are a few that you can find in "Racing a Champion": *once, at the time, in the early 1950s, one morning, then, ten minutes later, that night, several days later.* Words like these help you figure out when events are happening.

How well did you follow the sequence in "Racing a Champion"? Here are five events from the story. On a separate sheet of paper, rewrite them in the order in which they happened.

1. The race ends in a tie.
2. The man tells the teenager about how he trained.
3. The teenager watches an older man swim.
4. The man asks the teenager to race.
5. The teenager finds out who the man is.

Literary Skills

Rising Action

Have you noticed that as a story goes on the conflicts and events become more interesting and exciting? This is called **rising action.** Rising action keeps a reader interested in a story. Each new event helps build the story toward a **climax,** or high point in the action.

In "Racing a Champion," the swimming contest and the teenager's discovery about his opponent's background are the climax of the story. On a separate sheet of paper, list three events that are part of the rising action leading up to this high point.

Composition

Follow your teacher's instructions before completing *one* of these writing assignments.

1. If you were training for an important race or game, what would you do? In three or four sentences, list the most important things you would do to train. Tell them in the order you would do them.

2. Reread the next to the last paragraph of "Racing a Champion." In your own words, write a paragraph explaining what the man means. Also tell whether you agree or disagree with him.

$\mathcal{M}$ildred D. Taylor (Born 1943)

Many of the stories in Mildred D. Taylor's books come from stories told to her by her father. Some of these stories, in turn, came from her father's parents and grandparents.

Taylor was born in Jackson, Mississippi, but grew up in Toledo, Ohio. After graduating from college, she spent two years with the Peace Corps in Ethiopia, Africa. After returning home she worked at getting others to join the Peace Corps. She also taught other Peace Corps volunteers.

She then went to the University of Colorado School for Journalism for further education. At the university, she helped to organize a Black Studies program.

Her first book, *Song of the Trees,* was named a *New York Times* Outstanding Book of the Year. Her second book, *Roll of Thunder, Hear My Cry,* received the 1977 Newbery Medal. This book was also adapted for television in 1978. The selection you will read comes from *Let the Circle Be Unbroken.* All these books tell about a family named Logan and follow the lives of the children in that family as they grow to be adults.

113

THE EMERALD-BLUE

by Mildred D. Taylor

▶ Cassie loved the game of marbles, and there was one marble she couldn't wait to get her hands on. Could she do it? Should she do it?

It was Son-Boy who started it all. There I was sitting in Sunday school with my Bible verse firmly planted upon my lips when he pulled out the emerald-blue marble and he started flashing it to all the boys and girls securely hidden by the first row of students. Rolling it between his thumb and forefinger, he had every marble addict drooling over his prize. But true to his word, he allowed no one to touch it but himself. Finally, unable to stand it any longer, I whispered to Little Man beside me, "I'm gonna get that thing."

- emerald (EM uh ruld) **deep green color**
- forefinger (FOR fing ur) **the finger nearest the thumb; pointer or index finger**

114

Christopher-John, sitting on the other side of Little Man, turned toward me horrified. "C-Cassie, you can't! You know what Papa said!"

"I gotta have it."

"I betcha you gonna have a whippin' too," predicted Little Man.

"Maybe so, Papa find out, but I gotta figure out a way for Son-Boy to let go of that marble. Maybe——"

"Cassie?"

It was Mrs. Lettie Love, the elementary Sunday school teacher. I stood quickly. "Yes'm?"

"You learn your Bible verse for the week?"

"Yes'm. 'Thou shalt not covet thy neighbor's house or anything that is thy neighbor's'," I said dutifully without a moment's guilt.

Mrs. Love smiled, happy that one of her students had learned her verse so well. I sat down smiling too as I stared down the row at Son-Boy. He might as well get in his last few minutes of glory with that marble, because I planned for it to be mine within the hour.

Immediately after Sunday school Little Man and I found Maynard Wiggins and Henry Johnson, who had kept marbles jiggling in their pockets since school had begun and put a proposition to them. If they would put up their marbles against Son-Boy's ten, I would do the shooting with the promise that if I began to miss, Maynard or Henry could take over to recoup their losses. If I won, they would each be richer by the number of marbles they'd put up. If I lost, then that was just the chance we took. All I wanted from the deal was Son-Boy's emerald-blue. . . .

"Son-Boy ain't gonna hardly put up that emerald-blue," said Maynard.

"Yes he will," I said with confidence.

"How you know?" questioned Henry. "And how you know he gonna wanna play anyhow?"

" 'Cause he greedy, that's why! Look, y'all gonna give me your marbles or not? We only got half an hour to church time."

Maynard and Henry went off for a short conference, then came back agreed that they would risk their fortunes on me. We decided

- covet (KUV it) **want something that belongs to another**
- **dutifully** (DOO ti fuh lee) **doing something you think you should do; obediently**
- **proposition** (prop uh ZISH un) **offer**
- recoup (ri KOOP) **get back**

that it would be best for them to make the arrangements with Son-Boy. As they hurried off, I hollered after them, "Tell him he's gotta play all ten. It won't be no good 'less he play all of 'em . . . and don't say nothin' 'bout playing that emerald-blue. You do, he probably won't play."

Christopher-John, who had stood disapprovingly apart from these troubling proceedings, hurried over and tried to make me see the folly of my ways. "Cassie, Papa gonna skin you alive sure, he find out—ya know that? What's the matter with you, anyway? You gone crazy?"

He certainly had a point; but not even the thought of Papa's belt could turn me from the course I had set for myself. That emerald-blue had a nasty hold on me and if I could just get my hands on it, I promised myself and God that I'd never shoot marbles again. And perhaps, if luck was with me, Papa would never even have to know I'd disobeyed him.

Soon Maynard and Henry returned. The deal was set. We would meet Son-Boy down by the fallen tree about five minutes deep into the woods.

"What!" exclaimed Little Man, not too pleased about the chosen site. To reach the fallen tree we had to scurry through some pretty heavy growth, and chances of a stain were great. Little Man was a most particular boy when it came to his clothes, his school materials, his anything. He frowned down at his immaculate jacket, pants, and shoes, then at Henry and Maynard, and demanded, "Couldn't y'all find no place better'n that?"

"Can't play no closer to the church," replied Maynard, "Y'all goin' or not?"

"Yeah, we goin'," I said, hurrying toward the middle-grades class building. The path leading into the woods was behind it.

Little Man, deciding that too much was at stake to remain behind, followed with Maynard and Henry. Christopher-John pulled up the rear shouting warnings that not only was Papa going to get us but God too.

"Why don't you jus' go on back and stop bothering me?" I told

---

- **folly** (FOL ee) foolishness
- **immaculate** (i MAK yuh lit) **spotless; very clean**

him when we reached the fallen tree where Son-Boy and Don Lee, along with Curtis Henderson, were already gathered.

"Y'all come too!"

"Not till I get that emerald-blue," I whispered.

Pushing my coat out of the way, I dug into my dress pocket, the only useful feature in an uncomfortable garment, and pulled out the marbles Maynard and Henry had placed in my keeping. Then I settled down on my haunches trying to keep my dress from dragging in the dirt.

The battle began.

Luck was with Son-Boy. He got first shot, then immediately captured three of our men. Nervously, I made my shot and missed.

"Cassie!" cried Maynard, as he and Henry scowled down at their rapidly dwindling marbles. Their faith in me was quickly ebbing.

Son-Boy laughed. "Didn't y'all know couldn't no girl be good as me?" He shot again, but this time his shot marble hit nothing.

"Serve ya right," judged Little Man.

I went for my turn feeling the perspiration trickling down my arms despite the chilliness of the day. But before I could shoot, Maynard grabbed my arm. "Better let me shoot," he decided.

I snatched my arm from his grasp and, before he or Henry could object, shot and connected. After that, the game was mine. I sent the last of Son-Boy's marbles hurtling into our hands, then sat back on my ankles and stared across at Son-Boy, who looked as if he did not quite realize he had just been wiped out. Meanwhile, Little Man, Maynard, Henry, and yes, Christopher-John, too, were whooping it up at our victory.

"Would y'all shut up!" I demanded. It was almost time for the bell to ring, and there was still the matter of the emerald-blue. Immediately, everyone hushed.

"Look here, Son-Boy," I said, "to tell you the truth, I hate to see you wiped out like this. I mean, seeing Russell just give you them marbles."

I grew thoughtfully quiet as Son-Boy's face began to show signs of hope at my sympathetic attitude.

- haunches (HAWN chuz) **hips and thighs**
- dwindling (DWIND ling) **growing fewer**
- ebbing (EB ing) **fading**

117

"I tell you what," I said when I felt he was appropriately hopeful enough to hear my next statement. "If you want, we'll give you a chance to win all your marbles back, plus ours, with one shot—"

"Now hold on just a minute there, Cassie!" cried Maynard with Henry backing him up. Already they were dividing the marbles and had forgotten that I still did not have what I had come after.

I cut my eyes at them, copying the look Papa gave people when he was angry or deadly serious. Both Maynard and Henry grew silent.

"But—but I ain't got nothin' to shoot 'gainst," said Son-Boy.

"You got your emerald-blue."

Son-Boy's lower jaw dropped.

"You win," I propositioned, "you get to keep it. Not only that, but you'll have twenty other marbles jiggling in your pocket. What we'll do is both shoot for the emerald-blue. First one knocks it beyond the outer circle gets it." I inhaled deeply as I made my final ploy. "I'll even let you go first."

Little Man and Christopher-John looked at me in pure disbelief; Henry and Maynard just looked sick.

Son-Boy considered.

All was quiet.

He pulled the emerald-blue from his pocket and whirled it around in his palm.

The emerald-blue was almost mine, yet I couldn't help but feel sorry for Son-Boy. In a few minutes he had lost almost all of his treasure and if he was the boy I thought he was, he would risk the rest of it to try and get it back. But if he'd just use his head, he could keep the most precious part; the rest of the marbles were nothing compared to what he held in his hand. I decided that if Son-Boy played the emerald-blue, he was a fool.

"Okay," he said, placing the marble on the line of the inner circle.

Papa had been right. If gambling was anything like shooting marbles, then it was a sickness. But then, I hadn't totally used good sense either—risking one of Papa's no-nonsense whippings for a piece of glass. Maybe I was as big a fool as Son-Boy.

"Go on," I said. "Shoot."

• ploy (PLOY) **trick to get someone to do something**

Son-Boy nervously licked his lips and shot.

He missed.

I didn't.

"Ya done it, Cassie! Ya done it!" cried Little Man and Christopher-John, slapping me on my shoulders as I reached out to claim my prize.

Tenderly caressing the emerald-blue between my fingers, I held it toward the sun. It was a beautiful thing.

"We'd better get back," Christopher-John reminded us. "That bell's gonna start ringing."

We all jumped up, dusting each other off. Only Little Man had no need to dust. He'd seen to that.

Son-Boy, his face long, glanced at me and the emerald-blue with sad, vacant eyes and hurried on with Don Lee. I hadn't liked the feeling of that look. Son-Boy was my friend. Nevertheless, with the marble cradled in my hand, I didn't have time to think about Son-Boy now. I couldn't help it if he was a fool. I hurried with Little Man and Christopher-John after Henry and Maynard, and we emerged from the forest happily assessing our victory.

- caress (kuh RES) **touch in a soft and loving way**
- assess (uh SES) **judge the value**

ALL THINGS CONSIDERED ─────────────────────

1. When the story begins, Cassie is (a) in a forest. (b) in Sunday school. (c) at home.

2. The emerald-blue is a (a) marble. (b) dress. (c) precious ring.

3. The Bible verse Cassie learns is about (a) stealing. (b) wanting something that doesn't belong to you. (c) telling lies about your friends.

4. Cassie wants to shoot the marbles that belong to (a) Son-Boy and Little Man. (b) Christopher-John and Don Lee. (c) Maynard and Henry.

5. If Cassie wins, the boys will (a) get the emerald-blue. (b) claim they won. (c) have more marbles.

6. Christopher-John worries that (a) Cassie will lose all the marbles. (b) Cassie will get in trouble with Papa. (c) the teacher will keep them all after school.

7. Cassie and Son-Boy shoot marbles during the time (a) they are supposed to be in church. (b) they are supposed to be in Sunday school. (c) between Sunday school and church.

8. Maynard wants to shoot because (a) Cassie has lost some of the marbles. (b) he wants the emerald-blue. (c) he feels sorry for Son-Boy.

9. Cassie offers to let (a) Henry have the emerald-blue. (b) Son-Boy shoot his emerald-blue against all the other marbles. (c) someone else shoot for the emerald-blue.

10. At the end of the story, Cassie (a) wins the emerald-blue and loses the other marbles. (b) wins all the marbles except the emerald-blue. (c) wins all the marbles and the emerald-blue.

THINKING IT THROUGH ─────────────────────

1. Cassie says her Bible verse correctly in class. Do you think that she really learned the lesson of that verse? Why do you think that verse is mentioned in the story?

2. Why do you think the boys are willing to let Cassie shoot their marbles for them? How do you think Cassie sees herself as a marbles player?

3. On page 118, Cassie compares shooting marbles to gambling. Do you think she feels that what she is doing is right? What promise does she make? Do you think she will keep it?

4. How does Cassie feel when she wins the emerald-blue?

Building From Details

Inference

Often you understand something that isn't stated in a story. You figure it out from clues in the story and your own knowledge. When you figure out something from clues and your own knowledge, you are making an **inference** (IN fur uns).

Imagine that you didn't read the introduction to "The Emerald-Blue" or look at the pictures. Would you know whether the narrator is a girl or a boy? The name Cassie may be used by either. But on page 117, the narrator says, "I dug into my dress pocket." From that statement you can make the inference that Cassie is a girl.

You can make many inferences while you read. On a separate sheet of paper, write a sentence from the story that is a clue to each of the following inferences:

1. Many students in the Sunday school do not learn their verses well.
2. The children must be back for church.
3. Christopher-John is Cassie's brother.
4. Cassie's father is very strict.
5. Little Man is the only one who doesn't get dirty.

Composition

Follow your teacher's instructions before completing *one* of these writing assignments.

1. There are many ways of playing marbles. Different people have different rules. Write five rules for the way you play marbles. If you do not play marbles, write five rules for some other game you play.
2. What words would you use to describe Cassie? What facts in the story did you use to make your inferences about her? Write a paragraph telling whether you would like to have Cassie for a friend, and why.

▶ Some people look at sports and games with a sense of humor. Here are two poems that look at the funny side of things.

COME SKATING

by Shel Silverstein

They said come skating;
They said it's so nice.
They said come skating;
I'd done it twice.
They said come skating;
It sounded nice. . . .
I wore roller—
They meant *ice.*

THE ACROBATS

by Shel Silverstein

I'll swing
By my ankles,
She'll cling
To your knees
As you hang
By your nose
From a high-up
Trapeze.
But just one thing, please,
As we float through the breeze—
Don't sneeze.

WAYS OF KNOWING

1. Each poem contains an unexpected idea. What is the unexpected idea in "Come Skating"? What is the unexpected idea in "The Acrobats"?

2. How does repeating the line "They said come skating" help you realize why the skater made a mistake?

3. Look at the patterns of rhyming words in each poem. How are they alike? How are they different?

4. How does the poet make a game out of poetry? Do you enjoy this kind of humor? Explain your answer.

Oral Interpretation

Each of the poems you just read has a punch line. A punch line is a part at the end of a story, poem, or joke that makes the point and is funny. When you read something with a punch line, let the end be a surprise to your listener.

Choose one of the poems on page 122 to read aloud. First think about how you will read it. Then read it aloud to yourself. Read so that you seem to be telling an ordinary story—until the last line. When you are ready, find someone who might enjoy the joke and read the poem aloud to that person.

Here are some suggestions for reading:

- For "Come Skating," let your voice go up on the first line, down on the second, up on the third, and so on. On the last line, sound as if you are slipping on the ice.

- For "The Acrobats," let your voice swing back and forth. Pause before the last line. Then, as you read the last line, whisper, shout, plead, or . . . sneeze!

THE COURAGEOUS DODGER

by Martin Lader

▶ Some athletes show courage not just on the playing field, but in life as well. Campy, as Roy Campanella was called, was a hero in the game of life as well as in the game of baseball.

In the simplest terms, this was going to be the biggest game ever played in Brooklyn. Not only did it pack the usual tension of the seventh game of a World Series between two bitter rivals, but for the Brooklyn fans, it was perhaps a last chance to beat the hated New York Yankees. It was rumored that the Dodgers were moving out of Brooklyn.

Five times in the past, the Brooklyn Dodgers had met the Yankees in the World Series. And five times the Dodgers had lived up to their nickname of Bums.

It had come as no surprise, a few days earlier, that the Yankees brushed aside the Dodgers in the opening two games of the 1955 Series.

In the solemn Dodger clubhouse, no one dared raise his voice above a whisper following the second game. Then Jackie Robinson suddenly shouted to his teammates, "We've got to win this one. If we lose again, they'll be calling us choke-up guys the rest of our lives. Do we want that?"

A moment later a man with a barrel chest and muscular arms stood up and said, in a high voice, "Jackie's right. It's up to us to go out and get the job done. Let's go out and get 'em tomorrow."

The next afternoon when the Series shifted to Brooklyn, that man, Roy Campanella, was even better than his words. Campy, who had once thought he'd never get a chance to play in organized ball because of his color, smacked a two-run homer in the first inning. Then he added a double and a single as the Dodgers won 8–3.

There was more of the same the next

- **tension** (TEN shun) strain; feeling of worry
- rival (RY vul) one who is in a contest against another
- rumor (ROO mur) tell something that may or may not be true
- **solemn** (SOL um) serious and sad
- choke-up (CHOHK up) not able to succeed when necessary
- inning (IN ing) each team's turn to hit in baseball

124

day with Campanella again slugging a homer, a double, and a single to give Brooklyn an 8–5 victory. The teams then split the next two games, giving them 3 wins apiece and sending the World Series into the seventh game at Yankee Stadium. It was a game that seemed like a matter of life and death for the Brooklyn fans.

It was the forty-ninth game ever to be played by a Brooklyn team in eight World Series. And the Dodgers were still trying for their first championship. For the great Dodger players it was the single game that could distinguish their careers and could give meaning to all they had given to Brooklyn.

A crowd of 62,465 people turned out in Yankee Stadium. Once again it was the man with the high voice and explosive bat who made the difference and let Brooklyn celebrate the greatest day in its history.

Although he had never hit well in the Stadium, Campy delivered the first run of the game in the fourth inning. In the sixth inning Campy was in the middle again when the Dodgers scored for the last time. When the Yankees made the final out, the Dodgers had their first World Series championship. Campy could be seen racing to the mound, where he grabbed the pitcher in a hug and lifted him high off the ground.

It was the grandest moment ever for both the Brooklyn Dodgers and Roy Campanella. A month later it became even more special as Campy was voted the National League's Most Valuable Player for the third time.

A little more than two years later, Brooklyn no longer had a baseball team. The team had been moved to Los Angeles. Even sadder, Roy Campanella was to spend the rest of his life in a wheelchair, paralyzed, the victim of a car crash less than a mile from his home.

- distinguish (dis TING wish) **give special importance to**
- **league** (LEEG) **group of teams that play against each other**
- victim (VIK tum) **one who is injured**

Campy was born on November 19, 1921, in Philadelphia. He was the youngest of four children. Money was scarce, but there was always enough food, since his father sold fruits and vegetables.

Roy knew the meaning of hard work as a child. He would get up at 2:30 A.M. to help his brother run a milk route. Roy would go back to bed at 5:30. By 8:00 he'd be on his way to school. He'd also help his father load his delivery truck, and had other odd jobs such as cutting lawns and selling newspapers.

Even with work and school, there was always time for fun. Fun to Roy meant baseball. He was a good player. When he was 10, in the Nicetown section of North Philadelphia, he was the only boy of his age allowed to play with the bigger guys.

There were few people there who had money. Many of the boys didn't even have baseball gloves. The ball they used was beat-up and taped. The bats were cracked and had to be wired and taped. One time, Roy was catching and the mask he was using was too big for him. He took it off, and a foul tip smashed into his face and broke his nose.

As a kid, Roy pitched and played outfielder and catcher. He had first been a catcher when he went to a tryout for a school team and saw that none of the other kids wanted to be catcher. By volunteering for that position, he knew he would always have a place to play.

At 15, Roy played for the Nicetown Giants. Then Campy became the only black on his local American Legion team.

It was hard not to notice Campy then. He was big for his age, not so much tall as hefty, and he played ball like a man. In spring 1937 he joined the Bacharach Giants, a black semi-professional team in Philadelphia. This involved traveling, which didn't please his mother. But she gave in when she learned that Roy would be paid $35 for two games. That was more money than the family took in some weeks.

Roy played only one game with the Bacharach Giants before he was offered a chance to join the Baltimore Elite Giants of the Negro National League. That was the big leagues for blacks at a time when baseball was segregated.

Roy was only 15. He was to earn $60 a month. The day after his sixteenth birthday, Roy quit school, feeling he was grown up enough to go into the world and earn his own way.

In 1939 Campy became the Elite Giants' first-string catcher. They won the league championship, with Campy the hitting star.

- hefty (HEF tee) **big and powerful**
- semi-professional (sem ee pruh FESH un ul) **playing for money, but not as a full-time job**
- segregated (SEG ruh gay tid) **separated because of color or race**
- first-string—**chosen before others; most important**

126

In 1945 Campy played in an exhibition series against major-league stars. Charlie Dressen, a coach with the Brooklyn Dodgers, followed Roy into the clubhouse. He told him that Dodger president Branch Rickey wanted to meet with him the next morning. Roy came away from the meeting with the idea that Rickey was interested in him for a new Negro league.

But a week later Rickey and the Dodgers broke tradition with the signing of Jackie Robinson for their farm team at Montreal. Robinson was the first black player to break into white baseball. After Robinson came John Wright and Don Newcombe. Campanella became the fourth black to sign a contract.

He was sent to Nashua, a Class B team in New Hampshire. With so much professional experience behind him, Campy quickly proved himself at Nashua. He homered on opening day. It wasn't long before the other players began looking up to him. Nashua won the New England League championship, and Campanella was chosen Most Valuable Player.

There was another MVP award waiting for Campy at Montreal in 1947, leaving no question that he was ready for the majors.

Roy arrived in the Brooklyn dugout only two hours before a night game with the New York Giants. He was put into the lineup immediately. Campanella was soon the regular catcher.

- **tradition** (truh DISH un) **the way things have always been done**
- farm team—minor-league team that trains some players for the major leagues
- lineup (LYN up) list of regular players

Starting in 1949, Campanella caught in more than 100 games for a league record. He enjoyed a career that led to the Hall of Fame.

Besides having many offensive skills, Campy was a remarkable defensive player. Despite his size, Campy was very quick behind the plate. He could grab bunts with the lightness of a cat. He boasted a throwing arm that was both strong and accurate.

Being with the Dodgers also brought Campanella a lot of pain. He suffered many injuries and often played while hurt. Often his teammates would beg him to bear down more on runners sliding into the plate. But Roy, ever the nice guy, didn't want to risk hurting someone else.

What became a real worry for him was the tough luck his team had. In 1950, for instance, Brooklyn lost the pennant on the last day of the season. The next year the Dodgers lost a playoff to the Giants. Still, the Dodgers won five pennants in eight years.

Campanella was always a courageous player, a man who enjoyed baseball so much that he always seemed to do his best even after a serious injury. After having surgery in 1954, he called the Dodger office and said, "You're talking to the Most Valuable Player in the National League for 1955."

He wasn't joking. Campy fought back and became the MVP.

Early in the morning of January 28, 1958, Roy was driving home and thinking about the Dodgers' move to Los Angeles. He skidded into a telephone pole in a rented car and broke his neck.

The accident that nearly cost him his life left him paralyzed from the chest down. But he was a deeply religious man, and he always had the ability to accept and adapt. When he wrote a book about his life, he called it *It's Good to Be Alive,* and he was able to say, "I have so many good memories. This is not really a bad one. I have accepted this wheelchair and I have accepted life."

- offensive (uh FEN siv) **on the attack**
- defensive (di FEN siv) **protecting against attack**
- pennant (PEN unt) **flag given to the champion**
- playoff (PLAY awf) **contest to decide the winner among those tied for the lead**

ALL THINGS CONSIDERED

1. When the Dodgers first won the World Series, they were playing in (a) Philadelphia. (b) New York. (c) Los Angeles.
2. Most of the time, Roy Campanella played the position of (a) outfielder. (b) pitcher. (c) catcher.
3. He chose that position because (a) it was the only one he could play. (b) few players wanted it. (c) he was told it was the best position.
4. Campy did not think he would get a chance to play in the major leagues because (a) for many years the major leagues used white players only. (b) every time he tried out he was sent back to a farm team. (c) his father would not let him travel.
5. As a child Roy (a) had many jobs to earn money. (b) spent all his time playing baseball. (c) was hired as a professional ballplayer.
6. After speaking with Branch Rickey, Campanella (a) went right to the Dodgers. (b) proved his ability in Nashua, New Hampshire. (c) became the first black major league player.
7. When Campy joined the Dodgers, he (a) was a substitute player for a few months. (b) joined the lineup right away. (c) started as a pinch hitter.
8. Campanella was known as (a) mainly an offensive player. (b) mainly a defensive player. (c) both an offensive and defensive player.
9. People did not expect Campanella to win the Most Valuable Player award in 1955 because (a) he had just had surgery. (b) his game was getting worse. (c) he had recently been in a car accident.
10. After his accident, Campanella (a) was angry at everybody. (b) felt sorry for himself. (c) was glad to be alive.

THINKING IT THROUGH

1. In your opinion, what about Roy Campanella's childhood might have helped him develop into the person he became?
2. Roy Campanella showed courage at many times in his life. Find three events in the biography that show he had courage. How do you think most people would have reacted to each of these events?
3. This biography does not begin with the earliest part of Roy Campanella's life. Where does it begin? Why do you think it begins there? Where does it end? Why do you think the author told the story this way?

Relationships

Flashback

Many stories begin with the part that happens first. These stories then tell everything in the order in which events happened. But some stories begin with later events. A flashback is used to tell what happened earlier. A **flashback** is a look at something that happened before. This biography of Roy Campanella uses flashbacks.

Review the biography. Then follow the instructions below. Write your answers on a separate sheet of paper.

1. Find the pages that tell about the important World Series game that the Dodgers won in 1955. Write the page numbers.
2. Look for the paragraph that begins a flashback to the opening games of the 1955 World Series. Write the first six words of that paragraph.
3. Find the pages that tell about Roy Campanella's childhood. Write the page number and the first sentence of the paragraph that begins telling about his childhood. This part is also a flashback.
4. On what page do you learn what happened to Roy Campanella in 1958? Write the page number and the first ten words of the paragraph that tells what happened.

Composition

Follow your teacher's instructions before completing *one* of these writing assignments.

1. Pretend you are Roy Campanella. Think back over your life. Write four sentences about your experiences. In each, tell about something that makes you feel proud.
2. The biography tells how Campanella played the game of life as well as the game of baseball. Write a paragraph about what was outstanding in the way Campy played the game of life.

ONE THROW

by W. C. Heinz

▶ Pete Maneri was playing great baseball in the minor leagues. But he wanted a chance to play with the New York Yankees. The problem was that the team's manager wouldn't let the big leagues know about him. Then a stranger told him a way to get attention. All Pete had to do was— throw the game.

I checked into a hotel called the Olympia, which is right on the main street and the only hotel in the town. After lunch I was hanging around the lobby, and I got to talking to the guy at the desk. I asked him if this wasn't the town where that kid named Maneri played ball.

"That's right," the guy said. "He's a pretty good ballplayer."

"He should be," I said. "I read that he was the new Phil Rizzuto.*"

"That's what they said," the guy said.

"What's the matter with him?" I said. "I mean if he's such a good ballplayer what's he doing in this league?"

"I don't know," the guy said. "I guess the Yankees know what they're doing."

"What kind of a kid is he?"

"He's a nice kid," the guy said. "He plays good ball, but I feel sorry for him. He thought he'd be playing for the Yankees soon, and here he is in this town. You can see it's got him down."

"He lives here in this hotel?"

"That's right," the guy said. "Most of the older ballplayers stay in rooming houses, but Pete and a couple other kids live here."

He was leaning on the desk, talking to me and looking across the hotel lobby. He nodded his head. "This is a funny thing," he said. "Here he comes now."

The kid had come through the door from the street. He had on a light gray sport shirt and a pair of gray flannel slacks.

• **league** (LEEG) group of teams that play against each other

*Phil Rizzuto (fil ruh ZOO toh) shortstop for the New York Yankee baseball team in the 1940s and 1950s

131

I could see why, when he showed up with the Yankees in spring training, he made them all think of Rizzuto. He isn't any bigger than Rizzuto, and he looks just like him.

"Hello, Nick," he said to the guy at the desk.

"Hello, Pete," the guy at the desk said. "How goes it today?"

"All right," the kid said, but you could see he was exaggerating.

"I'm sorry, Pete," the guy at the desk said, "but no mail today."

"That's all right, Nick," the kid said. "I'm used to it."

"Excuse me," I said, "but you're Pete Maneri?"

"That's right," the kid said, turning and looking at me.

"Excuse me," the guy at the desk said, introducing us. "Pete, this is Mr. Franklin."

"Harry Franklin," I said.

"I'm glad to know you," the kid said, shaking my hand.

"I recognize you from your pictures," I said.

"Pete's a good ballplayer," the guy at the desk said.

"Not very," the kid said.

"Don't take his word for it, Mr. Franklin," the guy said.

"I'm a great ball fan," I said to the kid. "Do you people play tonight?"

"We play two games," the kid said.

"The first game's at six o'clock," the guy at the desk said. "They play pretty good ball."

"I'll be there," I said. "I used to play a little ball myself."

"You did?" the kid said.

"With Columbus," I said. "That's twenty years ago."

"Is that right?" the kid said.

That's the way I got to talking with the kid. They had one of those pine-paneled taprooms in the basement of the hotel, and we went down there. I had a couple and the kid had a soda, and I told him a few stories and he turned out to be a real good listener.

"But what do you do now, Mr. Franklin?" he said after a while.

"I sell hardware," I said. "I can think of some things I'd like better, but I was going to ask you how you like playing in this league."

"Well," the kid said, "I suppose it's all right. I guess I've got no kick coming."

"Oh, I don't know," I said. "I understand you're too good for this league. What are they trying to do to you?"

"I don't know," the kid said. "I can't understand it."

"What's the trouble?"

"Well," the kid said, "I don't get along very well here. I mean there's nothing wrong with my playing. I'm hitting .365 right now. I lead the league in stolen bases. There's nobody can field with me, but who cares?"

"Who manages this ball club?"

"Al Dall," the kid said. "You remember, he played in the outfield for the Yankees for about four years."

"I remember."

"Maybe he is all right," the kid said, "but I don't get along with him. He's on my neck all the time."

"Well," I said, "that's the way they are in the minors sometimes. You have to remember the guy is looking out for himself and his ball club first. He's not worried about you."

"I know that," the kid said. "If I get the big hit or make the play he never says anything. The other night I tried to take second on a loose ball and I got caught in the rundown. He bawls me out in front of everybody. There's nothing I can do."

- taproom (TAP room) **room that serves drinks and snacks in a hotel**
- kick (KIK) **complaint, something to be angry about**
- minors (MY nurz) **leagues whose players cannot yet play at the high levels needed by the major leagues**
- rundown (RUN down) **baseball play in which the runner is tagged out when caught between bases**

"Oh, I don't know," I said. "This is probably a guy who knows he's got a good thing in you, and he's looking to keep you around. You people lead the league, and that makes him look good. He doesn't want to lose you to Columbus or the Yankees."

"That's what I mean," the kid said. "When the Yankees sent me down here they said, 'Don't worry. We'll keep an eye on you.' So Dall never sends a good report on me. Nobody ever comes down to look me over. What chance is there for a guy like Eddie Brown or somebody like that coming down to see me in this town?"

"You have to remember that Eddie Brown's the big shot," I said, "the great Yankee scout."

"Sure," the kid said. "I never even saw him, and I'll never see him in this place. I have an idea that if they ever ask Dall about me he keeps knocking me down."

"Why don't you go after Dall?" I said. "I had trouble like that once myself, but I figured out a way to get attention."

"You did?" the kid said.

"I threw a couple of balls over the first baseman's head," I said. "I threw a couple of games away, and that really got the manager sore. I was lousing up his ball club and his record. So what does he do? He blows the whistle on me, and what happens? That gets the brass curious, and they send someone down to see what's wrong."

"Is that so?" the kid said. "What happened?"

"Two weeks later," I said, "I was up with Columbus."

"Is that right?" the kid said.

"Sure," I said, egging him on. "What have you got to lose?"

"Nothing," the kid said. "I haven't got anything to lose."

"I'd try it," I said.

"I might try it," the kid said. "I might try it tonight if the spot comes up."

I could see from the way he said it that he was madder than he'd said. Maybe you think this is mean to steam a kid up like this, but I do some strange things.

"Take over," I said. "Don't let this guy ruin your career."

- blow the whistle—report that someone is doing something wrong
- brass (BRASS) important people; people in power
- egg on (EG ON) urge or push to do something; encourage
- **career** (kuh REER) work a person has chosen to do

134

"I'll try it," the kid said. "Are you coming out to the park tonight?"

"I wouldn't miss it," I said. "This will be better than making out route sheets and sales orders."

It's not much of a ball park in this town—old wooden bleachers and an old wooden fence and about four hundred people in the stands. The first game wasn't much either, with the home club winning something like 8 to 1.

The kid didn't have any hard chances, but I could see he was a ballplayer, with a double and a couple of walks and a lot of speed.

The second game was different, though. The other club got a couple of runs and then the home club picked up three runs in one. They were in the top of the ninth with a 3—2 lead and two outs when the pitching began to fall apart and they loaded the bases.

I was trying to wish the ball down to the kid, just to see what he'd do with it, when the batter drives one on one big bounce to the kid's right.

The kid was off for it when the ball started. He made a backhand stab and grabbed it. He was deep now, and he turned in the air and fired. If it goes over the first baseman's head, it's two runs in and a panic—but it's the prettiest throw you'd want to see. It's right on a line, and the runner goes out by a step, and it's the ball game.

- route sheets and sales orders—**some of the papers a sales- person has to fill out**
- stab (STAB) **try; attempt**

I walked back to the hotel, thinking about the kid. I sat around the lobby until I saw him come in, and then I walked toward the elevator like I was going to my room, but so I'd meet him. And I could see he didn't want to talk.

"How about a soda?" I said.

"No," he said. "Thanks, but I'm going to bed."

"Look," I said. "Forget it. You did the right thing. Have a soda."

We were sitting in the taproom again. The kid wasn't saying anything.

"Why didn't you throw that ball away?" I said.

"I don't know," the kid said. "I had it in my mind before he hit it, but I couldn't."

"Why?"

"I don't know why."

"I know why," I said.

The kid didn't say anything. He just sat looking down.

"Do you know why you couldn't throw that ball away?" I said.

"No," the kid said.

"You couldn't throw that ball away," I said, "because you're going to be a major-league ballplayer someday."

The kid just looked at me. He had that same sore expression.

"Do you know why you're going to be a major-league ball-player?" I said.

The kid was just looking down again, shaking his head. I never got more of a kick out of anything in my life.

"You're going to be a major-league ballplayer," I said, "because you couldn't throw that ball away, and because I'm not a hardware salesman and my name's not Harry Franklin."

"What do you mean?" the kid said.

"I mean," I explained to him, "that I tried to needle you into throwing that ball away because I'm Eddie Brown."

• needle (NEE dul) **annoy; prod into action**

ALL THINGS CONSIDERED ────────────────────

1. The person telling the story is a (a) hotel manager. (b) stranger in town. (c) baseball player.
2. The stranger is introduced to Pete as (a) Nick. (b) Eddie Brown. (c) Mr. Franklin.
3. Pete and Mr. Franklin have a talk (a) in a taproom. (b) at the ball park. (c) in a hotel room.
4. Mr. Franklin says that he (a) sells hardware. (b) is a major-league baseball player. (c) is a scout.
5. Pete leads his league in (a) home runs. (b) stolen bases. (c) double plays.
6. Pete tells Mr. Franklin that his manager doesn't (a) send in good reports on him. (b) let him play enough. (c) try hard enough to help the team win.
7. Eddie Brown is known to be (a) a scout for the Yankees. (b) the manager of another minor-league team. (c) a Yankee shortstop.
8. Mr. Franklin suggests that Pete (a) telephone the Yankee manager and complain. (b) purposely lose a game. (c) try playing another position.
9. During the game Pete (a) throws the ball badly. (b) makes the play that wins the game. (c) strikes out.
10. Mr. Franklin turns out to be (a) Phil Rizzuto. (b) the Yankees' manager. (c) Eddie Brown.

THINKING IT THROUGH ────────────────────

1. Most teams want players who are good team players. What words best describe a good team player? Is Pete Maneri one? Give examples from the story to explain your answer.
2. Reread the second paragraph on page 134. What does Pete think of his manager? At that point in the story, what was your opinion of the manager? Did your opinion of him change at the end of the story? Explain.
3. Mr. Franklin tells Pete to hurt his team in order to help himself. What do you think of this advice? What do you think would have happened if Pete had listened to him?
4. At one point in the story, Pete Maneri makes an important decision. Where in the story does that happen?

Vocabulary and Sentence Meaning ————

Multiple Meanings

Many words have more than one meaning. For example, reread the title of the story. The word *throw* usually means "toss" or "pitch." But it can also mean "purposely lose a game." How do both meanings fit the story?

In Column A, you will find some other words from the story that have more than one meaning. Find two meanings in Column B for each word in Column A. On a separate sheet of paper, write both meanings next to the words from Column A.

A	**B**
1. right	**a)** kind of metal
2. fan	**b)** correct
3. brass	**c)** something to sew with
4. needle	**d)** side opposite left
	e) something to cool off with
	f) important people
	g) person who loves a game
	h) annoy

Composition ————

Follow your teacher's instructions before completing *one* of these writing assignments.

1. Here are more words with multiple meanings from the story.

> *light   spring   spot   mean   club*

Choose three of these words and figure out two meanings for each. Then write two sentences for each word, using a different meaning in each sentence.

2. If you could happily surprise someone, who would that person be? What would the surprise be, and how would you go about it? Answer these questions in a paragraph.

Literary Skills

Fiction and Nonfiction

You have been reading many different kinds of stories. Some of them have been true stories, and some have not.

Stories that are not true are called **fiction.** The characters and events have been made up by the author. Stories that are fiction are usually called **short stories.** You can probably figure out the reason for that name. Some longer works of fiction are called novels. Most of the works of fiction in this book are short stories. Plays may also be fiction. Later in this book you will read some plays.

Even if a story or play is fiction, some details may be real. For example, the setting may be a real place.

Stories that are true are called **nonfiction.** Nonfiction is about real people and events. Works of nonfiction include autobiographies, biographies, essays, articles, and diaries. Think about "The Greatest Woman Athlete" and "The Courageous Dodger," the two biographies you have read in this unit. Were they about real people and events? If you don't know, how can you find out?

The point to remember is that fiction is made up and nonfiction is true.

Look at the following list of stories from Units 1 and 2. You have probably read most of them. List the titles that you know on a separate sheet of paper. Then decide whether each is fiction or nonfiction. Next to each title write **F** for fiction or **N** for nonfiction. If you are not sure, write "not sure."

1. "The Cub"
2. "The End of My Long Night"
3. "A Taste of Life"
4. "Gold-Mounted Guns"
5. "The Horse of the Sword"
6. "The Comeback"
7. "The Greatest Woman Athlete"
8. "Racing a Champion"
9. "The Emerald-Blue"
10. "One Throw"

VOCABULARY AND SKILL REVIEW ─────────────

Before completing the exercises that follow, you may wish to review the **bold-faced** words on pages 107–137.

I. Match the words in Column A with their definitions in Column B.

A	B
1. dutifully	**a)** person on the opposite side
2. league	**b)** obediently
3. career	**c)** serious and sad
4. tradition	**d)** foolishness
5. solemn	**e)** offer
6. tourist	**f)** strain
7. folly	**g)** way things are always done
8. proposition	**h)** traveler
9. tension	**i)** group of teams
10. opponent	**j)** work one chooses to do

II. How good are you at making inferences? For each of the numbered sentences below, pick the statement that is the correct inference.

1. A boy accepts a swimming contest with a man over 60 years old.

a. The boy is afraid of the water.

b. The boy thinks his youth will give him an advantage.

c. The man has forgotten how to swim.

2. A boy agrees to play his best marble to win back the ones he's lost.

a. The boy doesn't really want his other marbles back.

b. The boy thinks he will probably win.

c. The boy hasn't really lost any marbles.

3. Somebody brings roller skates to an ice-skating party.

a. The person does not know how to ice-skate.

b. The person likes to roller-skate on ice.

c. The invitation only read *skating party.*

4. A baseball scout comes to a game to watch a minor-league player.

a. The scout wants to see if the player is good enough for the major league.

b. The minor-league manager has complained about the player.

c. The baseball scout has nothing else to do.

ATALANTA

retold by Eden Force Eskin

▶ This story from ancient Greece tells of a princess who ran faster than any man she had ever met. She was brave and beautiful. But she refused to marry anyone who could not outrun her. One man thought he had a way to beat her at the running game. Would his plan work?

The elderly servant looked with pity at the bundle he was carrying. His mission for the king was not a happy one. The king had wanted a son, and when a daughter was born, he was bitterly disappointed.

"This creature is not worth bringing up!" the king declared. "Take her away and leave her on a mountainside. The bitter cold weather and wild beasts will take care of her."

So the servant was given the task of carrying baby Atalanta (AT uh lan tuh) up the mountainside and leaving her to die. Because he was afraid to disobey the king, he followed orders and left the child alone in the mountains.

The baby's fate was to be very different from what the king, her father, had ordered. Artemis (AR tuh mis), the Greek goddess of hunting, had other plans for her. At Artemis's command, a she-bear found the infant and took her to raise like her own cub.

Being raised this way turned Atalanta into a brave, daring young girl who was wild and strong. After a while, some kind hunters came along and took a liking to Atalanta. They took her to live with them. She amazed them with her hunting skills. In fact, she was a better hunter than almost any man—and this was at a time when girls were not taught to hunt. And she ran like the wind. Like the wind, no one could catch her.

- **mission** (MISH un) job or task a person is sent to do
- bitterly (BIT ur lee) **painfully; in a manner that is hard to bear**
- **fate** (FAYT) something that is going to happen without anyone being able to change it; destiny; fortune

At this time, a fierce wild boar was destroying the countryside of Calydon (KAL i don). This vicious beast, known as the Calydonian (kal i DOH nee un) boar, attacked the cattle and murdered anyone who tried to stop him. Something had to be done.

The bravest men of Greece decided to organize a hunt to find and kill the Calydonian boar. Atalanta decided to join them. She came to the hunt looking very beautiful. A shining buckle clasped her robe at the neck. Her thick, long hair was arranged simply in a knot at her neck. An ivory quiver hung from her left shoulder, and her left hand held a bow. Her beautiful face attracted much attention and captured at least one man's heart.

- **fierce** (FEERS) wild; savage; violent
- **quiver** (KWIV ur) case for holding arrows

142

Several men objected to having a woman on this dangerous hunt, but they were soon forced to change their minds. When the hunting party found the boar and surrounded it, the vicious beast rushed at them and killed two men before anybody could move in to save them. In the wild confusion that followed, only Atalanta remained calm enough to take aim and shoot. Her arrow wounded the boar. Another hunter jumped in and gave the beast its final death blow, but Atalanta was honored for drawing the first blood.

When her father learned of her triumph, he was delighted. He decided to take her back. After all, he had wanted a son who was an outstanding hunter, and this daughter of his had turned out to be a greater hunter than almost any man.

There was one great problem. Her father wanted her to marry. But the goddess Artemis had warned her never to take a husband. If she did, harm would come to the man. Atalanta did not care much about marriage. She was happy with her life as a hunter and racer. She formed a plan to avoid marrying, without angering her father.

"I'll be glad to marry," she declared. "But the man I marry must be able to beat me in a race."

The king took her at her word. He made a proclamation that his daughter would marry the man who outran her in a footrace. But there was a catch. Anyone who raced her and lost would die.

In spite of these conditions, many young men wanted to challenge the princess. Some were attracted to her beauty, others admired her skills as a hunter and a racer. Fleet-footed men came willing to risk death for the prize of her hand. Each of them tried to outrun her, and all of them died.

One young man was more determined than the others. His name was Hippomenes (hi POM uh neez), and he decided that he needed help. So he turned to Aphrodite (af ruh DY tee), the goddess of love. Hippomenes knew that Aphrodite could not stand to see a beautiful young woman turn her back on marriage and love.

Aphrodite was delighted to help Hippomenes win the princess. The goddess gave him three apples of gold—apples so beautiful that nobody could see them and not want them.

- **proclamation** (prok luh MAY shun) **public announcement of something important**
- fleet-footed (FLEET FOOT id) **able to run very fast**

143

"These apples," Aphrodite told Hippomenes, "will win the princess for you. But you must do what I tell you."

Hippomenes stood beside Atalanta as the race was about to begin. She was more beautiful than he had ever seen her, and he was even more determined to win. As they started off, Hippomenes held the three golden apples in his hand. Atalanta flew straight as an arrow, with her long hair flowing behind her. She had gained a good lead when Hippomenes threw the first apple right in front of her. She bent to pick it up, giving Hippomenes a chance to catch up.

As Atalanta drew ahead again, Hippomenes threw the second apple, but this time he threw it slightly to Atalanta's side. She had to turn a bit out of her way to get it. This time, Hippomenes managed to run ahead of her, but once again she caught up and took the lead.

He had one more apple, and he cast it to the side. It rolled into the grass, and Atalanta could not resist racing after it. Before she realized what was happening, Hippomenes touched the goal. The princess was his!

The two were soon married, and after a while they had a son who was to become a great hero. But Artemis's warning was not to be ignored. Somehow, Atalanta and Hippomenes angered one of the other goddesses. She had them turned into lions, and together they raced through the forests.

* **resist** (ri ZIST) oppose; be successful in avoiding

ALL THINGS CONSIDERED ———————————

1. The young princess is first raised by (a) a she-bear. (b) a goddess. (c) her father, the king.

2. After a while, she goes to live with a group of (a) runners. (b) hunters. (c) servants.

3. She takes part in a famous hunt to (a) win some golden apples. (b) kill a wild boar. (c) prove that a goddess protected her.

4. Her father wants to take her back because (a) he has chosen a husband for her. (b) a goddess changes his mind. (c) she has proven herself to be a great hunter.

5. Atalanta says she will marry a man who can outrun her because she (a) admires good runners. (b) wants the king to have a son-in-law he can be proud of. (c) thinks nobody can beat her.

6. Anyone who loses the race will (a) marry someone else. (b) die. (c) be sent to the mountains.

7. Hippomenes wants to win, so he (a) plants some golden apples. (b) practices running for a year. (c) asks the goddess Aphrodite for help.

8. When Atalanta runs after the first and second apple, Hippomenes (a) stops running and admires her. (b) gains the distance he has lost. (c) falls further behind.

9. Hippomenes is able to win because (a) one of the apples injures Atalanta. (b) Atalanta really wants to marry him. (c) Atalanta runs off the course to pick up the third apple.

10. One inference you can make from the ending is that in Greek stories (a) the goddesses are not always right. (b) warnings of goddesses come true. (c) most animals were once people.

THINKING IT THROUGH ———————————

1. Parts of the story could really happen and parts could not. Find three events in the story that could happen and three events that could not.

2. Do you believe in fate? That is, do you believe that what is going to happen to a person will happen no matter what that person does? Or do you believe that a person's own choices and way of living determine his or her life? Give some examples from real life to support your ideas.

3. Do you think that Atalanta would have grown up differently if she had not been left in the mountains as an infant? Explain.

Literary Skills

Conclusion

Every story has a beginning, a middle, and an end. The end is often called the **conclusion.** The conclusion of a story must make sense for that story. It may be a surprise to the reader, or it may be expected. Either way, the conclusion must fit the story.

The beginning of "Atalanta" tells about Atalanta's childhood. At the beginning of the story, the reader learns that Atalanta starts life in a very unusual way. The middle of the story tells about her skills and deeds and explains why she does not plan to marry. The conclusion of the story tells how a conflict is resolved.

The main conflict of the story is between Atalanta—who does not want to marry—and her father and the young men—who want her to marry. As Atalanta and Hippomenes race, the conflict builds to the most exciting point, or the **climax** of the story.

The plot sentence for the story might be: "Atalanta thinks she is safe when she refuses to marry anyone who cannot outrun her, but Hippomenes finds a way to win by _____."

Can you finish the sentence? What is the conclusion? How does Hippomenes win without Atalanta going back on her word?

Tell the conclusion of the story in your own words. Use a separate sheet of paper. After you give the conclusion of the story, tell whether you think it is a good conclusion for *this* story. Explain why or why not.

Composition

Follow your teacher's instructions before completing *one* of these writing assignments.

1. Did you want Atalanta or Hippomenes to win the race? Write four sentences that tell why you wanted that person to win.
2. Can you think of a different conclusion for the story? Rewrite the last two paragraphs of the story. Make your paragraphs something that could happen based on the events in the story.

Mark Twain (1835-1910)

Mark Twain was one of America's greatest and most humorous writers. He had worked at many different jobs before he began to write. That's probably how he came to know many kinds of Americans and parts of America.

He was born Samuel Langhorne Clemens. He took the name "Mark Twain" from a call he heard while working as a riverboat pilot on the Mississippi River.

Several times he set out to seek his fortune in distant lands by mining for gold or other metals. Those attempts never worked out. Instead, he found his fortune writing articles, books, and stories.

The Adventures of Tom Sawyer is one of Twain's best-loved books. Tom's adventures take place in a small town in Missouri, very much like the town where Twain grew up.

THE GLORIOUS WHITEWASHER

from *The Adventures of Tom Sawyer* by Mark Twain

▶ Tom did not look forward to spending the afternoon painting the fence. But if he could make a game of it, maybe it wouldn't be so bad. He might even find some willing players.

Saturday morning had come, and all the summer world was bright and fresh and full of life. There was a song in every heart. There was cheer in every face. The trees were in bloom and the smell of blossoms filled the air. The hill beyond the village was green. It lay just far enough away to seem dreamy and inviting.

Tom appeared on the sidewalk with a bucket of whitewash and a long-handled brush. He looked at the fence, and all gladness left him. Thirty yards of fence nine feet high! Sighing, he dipped his brush and passed it along the topmost board. He repeated the step and did it again. He compared the whitewashed streak with the continent of unwhitewashed fence. Then he sat down discouraged.

Jim came skipping out of the gate with a pail. Bringing water from the town pump had always been hateful work in Tom's eyes. But now it did not strike him that way. He remembered that there was company at the pump. And he remembered that although the pump was only a short way off, Jim never got back with a bucket of water in less than an hour.

"Say, Jim, I'll fetch the water if you'll whitewash some," said Tom.

Jim shook his head and said, "Can't, Tom. The missis told me I got to go an' get the water and not stop to fool around with anybody. She said she expected that Tom was gonna ask me to whitewash. So she told me to tend to my own business."

"Oh, never you mind what Aunt Polly said, Jim. That's the way she always talks. Gimme the bucket. I won't be gone only a minute.

- **sigh** (SY) take a long breath
- strike (STRYK) come to mind

She won't ever know."

"Oh, I dasn't, Tom. She'd take my head off!"

"*She!* She never licks anybody. She talks awful, but talk don't hurt. Jim, I'll give you a marble."

Jim began to waver.

"And besides, Jim, if you will, I'll show you my sore toe."

Jim was only human. This attraction was too much for him. He put down his pail, took the marble, and bent over the toe while the bandage was being unwound. In another moment, Jim was flying down the street with his pail, and Tom was whitewashing. Aunt Polly was walking off with a slipper in her hand and triumph in her eye.

But Tom's energy did not last. He began to think of the fun he had planned for this day. Soon the boys would come along, and they would make fun of him for having to work. The very thought of it burnt him like fire.

- waver (WAY vur) **show doubt; be unsure of what to do**
- **attraction** (uh TRAK shun) **something of special interest**

He got out his worldly wealth and examined it—bits of toys, marbles, and trash. It was enough to buy an exchange of *work,* maybe, but not enough to buy so much as half an hour of pure freedom. He returned his things to his pocket and gave up the idea of trying to buy help. At this hopeless moment, an idea burst upon him! A great, magnificent idea!

He took up his brush and went calmly to work. Ben Rogers came into sight. He was eating an apple and pretending he was a steamboat.

Tom went on whitewashing and paid no attention to the steamboat.

Ben stared a moment and then said, "Hi-yi! *You're* stuck, ain't you?"

No answer. Tom studied his last touch with the eye of an artist. Then he gave his brush another gentle sweep and looked at his work. Ben came alongside him. Tom's mouth watered for the apple, but he stuck to his work.

Ben said, "Hello, you got to work, hey?"

Tom wheeled suddenly and said, "Why, it's you, Ben! I warn't noticing."

"Say, *I'm* going swimming, I am. Don't you wish you could? But of course you'd rather *work,* wouldn't you? Course you would!"

Tom looked at the boy a bit and said, "What do you call work?"

"Why, ain't *that* work?"

Tom went back to his whitewashing and answered carelessly, "Well, maybe it is and maybe it ain't. All I know is it suits Tom Sawyer."

"Oh come now! You don't mean to let on that you *like* it?"

The brush continued to move. "Like it? Well, I don't see why I oughtn't to like it. Does a boy get a chance to whitewash a fence every day?"

That put the thing in a new light. Ben stopped nibbling his apple. Tom swept his brush back and forth, added a touch here and there, and looked at his work again.

Ben watched every move and grew more and more interested. Before long, he said, "Say, Tom, let *me* whitewash a little."

Tom considered, was about to say yes, but he changed his mind,

• **worldly** (WURLD lee) **in this world**

"No, no, I reckon it wouldn't do, Ben. You see, Aunt Polly's awful particular about this fence—right here on the street, you know. If it was the back fence, I wouldn't mind and *she* wouldn't. Yes, she's awful particular about this fence. It's got to be done very careful. I reckon there ain't one boy in a thousand, maybe two thousand, that can do it the way it's got to be done."

"No? Is that so? Oh come now, lemme just try. Only just a little—I'd let *you*, if you was me, Tom."

"Ben, I'd like to, honest! But Aunt Polly—well, Jim wanted to do it, but she wouldn't let him. Now don't you see? If you was to tackle this fence and anything was to happen to it——"

"Oh, I'll be careful. Now lemme try. Say, I'll give you the core of my apple."

"Well—No, Ben, now don't. I'm afraid——"

"I'll give you *all* of it!"

Tom gave up the brush with unwillingness in his face but joy in his heart. And while Ben worked and sweated in the sun, Tom sat on a barrel in the shade. He dangled his legs, munched his apple, and planned to trap others. There were boys who came along every little while. They came to tease, but remained to whitewash.

By the time Ben was tired out, Tom had traded the next chance to Billy Fisher for a kite. And when Billy tired out, Johnny Miller brought in a dead rat and a string to swing it with—and so on, and so on, hour after hour.

When the middle of the afternoon came, from being a poor boy in the morning, Tom was rolling in wealth. He had, beside the things mentioned before, twelve marbles, a piece of blue bottle glass to look through, a spool, a key that wouldn't unlock anything, a piece of chalk, a bottle top, a couple of tadpoles, six firecrackers, a kitten with only one eye, a brass doorknob, a dog collar—but no dog—the handle of a knife, four pieces of orange peel, and an old window sash.

He had had a nice, good, idle time all the while, with plenty of company. And the fence had three coats of whitewash on it! If he hadn't run out of whitewash, he would have bankrupted every boy in the village.

- **tackle** (TAK ul) try to do
- **window sash**—frame that holds a window
- **bankrupt** (BANGK rupt) cause to lose all money or wealth

151

Tom had discovered a great law of human action, without knowing it. In order to make someone want a thing, it is only necessary to make the thing difficult to get. Maybe he understood that Work is whatever you have to do and Play is whatever you don't have to do.

The boy thought awhile about the great change which had taken place in his worldly wealth. Then he headed for the house to report on a job well done.

ALL THINGS CONSIDERED

1. At first, Tom is unhappy because (a) he wants to whitewash the fence and is not allowed to. (b) he has to whitewash the fence and doesn't want to. (c) the fence is too high for him to reach.

2. The first person he asks to do the job is (a) Jim. (b) Ben Rogers. (c) Aunt Polly.

3. He begins to work calmly after (a) Ben comes along. (b) he gets a great idea. (c) he realizes there is no hope.

4. When Ben comes along, Tom (a) asks Ben to do some of the work. (b) sends for the other boys. (c) pretends he enjoys whitewashing.

5. When Ben first offers to whitewash the fence, Tom says (a) he will be glad to have help. (b) Ben isn't tall enough. (c) Aunt Polly is very fussy about her fence.

6. Ben finally whitewashes the fence after (a) Tom gives him a toy. (b) Ben gives Tom an apple. (c) Jim says it's okay.

7. While Ben is whitewashing, Tom (a) helps. (b) reads. (c) rests.

8. When other boys come along they (a) ask to paint the fence, too. (b) tell Ben he is foolish. (c) ask Tom for toys.

9. The whitewashing job is done when (a) there are no more boys. (b) it is time for supper. (c) all the whitewash is gone.

10. Tom figures out that people (a) work only when they are paid. (b) like to help others. (c) don't mind work if they think it is play.

THINKING IT THROUGH

1. Reread the first paragraph. Why does the author begin this story in such a cheerful way? Does the picture he paints fit Tom's mood?

2. How did Tom get the boys to help him? Did anybody get hurt by his game?

3. In what ways does the author, Mark Twain, make the characters' speech seem true to life? Find two examples. How does this help you visualize the characters? Does it add humor to the story? Explain.

4. Look at the last sentence of the next to the last paragraph. Do you agree or disagree? Explain.

Vocabulary and Sentence Meaning

Context Clues

When reading, most people come across words they do not know. The context of a word helps readers guess at the meaning. **Context clues** are all the words around an unknown word.

On page 148, what *context clues* help tell the meaning of the word *whitewash?* The first clue is "bucket of whitewash." That clue tells that whitewash can be carried in a bucket. The next clue is that Tom "dips his brush" in the whitewash. A third clue is that whitewash leaves a streak on the board. In the case of this word, even the name *whitewash* is a clue.

Use all the clues about whitewash to state the exact meaning of the word.

Find clues to help you with the meanings of the following words. Remember to look at the context of each. Write the words and the meanings you figure out for them on a separate piece of paper.

1. continent (page 148)

2. fetch (page 148)

3. considered (page 150)

4. reckon (page 151)

5. particular (page 151)

Composition

Follow your teacher's instructions before completing *one* of these writing assignments.

1. Choose four words from those listed at the bottoms of pages 148–151. Use each word in a sentence. Try to include a clue for the meaning of the word.

2. What is work and what is play? Think of something you consider play that someone else might consider work. Or, think of something you consider work that others might consider play. Write a paragraph telling why you feel the way you do.

VOCABULARY AND SKILL REVIEW

Before completing the exercises that follow, you may wish to review the **bold-faced** words on pages 141–153.

I. On your paper, write the word in each line that means the same, or nearly the same, as the word in *italics.*

1. *fate:* wealth, destiny, peace, strength
2. *fierce:* huge, unhappy, wild, small
3. *sigh:* breathe slowly, complain loudly, cough hard, whistle
4. *attraction:* complaint, interesting thing, lie, bad movie
5. *tackle:* trust, hammer, giggle, try
6. *mission:* home, desire, job, adventure
7. *quiver:* arrow case, bow string, metal buckle, sharp knife
8. *proclamation:* discovery, system, announcement, lie
9. *bankrupt:* rich, poor, injured, false
10. *resist:* want, oppose, imagine, succeed

II. How good are you at using context clues? The conversation below comes from *Alice's Adventures in Wonderland* by Lewis Carroll. The Mock Turtle is telling Alice about his school. The words the Mock Turtle uses are real words. But they are not the correct words for the context. Write the word the Mock Turtle meant to use for each of the six underlined words.

Said the Mock Turtle with a sigh, "I only took the regular course."

"What was that?" inquired Alice.

"Reeling and Writhing, of course to begin with," the Mock Turtle replied, "and then the different branches of Arithmetic—Ambition, Distraction, Uglification, and Derision."

III. The following diagram shows the rising and falling action of a plot. Copy the diagram and add the terms rising action, climax, and conclusion.

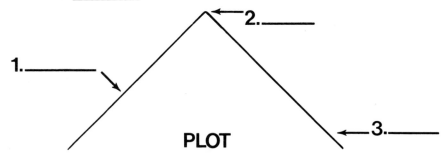

PLOT

155

UNIT REVIEW

I. Match the terms in Column A with their definitions in Column B.

A	B
1. climax	**a)** fight or struggle with oneself or between oneself and others
2. conclusion	**b)** getting a picture in your mind
3. conflict	**c)** sight, hearing, smell, taste, and touch
4. context clues	**d)** order
5. five senses	**e)** figuring out something from what is already known
6. inference	**f)** more than one sense to a word
7. multiple meanings	**g)** events getting more interesting as a plot continues
8. rising action	**h)** end of a story
9. sequence	**i)** the most exciting part or high point of a story
10. visualizing	**j)** information that helps you understand a word's meaning

Follow your teacher's instructions before completing *one* of these writing assignments.

II. Which story or poem in this unit was your favorite? To explain what you liked about that selection, use some terms you have learned in this unit. On a separate sheet of paper, write the name of the selection. Then tell at least three things that you liked. You may want to discuss the plot. Did it have rising action? Was the conclusion a good one? Was the climax exciting? You may want to discuss the details or the use of words.

III. Some of the selections in this unit might be closer than others to your idea of what a game is. Now that you have read about different kinds of games, choose one story and describe the game in that story. Begin by writing the title of the story.

SPEAKING UP

Warner Wolf is a sports reporter on television. Besides reporting sports, he sometimes gives his ideas about things he thinks need to be changed in the sports world. Turn the page for something he said on television about fights in hockey games.

Read the selection aloud as if you are reading it on television. Pronounce the words slowly and clearly so they can be understood easily. Put a lot of expression into your voice, and sound as if you mean what you say.

BOO ON HOCKEY FIGHTS

by Warner Wolf

Boo on hockey fights!

There's so much hypocrisy in hockey it's a joke. The owners keep saying they want a clean sport. Baloney! If the owners wanted to stop hockey fights all they would have to do is adopt a very simple rule. Every hockey fight begins the same way. The first thing the players do is throw down their gloves on the ice so they can grab and fight. My rule is easy: *He who throws down his gloves is automatically ejected from the game.*

If you think you can fight with those gloves on, you're not being realistic. You can *try* to fight. You can slap. But fight? No way! First of all, they're too cumbersome to hit anybody with. And second, you can't grab your opponent with one hand and hit him with the other if you have your gloves on. At best, if players kept their gloves on, they would wrestle each other to the ice and there would be no fights.

The beautiful thing is it's a blanket rule: *Take gloves off, out of the game.* Plus you can make the penalty more severe if you wish. Say the guy throws his gloves down and starts fighting with only two minutes to go in the game. "Big deal," he says, "I'm out of the game. So what? There's only two minutes left." Well, you say he's out of this game and the next game too for fighting.

That's a pretty simple rule if they really wanted to ban fighting. But the problem is, some of the owners are afraid people will stop coming to the games if there are no fights. This may be true, but for every person who will stop coming to a game because there are no more fights, I believe there are two people who will start showingup.

From GIMME A BREAK by Warner Wolf, copyright c 1983.
Reprinted by permission of McGraw-Hill Book Company.

- hypocrisy (hi POK ruh see) **pretending you believe in one set of ideas while acting on another set of ideas or beliefs**
- eject (i JEKT) **throw out; force to leave**
- cumbersome (KUM bur sum) **hard to handle; clumsy**

WRITING YOUR OWN PLOT

What do you think is happening in this picture? What happened just before this picture was taken? What will happen next? Your answers to these questions will become part of a plot paragraph.

1. **Prewriting:** List about five action words or phrases to describe what is happening in the picture. Then decide what happened before and what will happen next. You will have to make *inferences* based on your own experiences and the information in the picture.
2. **Writing:** Use your prewriting plan to write a paragraph. Write about events in the order in which they happen.
3. **Revising:** Reread your paragraph. Do events move in a natural order from beginning to end? Do you use action words? Check to see that all your sentences have subjects and verbs. Make corrections and then write your paragraph neatly.

UNIT 3

THE COMIC SPIRIT

A smile, a giggle, a chuckle, a laugh—these are the signs that humor is on the loose.

If you think that literature has to be serious, get ready to change your mind. Writers have always joined in the comic spirit. They've written about serious things in funny ways and about funny things just for fun.

Everyone has a sense of humor, but not the *same* sense of humor. What makes one person laugh out loud may make another only smile. That's the funny thing about the comic spirit!

THE KING AND
HIS COUNSELORS

adapted from Aesop

▶ Perhaps your comic spirit will be awakened by trickster tales. **Trickster tales** are stories about characters—human or animal—who live by their quick wits. These tales have been around since the earliest days of storytelling.

   The trickster in the following tale must think fast when the king asks him a question. Should he answer truthfully, or should he lie? What will the trickster do?

King Lion was crabby as he went to work one morning. The queen had told him his breath was somewhat unpleasant. Why had she said that? What did she mean?

King Lion burst into the throne room and let out a mighty roar just to let Secretary Rabbit know who was king. Then, mounting his throne, he growled, "Aren't the counselors in yet?"

"They are at their desks, Your Majesty," answered the secretary.

"Tell Counselor Sheep I need some counsel," the king muttered.

So Counselor Sheep came to the king, bowing low. "Dear Counselor," growled King Lion, "tell me, is it your opinion that my breath is unpleasant?" Then he opened wide, and Counselor Sheep tipped up a long, quivering nose to sniff.

Because he firmly believed that the only good counsel was honest counsel, Counselor Sheep said, "I am afraid, Your Majesty—yes, indeed—your breath—"

"Never mind!" the king interrupted. "Because your advice is wrong, as usual, I'll just—"

And he did; he bit off Counselor Sheep's head.

Then the king had his secretary summon Counselor Wolf.

- **unpleasant** (un PLEZ unt) not pleasing; annoying
- **counselor** (KOUN suh lur) one who gives advice
- counsel (KOUN sul) give an opinion; advise
- **opinion** (uh PIN yun) what a person thinks
- **quivering** (KWIV ur ing) shaking; trembling
- summon (SUM un) send for

"Dear Counselor," growled the king, "tell me, is it your opinion that my breath is unpleasant?" Again he opened wide, and Counselor Wolf tipped up a sharp, steady nose to sniff.

"Ah!" exclaimed Counselor Wolf, eyes closed in ecstasy. "Your breath is delightful. A spring breeze scented with violets, a—"

But those words caused the furious king to bite off Counselor Wolf's head too. "Flatterer," he growled. "I'll never have to listen to your false counsel again."

So now King Lion summoned Counselor Fox.

"Dear Counselor," growled the king to his third and last counselor, "tell me, is it your opinion that my breath is unpleasant?" And for the third time he opened his mouth for examination.

Counselor Fox coughed discreetly into a handkerchief. "Pardon me, Your Majesty," he whispered hoarsely. "Because I have one of those miserable head colds, I can smell nothing at all."

Excused by the king, Counselor Fox bowed low and retired to his office.

There are times when silence is golden.

- ecstasy (EK stuh see) **highest joy**
- **flatterer** (FLAT ur ur) **one who praises another too much**
- discreetly (di SKREET lee) **in a wise and careful way; with good judgment**
- retire (ri TYR) **leave; go back to another place**

ALL THINGS CONSIDERED _____

1. The story of King Lion and his counselors is a (a) biography. (b) lyric poem. (c) fable.

2. The king is worried because (a) he has caught a cold. (b) the queen has told him his breath is unpleasant. (c) he thinks his counselors are doing a bad job.

3. When asked to give his opinion, Counselor Sheep tries to (a) trick the king. (b) tell the king the truth. (c) flatter the king.

4. Counselor Wolf tries to (a) trick the king. (b) tell the king the truth. (c) flatter the king.

5. By pretending to have a cold, Counselor Fox (a) saves his life. (b) loses his job. (c) tricks Counselor Wolf.

6. Counselor Fox probably (a) does not have a cold. (b) has a very bad cold. (c) does not want the king to catch his cold.

7. The king seems to think that Counselor Fox is (a) telling the truth. (b) playing a trick on him. (c) coughing too much.

8. The trickster in this story is (a) King Lion. (b) Counselor Wolf. (c) Counselor Fox.

9. The word that best describes Counselor Fox is (a) foolish. (b) honest. (c) clever.

10. The moral, or lesson, of this story is (a) never tell the truth. (b) sometimes it's best to say nothing. (c) health is wealth.

THINKING IT THROUGH _____

1. Each animal character in most fables has only one main character trait. For example, in this fable, the lion is hard to please. The sheep is honest no matter what the result. What is the main character trait of the wolf? What is the main character trait of the fox?

2. How would you have answered the king? What does your answer tell you about yourself?

3. Think about the moral of the story: *There are times when silence is golden.* Imagine a time when it would be best for a person to be silent. Tell about it.

4. Now imagine a time when it would *not* be a good idea for a person to be silent. Share your ideas with the class.

5. The title of this fable is "The King and His Counselors." Suppose the title had been "When Silence Is Golden." Compare the two titles. Which title is better? Tell why you think so.

Relationships

Cause and Effect

A **cause** is an event or idea that leads to a certain result called an **effect.** For example, your alarm clock rings. What might be the result, or effect, that the ring will have?

One thing that is likely to happen is that the ring will cause you to wake up. In other words, the effect of the ringing alarm clock will be to wake you up.

CAUSE	EFFECT

The alarm clock rings,   so you wake up.

Here is another example of cause and effect. In this sentence, the effect is stated first.

EFFECT	CAUSE

You answered the questions correctly   because you studied.

As you can see, sometimes the cause is stated first in the sentence. At other times, the effect is stated first. Think to yourself: What idea or event happened first (the cause)? What was the result (the effect)?

A cause-and-effect statement often has a clue word. Some clue words are: *so, because, when,* and *since.*

On a separate piece of paper, complete each of the following sentences. Add either a cause or an effect as indicated in parentheses ( ).

1. King Lion is crabby because the queen . . . (cause).
2. Because Counselor Sheep tells the truth, King Lion . . . (effect).
3. When Counselor Wolf flatters King Lion, the king . . . (effect).
4. Counselor Fox says he cannot smell anything because he . . . (cause).
5. Since King Lion accepts the answer of Counselor Fox, the fox . . . (effect).

165

Composition

Follow your teacher's instructions before completing *one* of these writing assignments.

1. In the story, King Lion went to work in the throne room. Think about what might be in the throne room. Describe the room in two or three sentences.

2. Make up a new ending for the fable. First, tell what the fox said or did. Then, tell what the king did. Finally, end the story with a different moral (lesson). You may choose one of the morals below or make up your own.

Don't count your chickens until they're hatched.
Haste makes waste.
It's never too early to plan for your future.

Oral Interpretation

When you read aloud, you should say the words as you think the characters might say them. Here are some hints about what certain kinds of speaking show:

- Speaking slowly shows that a character is careful, thoughtful, or wise.

- Speaking fast shows excitement, fear, or anger.

Use these two hints as you practice reading the lines spoken by the lion, the sheep, the wolf, and the fox in "The King and His Counselors." Try to show how each character feels.

First, practice alone. Try to hear the words in your head as you read silently. Then practice with a friend. Take turns reading aloud. Help each other by offering suggestions for improvement.

Then, form groups—five students in each group since there are five speaking parts. With your classmates you can turn your reading into a short play to perform in front of the rest of the class.

BOUKI RENTS A HORSE

a Haitian folktale

retold by Harold Courlander

▶ This trickster tale shows how an underdog survives by being clever and sly. Not only that, it also shows how a problem can be changed into a laugh.

It was time to dig up the yams and take them to market. Bouki went out with his big hoe and dug up a big pile of yams and left them in the sun to dry. While they were drying, he began to consider how he would get them to the city. "I think I will borrow Moussa's donkey," he said at last. "As long as I have the donkey, I might as well dig up some more yams."

So he dug up some more yams, and then he went to Moussa's house for the donkey. But Moussa said, "Bouki, my donkey ran away yesterday, and we haven't found him yet. Why don't you rent a horse from Mr. Toussaint?"

"Toussaint!" Bouki said. "He'll charge more than I can get for the yams! He'll charge me even for *talking* to him!"

But finally Bouki went to Toussaint's house to see if he could rent a horse.

Toussaint said, "This is a good horse. He's too good to carry yams. But you can have him for one day for fifteen gourdes."

Bouki had only five gourdes.

"I'll take the five now," Toussaint said. "You can give me ten more tomorrow when you come for the horse."

Bouki went home. He went to sleep. In the morning when he got up to go to market, Moussa was waiting in front of his house with the donkey.

- **underdog** (UN dur DOG) **person who is not thought of as a winner; a person not favored to succeed**
- yam (YAM) **kind of sweet potato**
- gourde (GOORD) **Haitian money**

167

"Here's the donkey," Moussa said. "He came home in the middle of the night."

Bouki said, "But I already rented Toussaint's horse!"

"Never mind, go tell Toussaint you don't need the horse," Moussa said.

"But I already gave him five gourdes," Bouki complained. "I'll never get my money back!"

Just then Ti Malice came along. He listened to the talk. He said, "Take me along to Toussaint's. I'll get your money back for you."

Together Bouki and Ti Malice went to Toussaint's place.

"We've come for the horse," Ti Malice said.

"There he is under the tree," Toussaint said. "But first give me the ten gourdes."

"Not so fast," Ti Malice said. "First we have to see if he's big enough."

"He's big enough," Toussaint said. "He's the biggest horse around here. So give me the ten gourdes."

"First we have to measure him," Ti Malice said. He took a measuring tape from his pocket and stretched it over the horse's back. "Let's see, now," he said to Bouki. "You need about eighteen inches, and you can sit in the middle. I need about fifteen inches, and I can sit here. Madame Malice needs about eighteen inches, and she can sit behind me. Madame Bouki needs about twenty inches, and she can sit in the front."

"Wait!" Toussaint said. "You can't put four people on that horse!"

"Then," Ti Malice said, "Tijean Bouki can go here on the horse's neck. Boukino can sit in his lap, and we can tie Boukinette right here if we're careful."

"Listen!" Toussaint said, starting to sweat. "You must be crazy. A horse can't carry so many people!"

"He can try," Ti Malice said.

"You'll kill him!" Toussaint said.

"We can put my children *here,*" Ti Malice said, measuring behind the horse's ears, "but they'll have to push together."

"Just a minute!" Toussaint shouted. "You can't have the horse!"

"Oh yes, we can," Ti Malice said, still measuring. "You rented him to us, and today we are going to use him. Bouki, where will we put the baby?"

"Baby?" Bouki said. "Baby?"

"We'll put the baby here," Ti Malice said. "Madame Bouki can hold him. Then over here we can hang the saddlebags to carry the pigs."

"The deal is off!" Toussaint shouted. "This animal isn't a steamship!"

"Now don't try to back out of the deal," Ti Malice said, "or we'll take the matter to the police."

"Here!" Toussaint said. "Here's your five gourdes back!"

"Five!" Ti Malice said. "You rented him to us for *fifteen,* and now you want to give *five* back? What do you take us for?"

"Yes," Bouki said, "what for?"

"But Bouki only *gave* me five!" Toussaint said.

Ti Malice looked the horse over carefully.

"Where will we put Grandmother?" Bouki asked suddenly.

"Here!" Toussaint shouted. "Here!" He pushed fifteen gourdes into Ti Malice's hands. "And get away from my horse!" He jumped on its back and rode away.

Bouki and Ti Malice watched him go. Then they fell on the ground and began to laugh. They laughed so hard that they had to gasp for air.

Suddenly Bouki stopped laughing. He looked worried. He sat up straight.

"What's the matter?" Ti Malice asked.

"I don't think we could have done it," Bouki said.

"Done what?" Ti Malice asked.

"Put Grandmother on the horse," Bouki said.

ALL THINGS CONSIDERED ─────────────

1. Bouki needs a horse because (a) he has so many yams to take to the market. (b) a horse can dig up yams. (c) Moussa won't sell him a donkey.

2. At first Bouki does not want to rent a horse because (a) Toussaint probably will charge too much. (b) he is afraid of horses. (c) a horse cannot carry a big enough load.

3. Later Bouki's problem becomes how to (a) use Toussaint's horse without paying for it. (b) refuse Toussaint's horse and get his rent money back. (c) get his yams and his family to market.

4. Ti Malice uses a measuring tape to see (a) how many yams the horse can carry. (b) how tall the horse is. (c) how many riders the horse can carry.

5. First Ti Malice talks about loading (a) all the yams. (b) all the animals that he and Bouki own. (c) everyone in his family and in Bouki's family.

6. Then Ti Malice talks about hanging saddlebags to carry the (a) yams. (b) pigs. (c) people in the village.

7. When the load sounds too big, Toussaint (a) starts a fight. (b) wants to call off the deal. (c) calls the police and has Ti Malice arrested.

8. Finally, Toussaint agrees to give back the five gourdes and (a) ten more. (b) a bushel of yams. (c) the donkey he took from Ti Malice.

9. The trickster in this tale is (a) Toussaint. (b) Moussa. (c) Ti Malice.

10. The last line of the story suggests that Bouki (a) wants the horse after all. (b) does not have a grandmother. (c) does not realize that Ti Malice is only fooling Toussaint.

THINKING IT THROUGH ─────────────

1. What is the difference between Ti Malice and a thief who tiptoes into Toussaint's house and steals ten gourdes? Why might you like Ti Malice and not like a thief?

2. Look back through the story and find the sentences that make you laugh. Are you laughing because something funny has been said? Or are you laughing because Toussaint is getting what he deserves?

Vocabulary and Sentence Meaning

Dialogue

Characters talking to one another is called **dialogue.** When authors show the exact words of a character, they follow these rules:

1. Quotation marks go around the spoken words: "We've come for the horse," Ti Malice said.

2. A period or comma at the end of the spoken words goes inside the quotation marks: Toussaint said, "But first give me the ten gourdes." "Not so fast," Ti Malice said.

3. If a phrase such as *He said* comes before the spoken words, a comma goes after the *said:* He said, "Not so fast."

4. The first word of the spoken sentence begins with a capital letter, even after a comma: He said, "Not so fast."

5. Each time a new character speaks, the words begin on a new line.

The following sentences need quotation marks, periods, commas, and capital letters. Write these sentences correctly on your paper.

1. here's the donkey Moussa said

2. Bouki said I already rented Toussaint's horse

3. never mind Moussa said

4. Bouki said I already paid Toussaint five gourdes

Composition

Follow your teacher's instructions before completing *one* of these writing assignments.

1. Copy the lines of dialogue from page 169 that begin with the word "Listen!" (spoken by Toussaint) and end with the words "but they'll have to push together" (spoken by Ti Malice). Be sure to put the quotation marks exactly where they belong.

2. Write four lines of dialogue. Pretend that Bouki and Moussa are talking. Bouki wants to rent Moussa's donkey for five gourdes, but Moussa wants to charge ten gourdes.

CLEVER MANKA

retold by Ethel Johnston Phelps

▶ Do you like to solve riddles? Try matching wits with Manka. She has a ready answer for each question she is asked.

Long ago in the villages of Europe, disputes among the citizens were settled by the mayor. Right or wrong, the mayor's opinion was accepted.

It was in those days, then, that a certain village had a very young mayor who was not at all experienced. He was honest, however, as everyone could see from the plainness of his house. The front door opened directly into a sitting room where the young mayor heard all disputes. A seat on one side of the fireplace was his, and a bench on the other side was for those who brought their differences to him.

He had but one decorative piece on the wall, a pretty cloth with these words embroidered on it: "He who would be just must first be wise."

In this village there lived a rich farmer who was as selfish as he was rich. This farmer owed one of his neighbors, a poor shepherd, the payment of a calf. When the time for the payment came, the farmer refused to give the shepherd the calf. This forced the shepherd to bring the matter before the mayor.

After the mayor heard both sides, he thought a bit. Finally he said, "Instead of making a decision on this case, I will ask you both a riddle. The man who makes the best answer shall have the calf. Are you agreed?"

The farmer and the shepherd agreed, so the mayor said, "Well then, here is my riddle: What is the swiftest thing in the world? What is the sweetest thing? What is the richest? Think out your answers and bring them to me at this same time tomorrow."

- **dispute** (dis PYOOT) **argument**
- decorative (DEK ur uh tiv) **serving to give something a better look**

172

The farmer went home angry. "What kind of a mayor is this young fellow!" he growled. "If he had let me keep the calf, I'd have sent him a bushel of pears. Now I may lose the calf, for I can't think of an answer to his foolish riddle."

"What is the riddle?" asked his wife. "Perhaps I can help you." The farmer told her the riddle. His wife said that of course she knew the answers.

"Our gray mare must be the swiftest thing in the world," she said. "You know that nothing ever passes us on the road. As for the sweetest, did you ever taste any honey sweeter than ours? And I'm sure there's nothing richer than our chest of gold coins we've saved up over the years."

The farmer was delighted. "You're right! Now we will be able to keep the calf!"

Meanwhile the shepherd walked sadly homeward. He lived with his daughter Manka in a cabin of three small rooms. Manka was sitting by the stove when he entered, partly to keep warm and partly to keep an eye on the supper she had prepared. She could see that her poor father was sad, so she asked what troubled him.

The shepherd sighed. "I'm afraid I've lost the calf. The mayor gave us a riddle, and I know I shall never solve it."

"What is the riddle? Perhaps I can help you," said Manka.

The shepherd told her the riddle, and Manka quickly told him the answers.

The next day, when the shepherd reached the mayor's house, the farmer was already there. The mayor repeated the riddle and turned to the farmer.

With a pompous air the farmer said, "The swiftest thing in the world? Why, that's my gray mare, of course, for no other horse ever passes us on the road. The sweetest? Honey from my beehives. The richest? What can be richer than my chest of gold coins?"

"Hmmm," said the mayor. "And what answers does the shepherd make?"

"The swiftest thing in the world," said the shepherd, "is thought, for thought can run any distance in the twinkling of an eye. The sweetest thing of all is sleep, for when a person is tired and sad, what can be sweeter? The richest thing is the earth, for out of the earth come all the riches of the world."

"Good!" cried the mayor. "The calf goes to the shepherd."

Later the mayor said to the shepherd, "Tell me now, who gave you those answers? I'm sure you never thought of them yourself."

The shepherd was unwilling to tell, but finally he confessed that the answers came from his daughter Manka.

The mayor, who wanted to be wise in order to be just, became very interested in Manka. He sent his housekeeper for ten eggs and gave them to the shepherd. "Take these eggs to Manka," he said. "Tell her to have them hatched by tomorrow and bring me the chicks."

• **mare** (MAIR) female horse

The shepherd went home and gave Manka the eggs and the message. Manka laughed and said, "Take a handful of corn to the mayor with this message: 'My daughter says to plant this corn, grow it, and have it harvested by tomorrow. Do this, and she will bring you the ten chicks to feed on the ripe corn.'"

When the mayor heard this answer, he laughed heartily. "That's a very clever daughter you have! I'd like to meet her. Tell her to come to see me, but she must come neither by day nor by night, neither riding nor walking, neither dressed nor undressed."

Manka smiled when she received this message. The next dawn, when night was gone and day not yet come, she set out. She had wrapped herself in a fishnet. She rode on a goat with one leg over its back and one foot on the ground.

Now I ask you, did she go dressed?

No, she wasn't dressed, for a fishnet isn't clothing. Did she go undressed? Of course not, for wasn't she covered with a fishnet? Did she walk to the mayor's? No, she didn't walk, for she went with one leg thrown over a goat. Then did she ride? Of course she didn't ride, for wasn't she walking on one foot?

When she reached the mayor's house, she called out, "Here I am, and I've come neither by day nor by night, neither riding nor walking, neither dressed nor undressed."

The young mayor was so delighted with Manka's cleverness that he proposed to her. In a short time they were married.

"But understand, my dear Manka," he said, "you are not to use your cleverness to interfere in any of my cases. Do not give advice to those who come to me for judgment. If you do, I'll send you home to your father."

"Very well," said Manka. "I agree not to give advice in your cases unless you ask for it."

All went well for a time. Manka was busy with housekeeping. She was careful not to interfere in any of the mayor's cases.

Then one day two farmers came to the mayor to have a dispute settled. One of the farmers owned a mare that had given birth in the marketplace. The colt had run under the wagon of the other farmer, and the owner of the wagon claimed the colt as his property.

The mayor was thinking of something else while the case was being argued, so he answered carelessly. "The man who found the colt under his wagon is the owner of the colt," he said.

The farmer who owned the mare met Manka as he was leaving the house, and stopped to tell her about the case. Manka was ashamed that her husband had made so foolish a decision. She said to the farmer, "Come back this afternoon with a fishing net and stretch it across the dusty road. When the mayor sees you, he will come out and ask what you are doing. Tell him you are catching fish. He will ask how you can expect to catch fish in a dusty road. Tell him it's just as easy to catch fish in a dusty road as it is for a wagon to give birth to a colt. He'll see the injustice of his decision and have the colt returned to you. But remember one thing—you must not let him know that I told you to do this."

That afternoon when the mayor looked out of his window, he saw a man stretching a fishnet across the dusty road. He went out and asked, "What are you doing?"

"Fishing."

"Fishing in a dusty road?"

"Well," said the man, "it's just as easy for me to catch fish in a dusty road as it is for a wagon to give birth to a colt."

Then the mayor realized he had made a careless and unjust decision. "Of course, the colt belongs to your mare," he said. "It will be returned to you. But tell me, who put you up to this? You didn't think of it yourself!"

The farmer tried not to tell, but the mayor insisted. When he found out that Manka was at the bottom of it, he became very angry. He rushed into the house and called his wife.

"Manka," he said, "I told you what would happen if you interfered in any of my cases! I won't hear any excuses. Home you go this very day. You may take with you the one thing you like best in the house."

Manka did not argue. "Very well, my dear husband. I shall go home to my father's cottage and take with me the one thing I like best in the house. But I will not go until after supper. We have been very happy together. I should like to eat one last meal with you. Let us have no more angry words, but be kind to each other as we've always been. Let us part as friends."

The mayor agreed to this, and Manka prepared a fine supper of all the dishes her husband liked. The supper was so good that he ate and ate and ate. And the more he ate, the more he drank. At last he grew drowsy and fell sound asleep in his chair. Then, without awakening him, Manka had him carried out to the wagon that was waiting to take her home to her father.

• injustice (in JUS tis) **unfairness**

175

The next morning, when the mayor opened his eyes, he found himself lying in the shepherd's cottage.

"What does this mean?" he roared.

"Nothing, dear husband," said Manka. "You know you told me I might take with me the one thing I liked best in your house. So I did! I took you! That's all."

The mayor stared at her in amazement. Then he laughed loud and heartily to think how Manka had outwitted him.

"Manka," he said, "you're too clever for me. Come, my dear, let's go home."

So they climbed back into the wagon and drove home.

The very next day the mayor had the embroidered words on his wall changed. Instead of saying "He . . . ," the words now said "They who would be just must first be wise."

Indeed, the mayor never again scolded his wife. And whenever a very difficult case came up, he always said, "I think we had better consult my wife. You know she's a very clever woman."

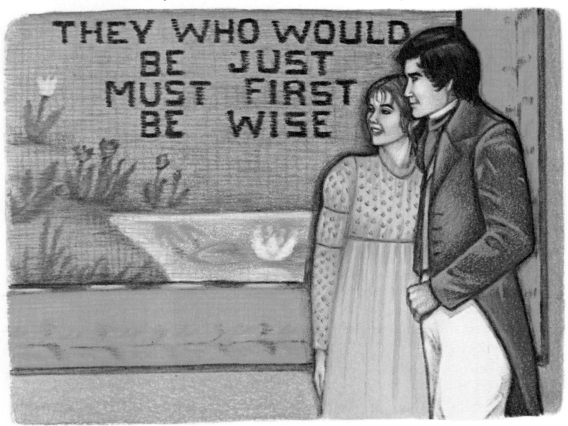

- **outwit** (out WIT) act in a more clever way than someone else
- **consult** (kun SULT) seek the advice of

ALL THINGS CONSIDERED _____

1. A farmer and a shepherd have an argument over the payment of a (a) calf. (b) lamb. (c) colt.

2. To decide the case, the mayor asks a riddle that is correctly answered by the (a) farmer's wife. (b) shepherd's daughter. (c) mayor's helper.

3. The swiftest thing in the world is said to be (a) a bird. (b) time. (c) thought.

4. When the mayor learns of Manka's cleverness, he (a) goes to see her. (b) asks her to come see him. (c) makes her an assistant judge.

5. To travel "neither by day nor by night," Manka goes (a) at sunset. (b) at dawn. (c) during a holiday.

6. The mayor marries Manka because she is so (a) beautiful. (b) lonely. (c) clever.

7. Manka promises her husband that she will (a) help him decide his cases. (b) not interfere with his cases. (c) not ask any more riddles.

8. Manka tells a farmer to say that it is as easy to catch fish in the road as it is for (a) fish to swim in a wagon. (b) fish to swim in the sea. (c) a wagon to give birth to a colt.

9. When Manka is told to leave the mayor's house with only the one thing that she likes best, she takes (a) her husband. (b) the money chest. (c) a calf.

10. In the end, the mayor is happy to (a) live alone. (b) decide all the cases by himself. (c) ask his wife for help.

THINKING IT THROUGH _____

1. The story of Manka takes place in the past. What details in the story show this? Do you think Manka would fit in today? Explain your answer.

2. Do you think the mayor knew the answers to his own riddle? What would you answer if asked, "What is the swiftest thing in the world? What is the sweetest? What is the richest?"

3. Why did Manka send corn to the mayor when he sent her eggs? Explain her message.

4. If you were choosing a husband or a wife, would a sense of humor and a clever mind be more or less important than wealth or beauty? Explain your answer.

177

Literary Skills

Understanding Setting

A story happens in a certain place and at a certain time. The place and time of a story are its **setting.** To understand setting, it is helpful to ask *where* and *when* a story happens. The answer to *where* a story happens can be general (in the country or in the city), or it can be specific (in the kitchen of a small house). The answer to *when* a story happens can also be general (in the past or in the future) or specific (on a summer's night in the 1940s).

To understand the setting, look for details or descriptions in the story itself. There are usually descriptions of the place and time. These descriptions are often at the beginning of the story. For example, "Clever Manka" begins: "Long ago in the villages of Europe . . ." This tells, in a general way, when and where the story takes place.

Write your answers to the following on a separate sheet of paper.

1. Reread the second paragraph of "Clever Manka." Does this paragraph tell about the setting? Why?
2. Find the paragraph that describes Manka's house. Do you think that knowing that Manka is sitting by the stove is part of the setting? Explain your answer.
3. In one or two sentences, tell why you think the mayor's house is described more thoroughly than Manka's house.

Composition

Follow your teacher's instructions before completing *one* of these writing assignments.

1. Which of the following words or phrases fit the description of the mayor's house? List them on your paper. Then use one or two of the words or phrases in a sentence about the mayor's house.
*fancy–plain   painting–embroidered piece
sitting room–dining room   fireplace–stove   couch–bench*
2. In your own words, explain the saying, "They who would be just must first be wise." Who are "they"? What is meant by being just?

VOCABULARY AND SKILL REVIEW

Before completing the exercises that follow, you may wish to review the **bold-faced** words on pages 162–176.

I. Choose the answer that best completes each sentence.

1. A *counselor* is someone who (a) gives advice. (b) makes excuses. (c) entertains guests.
2. *Mare* is the term used for a (a) male horse. (b) female lion. (c) female horse.
3. An *unpleasant* task is likely to be (a) annoying. (b) fun. (c) exciting.
4. Think of *dialogue* as (a) action. (b) conversation. (c) setting.
5. A *flatterer* can be counted on to (a) insult you. (b) confuse you. (c) praise you.
6. When you give an *opinion,* you (a) say what you think. (b) tell only the facts. (c) have nothing to say.
7. The *underdog* in any contest is the one (a) expected to win. (b) not expected to win. (c) keeping score.
8. To *outwit* an opponent, you have to be (a) friendly. (b) silly. (c) clever.
9. It is a good idea to *consult* others before making a big decision by (a) asking them for advice. (b) not discussing the matter with them. (c) asking them to make the decision for you.
10. *Dispute* is another word for (a) agreement. (b) argument. (c) arrangement.

II. Review the rules of dialogue on page 171. Then read the sentences below and look for errors. Rewrite the sentences correctly on your paper.

1. "Perhaps I can help you, said Manka.
2. Take these eggs to Manka, he said.
3. He went out and asked, "what are you doing?"
4. She said to the farmer Come back this afternoon with a fishing net.
5. "What does this mean?" he roared. "Nothing, dear husband," said Manka.

Tall tales are funny, exaggerated stories. They fit the saying, "larger than life." Characters in tall tales usually have super strength and perform impossible tasks. Each time a tall tale is told, it may get even more fantastic.

Some, but not all, tall tales begin in an ordinary way. The characters and events seem believable. Then, the **exaggeration** (ig ZAJ uh RAY shun) begins. The facts are stretched. Everything becomes bigger or smaller, longer or shorter, higher or lower, than it can possibly be.

Many American tall tales are set in the Old West. In the days of the early settlers, the people faced many hardships. The spaces were vast. The weather was extreme. It took a great deal of effort to cross the mountains, to brave the dangers, and to tame the land. So the tales that were told by these early settlers tended naturally to stretch the truth beyond belief.

TALL-TALE SAMPLER

▶ Tall tales can get so big, it's a good idea to start out small. Here are a few tall tales that are as wild as they are brief.

In Idaho, a great potato state, they tell this story. A man from the East asked a farmer to sell him 200 pounds of potatoes. The farmer wouldn't do it. Why? "I won't cut one of my potatoes in half for anybody," he said.

The corn grows really tall in Kansas. Once a farmer climbed up a stalk of corn to check its top ears. The corn kept on growing while he was up there. In fact, it was growing up faster than he could climb down. Finally, his friends had to send a balloon up to save him.

Folks in California say that the sunshine and air in their state are the best in the land. To prove what they say is true, they tell how a girl rode her bicycle from California to New York to see her sick aunt. Her poor aunt was almost dead when she got there. The doctor said the aunt needed sunshine and fresh air to save her. The girl quickly let the air out of one of her bicycle tires. The California sunshine and fresh air that rushed out saved the aunt's life!

ALL THINGS CONSIDERED _____

1. The first tall tale exaggerates the (a) size of Idaho. (b) number of potatoes a farmer can grow. (c) size of a potato.
2. The second tall tale suggests it is possible for a stalk of corn to grow (a) faster than a person can climb down it. (b) higher than a balloon can fly. (c) bigger than the state of Kansas.
3. The third tall tale suggests that (a) the air in a bicycle tire from California can improve the health of a woman in New York. (b) people in California live forever. (c) a girl can ride her bicycle from California to New York without stopping.
4. The third tall tale wants you to make the *inference* (see page 121) that New York has (a) plenty of sunshine and fresh air. (b) the same amount of fresh air as California. (c) little sunshine and fresh air.
5. The people who made up these tall tales seem to be (a) ashamed of their home states. (b) proud of their home states. (c) unable to laugh at themselves.

THINKING IT THROUGH _____

1. Do you suppose there is any truth in the tall tales you just read? Are the potatoes in Idaho big? Is the corn in Kansas tall? Is there plenty of sunshine and fresh air in California?
2. In what state do you live? Is there anything your state is known for that you could turn into a tall tale? Try it. And don't forget— *exaggerate.*

ADVENTURES OF ISABEL

by Ogden Nash

▶ Isabel is no ordinary young lady. This poem describes three
of her unusual adventures.

Isabel met an enormous bear,
Isabel, Isabel, didn't care;
The bear was hungry, the bear was ravenous,
The bear's big mouth was cruel and cavernous.
The bear said, Isabel, glad to meet you,
How do, Isabel, now I'll eat you!
Isabel, Isabel, didn't worry,
Isabel didn't scream or scurry.
She washed her hands and she straightened her hair up,
Then Isabel quietly ate the bear up.

Once in a night as black as pitch
Isabel met a wicked old witch.
The witch's face was cross and wrinkled,
The witch's gums with teeth were sprinkled.
Ho ho, Isabel! the old witch crowed,
I'll turn you into an ugly toad!
Isabel, Isabel, didn't worry,
Isabel didn't scream or scurry.
She showed no rage and she showed no rancor,
But she turned the witch into milk and drank her.

* ravenous (RAV uh nus) **very hungry; starving**
* cavernous (KAV urn us) **hollow; empty**
* scurry (SKUR ee) **run fast**
* rancor (RANG kur) **anger; bitter feeling**

Isabel met a hideous giant,
Isabel continued self-reliant.
The giant was hairy, the giant was horrid,
He had one eye in the middle of his forehead.
Good morning Isabel, the giant said,
I'll grind your bones to make my bread.
Isabel, Isabel, didn't worry,
Isabel didn't scream or scurry,
She nibbled the zwieback that she always fed off,
And when it was gone, she cut the giant's head off.

WAYS OF KNOWING

1. There are three groups of lines, called **stanzas** (STAN zuz), in this poem. Each stanza describes an adventure of Isabel. Each is like a tall tale. Which do you think makes the best tall tale? Why?

2. The rhyming words in this poem are part of the humor. For example, the bear is hungry and *ravenous*, his mouth is cruel and *cavernous*. Find other pairs of rhyming words and read the lines aloud.

3. Do you notice that there are no quotation marks around the words of characters in the poem? Tell where quotation marks would be if the poet had chosen to use them. Look back to page 171 for rules of dialogue.

4. Does the poem remind you of nursery rhymes you heard as a child? In what ways is it like a nursery rhyme? In what ways is it different?

- hideous (HID ee us) **very ugly; awful looking**
- **self-reliant** (SELF ri LY unt) **able to get along alone; depending on oneself**
- zwieback (ZWY bak) **sweet toast**

183

PECOS BILL

retold by Edward O'Reilly

▶ When three-year-old Pecos Bill falls out of a covered wagon
on a lonely road, nobody in his family misses him. How will
he get along? Be prepared for some strange happenings!

Poor little Bill! He was sitting in the Texas dust, watching his
family's covered wagon go bouncing down the rocky road. He could
see his nine brothers and ten sisters as they played inside the
wagon. But not one of them noticed that their three-year-old brother
had fallen out.

Little Bill didn't call to them. He thought maybe this was a new
kind of game. He just watched the wagon disappear into the West.
Then he waited to see what would happen next.

Soon the wagon was out of sight, and night began to fall. Coyotes came out to sit on the hilltops. Lifting their heads, they howled
at the moon. Bill thought this must be part of the game too. So he
started to howl. At first he didn't howl just right. But he kept on
trying, until pretty soon he could howl as well as any coyote pup.

A grown-up coyote heard Bill. The animal ran down the hill to the
lost child. "Now that's a mighty strange-looking coyote pup," the
animal thought to himself. "But I'd better take it home with me."

The coyote pups watched as Bill was led into their den. They
howled with laughter.

"If that's a coyote, then I'm a rattlesnake," cried one pup.

"And he's got no tail," laughed another.

"His ears aren't even pointy," teased a third. He pulled one of
Bill's ears to prove it.

Bill laughed. "What a wonderful game," he thought. He reached
out and pulled the ears of the pups. But he didn't stop there. He
swung the pups high into the air until they howled with pain. After
that, they quickly learned to respect Bill. Not only did they let him
stay, they even made him their leader. And that's how Bill got to be
chief of the coyotes.

> • coyote (ky OH tee) **kind of small wolf**
> • **respect** (ri SPEKT) **look up to; admire**

The years flew by, Bill grew very tall, and at thirteen years old he was famous. All the animals in the West knew about Pecos Bill. They knew that he could beat up rattlesnakes, mountain lions, and bears. Indeed, they knew that he could beat up anything that flew, walked, or crawled. Soon Bill came to be known as the West's king of beasts.

Now, this made a certain mountain lion very jealous. The lion felt that such a title belonged only to himself and to his lion cousins in Africa. "I can't let that coyote boy get away with this," thought the lion.

One morning, the lion saw Bill standing in front of a big rock. Bill was giving lessons to some coyote pups on how to howl. The lion climbed to the top of the rock and waited. Then, when Bill threw back his head to howl, the lion made a mighty leap. He knocked Bill into the dust. But the coyote chief didn't stay on the ground for long. Springing to his feet, he grabbed the lion around the middle.

"I could squeeze you to death," said Bill. "I've killed more than a hundred bears that way. But I have something else in store for you." Saying that, the boy leaped on the lion's back.

"Get off! Get off!" growled the mountain lion. He leaped and twisted and shook himself wildly. But he couldn't get Bill off his back.

"I won't get off until you agree to do just as I say," called Bill.

"Never!" roared the lion. He began to leap and kick some more. He jumped from side to side and did flips in the air. But the boy just laughed and held on tight.

After a while the lion grew very tired. He stood there, panting for breath. "You win," he gasped finally. "Just spare my life, and I'll always carry you wherever you want to go."

Bill smiled, and the coyote pups cheered. But Bill held up his hand. "Sh," he said. "Listen. Do you hear what I hear?" Quickly he rode the lion to the top of a hill.

Looking down, Bill saw a two-legged creature running across the plain. It was a man, but Bill thought it was a coyote like himself. After all, he hadn't seen any fellow human beings since the day he fell out of the wagon.

The man had been moving a herd of cattle along a trail. But an angry bull had left the herd and was now chasing the cowboy. "Help! Help!" cried the poor man.

Bill didn't waste a second. He whistled loudly, and hundreds of rattlesnakes crawled out from under the nearby rocks. Slipping and

sliding, they rushed toward Bill. He tied the snakes together, one after another, and made a loop at one end of his snake rope. That was the original lasso. These were the early days of the West, and things like lassos and hitching posts hadn't been invented yet. (In fact, Bill was later to become the greatest of all inventors.)

Bill could see that the cowboy had given up. The poor man had fallen to the ground. He was lying there with his face buried in his arms. The huge bull was rushing straight toward him.

Bill rode down the hill swinging his lasso in the air. Suddenly he sent it flying out over the bull. The loop came down over his huge horns. The surprised beast was pulled to a sudden stop. For a moment he looked around wildly. Then he started to struggle. He yanked and pulled to get free. How that beast kicked and tugged and snorted! He kept it up for a full half-hour. But he could have saved himself the trouble.

• **original** (uh RIJ uh nul) first; earliest

186

Bill gave a tug on the lasso that yanked the bull right off his feet. He swung the animal round and round in the air. When Bill let loose, the beast went flying over the plain for five miles.

Finally the scared cowboy opened his eyes and looked up. "I'm safe," he cried. "I'm safe!" Happily, he jumped to his feet. But then he froze in his tracks. He had caught sight of Pecos Bill and his friends.

"Mountain lion! Rattlesnakes!" cried the cowboy. And he began to shake from head to toe.

"Don't be frightened," called Bill. "They won't hurt you. They're my friends."

It took a while, but the cowboy finally saw that there was nothing to fear. In fact, Bill even taught him how to use the lasso.

"This is a great invention," said the cowboy. "It will help tame the West. I can't wait to tell my friends about this. And I'll tell them that you taught me to use it. Say, just who are you anyway?"

"A coyote," said Bill, "just like you. But to tell the truth, until now I thought that I was the only funny-looking coyote around these parts."

The cowboy laughed. "You're no coyote! You're a boy," he said. "You must have been lost out here for a long time. Why don't you come back to my ranch with me? You can teach all the cowboys how to use the lasso. And you can teach us how to tame animals so we can ride them."

Bill liked that idea. He went back to his coyote friends and told them he was going away for a while. "But I'll be back," he promised. Then Bill rode off on the back of his mountain lion.

Soon Bill was enjoying life as a cowboy teacher. He wore fancy cowboy clothes and cowboy boots. And he invented the ten-gallon hat to go with the rest of his outfit.

The cowboys liked him very much. They came from far and wide to take lessons from him. At first, he tried to teach them to ride mountain lions. But the men weren't too happy about the idea. That's when Bill thought of teaching them to bust broncos. (That's a term that Bill made up. It just means that the men were taught to tame wild horses.)

Bill also taught the men to use lassos. The cowboys made theirs out of rope, but Bill stuck to his famous snake lasso. He did many wonderful tricks with it, and people from all over the country came to see him perform.

The most famous use of Bill's lasso took place one day in March. That morning, a band of cowboys came riding up to Bill. "Run for your life!" they shouted. "A big cyclone is on its way. And they say that it's coming to get *you*!"

During the weeks before this, the cyclone had been very busy tearing up towns in Oklahoma and Arizona. But when it heard about Pecos Bill and his famous lasso, the cyclone came tearing into Texas.

Everyone but Bill ran to hide. He'd never seen a cyclone before, so he just waited in the front yard for it to come along. While he waited, he invented a few things. In the first five minutes, he invented the hitching post. In the next five minutes, he thought up the sheriff's star, law and order, and the Pony Express. He would have invented a few more things too, but just then the cyclone came spinning into view.

● cyclone (SY clohn) **heavy windstorm moving toward a calm area**

Bill stared calmly at the great twister. "So you're after me, are you?" he said to himself. "We'll soon see about that." Then Bill gave a loud whistle, and every rattler in Texas rushed up to him. Within minutes, Bill had a lasso that could reach to New Mexico and back.

The cyclone came tearing along. To show its strength, it sent houses and horses flying into the air. And all the while, it kept its eye on Bill.

Bill waited until the cyclone was just a mile away. Then — *whoosh! whoosh!* — the lasso went spinning into the sky. It cut through the clouds and dropped right over the top of the cyclone.

This made the cyclone so angry that it leaped ten miles into the sky. Bill just held onto his lasso. Then, hand over hand, he started to pull himself up. Finally he was sitting on the cyclone's back.

The cyclone flew into a rage. It flipped forward and backward and sideways. It shook like five thousand wild horses.

"Ho-hum," said Bill. "I wish I had something exciting to do today."

When the cyclone heard that, it grew wilder than ever. It bounced like ten thousand wild bulls. It crashed through canyons and leaped over mountains. It shivered and shook. It twisted and turned. But it couldn't shake Bill off its back. The wild ride went on until the cyclone was almost out of wind. Then it began to get smaller and smaller. Soon it was only a breeze.

Some people say the cyclone rained itself out under Pecos Bill. But Bill told his friends that the cyclone had really cried itself out. He said he had even heard the poor worn-out thing sobbing.

Only after the cyclone had promised to be nice to people from then on did Bill let it go. And the cyclone has kept its promise. In fact, you may have met that poor deflated cyclone yourself and not known it. It's that sudden little breeze that makes people feel so good on hot summer evenings.

- **twister** (TWIS tur) **rough windstorm; cyclone or tornado**
- **rage** (RAYJ) **fit of anger**
- **deflate** (di FLAYT) **let air out of; make something become smaller**

189

ALL THINGS CONSIDERED ──────────────

1. Pecos Bill is raised by coyotes from the time he is (a) born. (b) three years old. (c) ten years old.

2. When he is thirteen, Bill becomes known as (a) Lasso Bill. (b) the West's king of beasts. (c) the best bronco buster in the West.

3. Just as cowboys tame wild horses, Bill tames a (a) mountain lion. (b) buffalo. (c) hawk.

4. By tying rattlesnakes together, Bill invents the (a) hitching post. (b) cyclone. (c) lasso.

5. Bill learns that he is not a coyote when he (a) saves a cowboy's life. (b) travels to a ranch. (c) goes back to his family's covered wagon.

6. Bill teaches the cowboys to (a) ride mountain lions. (b) howl like coyotes. (c) use lassos.

7. A cyclone comes to Texas to (a) frighten away the rattlesnakes and coyotes. (b) help the cowboys round up cattle. (c) fight Pecos Bill.

8. Bill catches the cyclone (a) in his arms. (b) with his rattlesnake lasso. (c) in a huge trap.

9. To tame the cyclone, Bill (a) rides it like a bucking bronco. (b) feeds it rattlesnake meat. (c) attacks it while on an angry mountain lion.

10. As the story ends, the cyclone promises to (a) leave the West and never return. (b) be nice to people. (c) only shake old buildings.

THINKING IT THROUGH ──────────────

1. There are many exaggerations in this tall tale. Which one creates the wildest picture in your mind? Explain.

2. According to the story, Pecos Bill is an inventor. The original lasso that he invents is described and the story tells how Bill came to invent it. Choose one other thing he invents. Describe it and tell how you think Bill came to invent it.

3. Suppose "Pecos Bill" had been a true story instead of a tall tale. Tell what might happen to Bill after he falls from the wagon. Make it a "true" adventure story.

Literary Skills

Visualizing the Setting

You've had experience visualizing characters and events. Visualizing the setting of a story completes the picture. To visualize the setting, picture when and where a story happens. A good way is to imagine that *you* are there.

Reread the first paragraph of the story and imagine that you are there. Then look at the drawing below. It probably does *not* fit the setting as you visualize it. List three ways in which it differs.

Composition

Follow your teacher's instructions before completing *one* of these writing assignments.

1. Turn these sentences into exaggerations. For example, you might rewrite the first sentence to read, "My brother has feet so big that he wears boats for shoes."
   a) My brother has big feet.
   b) I read some books last summer.
   c) The bread dough rose high.
2. In making up an excuse, have you ever ended up with a tall tale? Write a paragraph telling a friend why you missed her party. Exaggerate!

191

THREE STRONG WOMEN

adapted by Claus Stamm

▶ Put yourself in the place of a big strong wrestler, the best in all Japan. Could there be anyone stronger than you?

Long ago in Japan there lived a famous wrestler who was on his way to wrestle before the Emperor.

He strode down the road on legs as thick as the trunks of trees. He had been walking for seven hours, but he was not weary. He could walk for seven more without getting tired.

The time was autumn. The sky was a cold, watery blue. The air was chilly. In the small bright sun, the trees along the roadside glowed red and orange.

The wrestler hummed "Zun-zun-zun" in time with the long swing of his legs. Wind blew through his thin brown robe, and he wore no sword at his side. He felt proud that he needed no sword, even in the darkest and loneliest places. The icy air on his body only reminded him that few tailors would have been able to make warm clothes for a man so broad and tall. He felt much as a wrestler should—strong, healthy, and rather conceited.

The roar of fast-moving water beyond the trees told him that he was passing above a riverbank. He "zun-zunned" louder. He loved the sound of his voice and wanted it to sound clearly above the rushing water.

He thought: "They call me Forever-Mountain because I am such a big strong wrestler. Forever-Mountain, that's me—a fine big brave man and far too modest ever to say so."

Just then he saw a girl who must have come up from the river, for she steadied a bucket on her head.

Her hands were small, and there was a dimple on each thumb, just below the knuckle. She was a round girl with red cheeks and a nose like a friendly button. Her eyes looked as though she were thinking of ten thousand funny stories at once. She stepped up onto the road and walked ahead of the wrestler.

"If I don't tickle that girl, I shall regret it all my life," said the wrestler under his breath. "She's sure to go 'squeak' and I

- **strode** (STROHD) **past tense of** *stride;* **walked with long steps**
- **conceited** (kun SEE tid) **overly proud**
- **modest** (MOD ist) **not proud; humble and bashful**

shall laugh and laugh. If she drops her bucket, that will be even funnier. I can always run and fill it again and even carry it home for her."

He tiptoed up and poked her lightly in the ribs with one huge finger.

"Kochokochokocho!" he said—a fine, ticklish sound in Japanese.

The girl gave a satisfying squeal, giggled, and brought one arm down so that the wrestler's hand was caught between it and her body.

"Ho-ho-ho! You've caught me! I can't move at all!" said the wrestler, laughing.

"I know," said the jolly girl.

He felt that it was very good-tempered of her to take a joke so well, and started to pull his hand free.

Somehow, he could not.

He tried again, using a little more strength.

"Now, now—let me go," he said. "I am a very powerful man. If I pull too hard I might hurt you."

"Pull," said the girl. "I admire powerful men."

She began to walk, and though the wrestler tugged and pulled until his feet dug great furrows in the ground, he had to follow. She couldn't have paid him less attention if he had been a puppy—a small one.

Ten minutes later, the girl was still tugging Forever-Mountain helplessly after her. He was glad that the road was lonely and no one was there to see.

"Please let me go," he pleaded. "I am the famous wrestler Forever-Mountain. I must go and show my strength before the Emperor"—he burst out weeping from shame and confusion—"and you're hurting my hand!"

The girl steadied the bucket on her head with her free hand. "You poor, sweet little Forever-Mountain," she said. "Are you tired? Shall I carry you? I can leave the water here and come back for it later."

"I do not want you to carry me. I want you to let me go. Then I want to forget I ever saw you. What do you want with me?" moaned the pitiful wrestler.

"I only want to help you," said the girl, now pulling him steadily up a narrow mountain path. "Oh, I am sure you'll have no more trouble than anyone else when you come up against the other wrestlers. You'll win, or else you'll lose, and you won't be too badly hurt either

• furrow (FUR oh) long, deep groove

way. But aren't you afraid you might meet a really strong man someday?"

Forever-Mountain turned white. He stumbled. He was imagining being laughed at throughout Japan as "Hardly-Ever-Mountain."

She glanced back.

"You see? Tired already," she said. "I'll walk more slowly. Why don't you come along to my mother's house and let us make a strong man of you? The wrestling in the capital isn't due to begin for three months. I know, because Grandmother thought she'd go. You'd be spending all that time in bad company and wasting what little power you have."

"All right. Three months. I'll come along," said the wrestler. He felt he had nothing more to lose. Also, he feared that the girl might become angry if he refused. And what would she do then? Something awful, perhaps, like place him in the top of a tree until he changed his mind.

"Fine," she said happily. "We are almost there."

She freed his hand. It had become red and a little swollen. "But if you break your promise and run off, I shall have to chase you and carry you back."

Soon they arrived in a small valley. A simple farmhouse with a thatched roof stood in the middle.

"Grandmother is at home, but she is an old lady and she's probably sleeping." The girl shaded her eyes with one hand.

"But Mother should be bringing our cow back from the field. Oh, there's Mother now!"

She waved. The woman coming around the corner of the house put down the cow she was carrying and waved back.

She smiled and came across the grass, walking with a lively bounce.

"Excuse me," she said, brushing some cow hair from her dress and smiling. "These mountain paths are full of stones. They hurt the cow's feet. And who is the nice young man you've brought, Maru-me?"

The girl explained. "And we have only three months!" she finished anxiously.

"Well, it's not long enough to do much, but it's not so short a time we can't do something," said her mother, looking thoughtful. "But he does look terribly feeble. He'll need a lot of good things to eat. Maybe when he gets stronger he can help Grandmother with some of the easy work about the house."

"That will be fine!" said the girl, and she called her grandmother—loudly, for the old lady was a little deaf.

"I'm coming!" came a creaky voice from inside the house. A little old woman leaning on a stick and looking very sleepy tottered out of the door. As she came toward them she stumbled over the roots of a great oak tree.

"Heh! My eyes aren't what they used to be. That's the fourth time this month

---

- thatched (THACHT) **made of straw**
- **feeble** (FEE bul) **weak; not strong**
- totter (TOT ur) **walk in an unsteady way**

I've stumbled over that tree," she complained. Then, wrapping her skinny arms about its trunk, she pulled it out of the ground.

"Oh, Grandmother! You should have let me pull it up for you," said Maru-me.

"Hm. I hope I didn't hurt my poor old back," muttered the old lady. She called out, "Daughter! Throw that tree away like a good girl, so no one will fall over it. But make sure it doesn't hit anybody."

"You can help Mother with the tree," Maru-me said to Forever-Mountain. "On second thought, you'd better not help. Just watch."

Her mother went to the tree, picked it up in her two hands, and threw it. Up went the tree, sailing end over end, growing smaller and smaller as it flew. It landed with a faint crash far up the mountainside.

"Ah, how clumsy," she said. "I meant to throw it over the mountain. It's probably blocking the path now, and I'll have to get up early tomorrow to move it."

The wrestler was not listening. He had very quietly fainted.

"Oh! We must put him to bed," said Maru-me.

"Poor, feeble young man," said her mother.

"I hope we can do something for him. Here, let me carry him. He's light," said the grandmother. She slung him over her shoulder and carried him into the house, creaking along with her cane.

The next day they began the work of making Forever-Mountain over into what they thought a strong man should be. They gave him the simplest food to eat, and the toughest. Day by day they prepared his rice with less and less water, until no ordinary man could have chewed or digested it.

Every day he was made to do the work of five men. Every evening he wrestled with Grandmother. Maru-me and her mother agreed that Grandmother, being old and feeble, was the least likely to injure him accidentally. They hoped the exercise might be good for the old lady's rheumatism.

He grew stronger and stronger but was hardly aware of it. Grandmother

- **slung** (SLUNG) past tense of *sling;* threw
- **rheumatism** (ROO muh tiz um) disease of the joints that brings pain and stiffness

195

could still throw him easily into the air— and catch him again—without ever changing her sweet smile.

He quite forgot that outside this valley he was one of the greatest wrestlers in Japan and was called Forever-Mountain. His legs had been like logs. Now they were like pillars. His big hands were hard as stones. When he cracked his knuckles, the sound was like trees splitting on a cold night.

Sometimes he did an exercise that wrestlers do in Japan—raising one foot high above the ground and bringing it down with a crash. When he did this the people in nearby villages looked up at the winter sky and told one another that it was very late in the year for thunder.

Soon he could pull up a tree as well as the grandmother. He could even throw one—but only a small distance. One evening, near the end of his third month, he wrestled with Grandmother and held her down for half a minute.

"Heh-heh!" She laughed and got up. "I would never have believed it!"

Maru-me squealed with joy and threw her arms around him—gently, for she was afraid of cracking his ribs.

"Very good, very good! What a strong man," said her mother, who had just come home from the fields, carrying, as usual, the cow. She put the cow down and patted the wrestler on the back.

They agreed that he was ready to show *real* strength before the Emperor.

"Take the cow along with you tomorrow when you go," said the mother. "Sell her and buy yourself a belt—a silken belt. Buy the fattest and heaviest one you can find. Wear it when you appear before the Emperor. It will be a souvenir from us."

"I wouldn't think of taking your only cow. You've already done too much for me. And you'll need her to plow the fields, won't you?"

They burst out laughing. Maru-me squealed. Her mother roared. The grandmother cackled so hard she choked and had to be pounded on the back.

"Oh, dear," said the mother, still laughing. "You didn't think we used our cow for anything like *work!* Why, Grandmother here is stronger than five cows!"

"The cow is our pet." Maru-me giggled. "She has lovely brown eyes."

"But it really gets tiresome having to carry her back and forth each day so that she has enough grass to eat," said her mother.

"Then you must let me give you all the prize money that I win," said Forever-Mountain.

"Oh, no! We wouldn't think of it!" said Maru-me. "It is not proper to accept gifts of money from strangers. And we all like you too much to sell you anything."

"True," said Forever-Mountain. "I will now ask your mother's and grandmother's permission to marry you. I want to be one of the family."

- pillar (PIL ur) **column, often made of marble**
- **souvenir** (SOO vuh neer) **item kept as a reminder**

"Oh! I'll get a wedding dress ready!" said Maru-me.

The mother and grandmother pretended to consider the proposal very seriously, but they quickly agreed.

Next morning Forever-Mountain tied his hair up in the topknot that all Japanese wrestlers wear, and said goodby. He thanked Maru-me and her mother and bowed very low to the grandmother, for she was the oldest and had been a fine wrestling partner.

Then he picked up the cow and trudged up the mountain. When he reached the top, he slung the cow over one shoulder and waved goodby to Maru-me.

At the first town he came to, Forever-Mountain sold the cow. She brought a good price because she was unusually fat from never having worked in her life. With the money, he bought the heaviest silken belt he could find.

When he reached the palace grounds, many of the other wrestlers were already there. They sat about, eating enormous bowls of rice, comparing one another's weight, and telling stories. They paid little attention to Forever-Mountain except to wonder why he had arrived so late this year. Some of them noticed that he had grown very quiet and took no part at all in their boasting.

All the ladies and gentlemen of the court were waiting in a special courtyard for the wrestling to begin. The gentlemen had long swords so heavy with gold and precious stones that they could never have used them, even if they had known how. The court ladies had long black hair. Their faces were painted white, which made them look frightened. They had pulled out their real eyebrows and painted new ones high above the place where eyebrows are supposed to be. This made them look as though they were very surprised at something.

Behind a screen sat the Emperor—by himself, because he was too noble for ordinary people to look at. He was a lonely old man with a kind, tired face. He hoped the wrestling would end quickly so that he could go to his room and write poems.

The first two wrestlers chosen to fight were Forever-Mountain and a wrestler who was said to have the biggest stomach in the country. He and Forever-Mountain both threw some salt into the ring. It was understood that this drove away evil spirits.

Then the other wrestler, moving his stomach somewhat out of the way, raised his foot and brought it down with a fearful stamp. He glared fiercely at Forever-Mountain as if to say, "Now you stamp, you poor frightened man!"

Forever-Mountain raised his foot. He brought it down.

There was a sound like thunder. The earth shook. And the other wrestler bounced into the air and out of the ring,

---

- topknot (TOP not) **large knot of hair on head**
- glare (GLAIR) **stare in an angry way**

as gracefully as a soap bubble.

He picked himself up and bowed to the Emperor's screen.

"The earth-god is angry. Possibly there is something the matter with the salt," he said. "I do not think I shall wrestle this season." And he walked out, looking very suspiciously over one shoulder at Forever-Mountain.

Five other wrestlers then and there decided that they were not wrestling this season, either. They all looked annoyed with Forever-Mountain.

From then on, Forever-Mountain brought his foot down lightly. As each wrestler came into the ring, he picked him up very gently, carried him out, and placed him before the Emperor's screen. Then, most courteously, he bowed.

The court ladies' eyebrows went up even higher. The gentlemen looked disturbed and a little afraid. They loved to see fierce, strong men tugging and grunting at each other, but Forever-Mountain was a little too much for them. All the other wrestlers were sitting on the ground and weeping with disappointment like great fat babies. Only the Emperor, behind his screen, was happy.

Now, with the wrestling over so quickly, he would have that much more time to write his poems. He quickly ordered all the prize money handed over to Forever-Mountain.

"But," he said, "you had better not wrestle anymore."

Forever-Mountain promised not to wrestle anymore. Everybody looked relieved. The wrestlers sitting on the ground almost smiled.

"I think I shall become a farmer," Forever-Mountain said. And he left at once to go back to Maru-me.

When Maru-me saw him coming, she ran down the mountain, picked him up, and carried him halfway up the mountainside. Then she giggled and put him down. The rest of the way she let him carry her.

Forever-Mountain kept his promise to the Emperor and never wrestled in public again. His name was forgotten in the capital. But up in the mountains, sometimes, the earth shakes and rumbles. They say that it is Forever-Mountain and Maru-me's grandmother wrestling in the hidden valley.

198

ALL THINGS CONSIDERED ———————————

1. The story is set in (a) Canada at the present time. (b) ancient Japan. (c) the Old West.

2. The main character in the story is (a) Forever-Mountain. (b) Maru-me's grandmother. (c) the Emperor.

3. At the beginning of the story, Forever-Mountain is (a) conceited about his strength. (b) unaware of his strength. (c) modest about his strength.

4. Forever-Mountain meets Maru-me (a) in the capital. (b) at a dance. (c) near a river.

5. Forever-Mountain weeps with shame and confusion when Maru-me (a) refuses to marry him. (b) calls him names. (c) drags him by the hand.

6. Maru-me's grandmother stumbles over the roots of a tree and (a) breaks her leg. (b) pulls the tree from the ground. (c) cuts down the tree.

7. When Maru-me's mother tosses away the tree, Forever-Mountain (a) quietly faints. (b) catches it. (c) laughs.

8. After three months of training, Forever-Mountain can (a) throw a tree over a mountain. (b) beat Maru-me in wrestling. (c) hold Grandmother down for half a minute.

9. Forever-Mountain wins the wrestling matches at the capital (a) with difficulty. (b) with ease. (c) by only a few points.

10. Some say the earth shakes from time to time because (a) thunder is wrestling with lightning. (b) Forever-Mountain is wrestling with Grandmother. (c) the three strong women are quarreling.

THINKING IT THROUGH ———————————

1. If you were acting out this story, which character would you like to play? Tell how you would play the part.

2. There are many examples of exaggeration in the story. Tell about the one you think paints the wildest picture.

3. Forever-Mountain plans to trick Maru-me into laughing by tickling her. Who turns out to be the trickster? Explain.

4. Are the wrestling matches more fun for the ladies and gentlemen of the court *before* or *after* Forever-Mountain becomes really strong? Why?

5. The wrestling matches are held for the Emperor. But he'd rather write poems than watch wrestling. What does this tell you about him?

199

Literary Skills

Kinds of Settings

Familiar settings are those you can picture easily. You know these settings because you have seen similar places before. An example of a familiar setting is a classroom. If you were reading a story that took place in a classroom, you would picture desks, a chalkboard, students, and a teacher.

Unfamiliar settings are those you cannot visualize easily. The place may be far away. The time may be the past or the future. You may not know what to expect.

Is the setting of "Three Strong Women" familiar or unfamiliar? You are told in the first line that the place is Japan and the time is the past. For many readers, this setting is unfamiliar. Can you picture the courtyard where the wrestling takes place? Did you expect the Emperor to sit behind a screen or a wrestling match to take place in a royal court?

On a separate sheet of paper, complete the following sentences with details from the story. (See the third paragraph.) Then put a check (✔) next to those parts of the setting that are familiar to you.

1. The time was _____.
2. The sky was a cold, _____.
3. The _____ was chilly.
4. The trees along the _____ glowed _____.

Composition

Follow your teacher's instructions before completing *one* of these writing assignments.

1. From this list, select the setting details that are familiar to you: snow-covered lawn in February, palm trees in summer, tall buildings at night. Use each of the details you select in a separate sentence.
2. Picture a setting that is familiar to you, such as a room in your house. Write a paragraph describing the setting.

200

William Saroyan (1908-1981)

The characters in William Saroyan's stories show a reckless joy for life that overcomes all sorrow. Saroyan's characters (many of them young boys) are like this because he was like this. He had an enthusiasm for life that shone through everything he wrote.

Perhaps knowing poverty so well helped Saroyan appreciate life. His father died when he was two, and his mother was too poor to support the family. The children had to live in an orphanage for five years. At eight, William had his first job. In the years that followed, he had many odd jobs, all in his hometown of Fresno, California. Finally, when he was 25, he was able to earn enough money by writing to become a full-time writer.

Saroyan never quite trusted formal education (as you will see in the following selection), just as he never quite trusted high-class ideas of literature. He wrote what he felt, always believing that whatever was wrong would turn out right in the end. Usually it did. *My Name is Aram,* his book of stories about a young boy and his family, became very popular. Later, he won a Pulitzer Prize for the play, *The Time of Your Life.* He loved the attention, but he refused the prize. He did not believe that the people sponsoring the prize should be the judges of literature.

ONE OF OUR FUTURE POETS, YOU MIGHT SAY

by William Saroyan

▶ The setting of this story is modern. But the main character has something in common with characters like Pecos Bill. Doing the impossible comes naturally to him, too.

When I was the fourteenth brightest pupil in the class of fifteen third-graders at Emerson School, the whole school district took a day off one day to think things over.

This was years ago.

I was eight going on nine or at the most nine going on ten, and good-natured.

In those days the average school district didn't make a fuss over the children of a small town. If some of the children seemed to be behind other children, the average school district assumed that this was natural and let it go at that.

Certain public speakers, however, saw more promise in us. They looked out at the sea of young faces and said: "You are the future leaders of America, the future captains of industry. You are the future statesmen, and, I might say, the future poets."

This sort of talk always pleased me. I liked to imagine what sort of future captains of industry pals of mine like Jimmy and Frankie were going to make.

I knew these boys.

They were great baseball players, but by nature high-grade idiots: healthy, strong, and spirited. I didn't think they would develop into captains of industry. Neither did they. If they were asked what career they planned to shape for themselves, they would honestly say, "I don't know. Nothing, I guess."

- captain of industry—**person in charge of a large company**
- statesman (STAYTS mun) **leader in government**
- **spirited** (SPIR i tid) lively

Anyway, one day our school district took a day off to think things over. After seven hours of steady thinking, they decided to put every public school pupil through a physical examination. They wanted to solve, if possible, the mystery of health in the youngsters of the poorer neighborhoods.

According to all published reports, the youngsters in my neighborhood should have had badly shaped heads, sunken chests, faulty bones, hollow voices, no energy, and at least six or seven other problems.

According to each public school teacher, however, these children had well-shaped heads, sound chests, strong bones, loud voices, too much energy, and a constant need to misbehave.

Something was wrong somewhere.

Our school district decided to try to find out what.

They *did* find out.

They found out that the published reports were wrong.

It was at this time that I first learned that I was a poet. I remember being in the public auditorium of my hometown with six hundred other future statesmen. And I remember hearing my name sung out by Miss Ogilvie in a clear tense soprano.

The time had arrived for me to climb the seventeen steps to the stage, walk to the center of the stage, strip to the waist, inhale, exhale, and be measured all over.

I had a moment of confusion followed quickly by a bright idea. I decided to behave with style. This I did, to the horror and bewilderment of three doctors, a half-dozen nurses, umpteen teachers and supervisors, and six hundred future captains of industry.

Instead of climbing the seventeen steps to the stage, I *leaped.*

I remember Miss Ogilvie turning to Mr. Rickenbacker, Superintendent of Public Schools, and whispering fearfully: "This is Garoghlanian—one of our future poets, I might say."

Mr. Rickenbacker took one quick look at me. "Oh, I see," he said. "Who's he sore at?"

"Society," Miss Ogilvie said.

"Oh, I see," Mr. Rickenbacker said. "So am I, but I can't jump like that. Let's say no more about it."

I flung off my shirt and stood stripped to the waist, a good deal of hair bristling on my chest.

• umpteen (ump TEEN) **a great many**

203

"You see?" Miss Ogilvie said. "A writer."

"Inhale," Mr. Rickenbacker said.

"For how long?" I asked.

"As long as possible," Mr. Rickenbacker said.

I began to inhale. Four minutes later I was still doing so. Naturally, the examining staff was a little amazed. They called a speedy meeting while I continued to inhale. After two minutes of heated debate the staff decided to ask me to stop inhaling. Miss Ogilvie explained that unless they *asked* me to stop I might go on inhaling all afternoon.

"That will be enough for the present," Mr. Rickenbacker said.

"Already?" I said. "I'm not even started."

"Now exhale," he said.

"For how long?" I said.

"Good grief!" Mr. Rickenbacker said.

"You'd better tell him," Miss Ogilvie said. "Otherwise he'll exhale all afternoon."

"Three or four minutes," Mr. Rickenbacker said.

I exhaled for four minutes. Then they asked me to put on my shirt and go away.

"How are things?" I asked the staff. "Am I in pretty good shape?"

"Let's say no more about it," Mr. Rickenbacker said. "Please go away."

• heated (HEE tid) **angry; excited**

204

The following year our school district decided not to give physical examinations. Examinations the year before had gone along all right as far as future captains of industry were concerned, and future statesmen, but when it came to future poets the examinations ran helter-skelter and amuck. Nobody knew what to do or think.

ALL THINGS CONSIDERED

1. The events in the story take place when the narrator is in the (a) third grade. (b) sixth grade. (c) ninth grade.
2. The boy describes himself as (a) very quiet. (b) quick to anger. (c) good-natured.
3. He finds it amusing that certain people see the students as future (a) athletes. (b) leaders and poets. (c) astronauts.
4. Published reports suggested that the students from poorer neighborhoods should be (a) healthy. (b) unhealthy. (c) happy.
5. The teachers say that these students are (a) healthy. (b) unhealthy. (c) happy.
6. The school district decides to give every student a (a) math test. (b) reading test. (c) physical examination.
7. When asked to inhale, the narrator (a) inhales for only one minute. (b) inhales until asked to stop. (c) exhales.
8. Miss Ogilvie seems sure the narrator will be a (a) future statesman. (b) future captain of industry. (c) future poet.
9. When the examination is over, the superintendent asks the boy to (a) inhale again. (b) come back the next day. (c) go away.
10. The narrator says that because of the future poets (a) the superintendent quit. (b) the examination was not given again. (c) Jimmy and Frankie became ballplayers.

THINKING IT THROUGH

1. Why does Miss Ogilvie describe Garoghlanian as a future poet?
2. What is exaggerated in this story? How is it different from what is exaggerated in "Pecos Bill"?
3. Garoghlanian describes himself as good-natured. Would you agree? Give examples from the story to support your answer.

- helter-skelter (HEL tur SKEL tur) **any which way**
- amuck (uh MUK) **opposite of smoothly; wild**

Literary Skills

Point of View

Think of **point of view** as the angle you have on a story. If you learn about the characters, events, and setting through the eyes of *a character in the story,* then the point of view is **first person.** Words such as *I, me,* and *we* are used. If you learn about the story through the eyes of *a narrator outside the story,* the point of view is **third person.** Words such as *he, she,* or *they* are used.

"One of Our Future Poets, You Might Say" is an example of a story told in the first person. Garoghlanian is a character in the story, and he is the storyteller. You "see" everything through his eyes:

> This sort of talk always pleased *me. I* liked to imagine what sort of future captains of industry pals of *mine* like Jimmy and Frankie were going to make.

Imagine that the story had been told in the third person. On a separate sheet of paper, rewrite the above paragraph using words such as *him, he,* and *theirs.* (If you wish, use the third-person point of view to rewrite a different paragraph from the story.)

Composition

Follow your teacher's instructions before completing *one* of these writing assignments.

1. In one or two complete sentences, tell if you liked the story you just read. Then ask a classmate what he or she thought of the story, and write that in one or two sentences.

2. What do you hope to be after you finish school? In a paragraph, tell what you wish to be and why. If you prefer, you can interview a classmate about his or her future plans and write about that. Notice that your point of view will change.

VOCABULARY AND SKILL REVIEW

Before completing the exercises that follow, you may wish to review the **bold-faced** words on pages 182–205.

I. Match the words in Column A with their definitions in Column B.

	A		B
1.	souvenir	**a)**	look up to; admire
2.	feeble	**b)**	rough windstorm
3.	original	**c)**	groups of lines in a poem
4.	respect	**d)**	item kept as a reminder
5.	slung	**e)**	weak; not strong
6.	self-reliant	**f)**	threw
7.	stanzas	**g)**	lively
8.	rheumatism	**h)**	first; earliest
9.	spirited	**i)**	able to get along alone
10.	twister	**j)**	disease of the joints

II. Read the descriptions below and try to visualize each setting. You will need to use your imagination to complete the picture in your mind. Take a few minutes to think. Then choose one setting. Write a few sentences to describe that setting in more detail. Remember to add specific details of time and place.

1. The air felt cold and crisp, and I hesitated to push off the warm covers. Finally I stood and walked to the window.

2. I had never been in a palace before. Only in my dreams had I imagined surroundings so magnificent.

3. It wasn't the sort of place most people would like. But to the young man it was a place to relax—a place to "get away from it all" and plan his future.

4. The cry of the seagull caused her to raise her head. She shaded her eyes and gazed at the sunset.

5. Together they strolled down the streets of the unfamiliar city. The smell of foods cooking was strong.

MATILDA

by Hilaire Belloc

Matilda told such awful lies
It made one gasp and stretch one's eyes.
Her aunt, who from her earliest youth
Had kept a strict regard for truth,
Attempted to believe Matilda.
The effort very nearly killed her,
And would have done so, had not she
Learned of the girl's infirmity.
For once, around the close of day,
Matilda, growing tired of play,
And finding she was left alone,
Went tiptoe to the telephone
And called for the immediate aid
Of London's noble fire brigade.
Within an hour the gallant band
Came pouring in on every hand.
From Putney, Hackney Downs, and Bow,
With courage high and hearts aglow,
They raced as news spread through the town:
"Matilda's house is burning down!"
Inspired by cheering, clear and loud,
That rose up from the anxious crowd,
They ran their ladders through a score
Of windows on the second floor.
They sprayed the furniture and walls
And doused the pictures in the halls
Until Matilda's aunt succeeded
In showing them they were not needed.
And even then she had to pay
To get the men to go away!

- infirmity (in FUR mi tee) **weakness; sickness**
- fire brigade (FYUR bri GAYD) **fire department**
- **gallant** (GAL unt) **brave; ready for action**
- inspire (in SPYUR) **fill with good thoughts and good feelings; cause to act**
- score (SKOR) **group of 20**
- douse (DOUS) **spray with water**

It happened that a few weeks later
Her aunt was off to the theater.
She had refused to take her niece
To see the entertaining piece—
A punishment both just and wise
For one who told such dreadful lies.
That night a fire *did* break out—
You should have heard Matilda shout!
You should have heard her scream and bawl
And seen her from the window call
To people passing in the street.
The rapidly increasing heat
Encouraged her to try to gain
Their sympathy—but all in vain.
For every time she shouted "Fire"
They only answered "Little liar!"
The flames rose up and seared the walls.
Still no one cared to hear her calls.
So poor Matilda had to leap
And, landing in a twisted heap,
Had to be straightened out in bed
For months and weeks. She was not dead.
She was not even boiled or fried.
But she regretted she had lied
And never would again, she swore.
But on her face a smirk she wore.

WAYS OF KNOWING

1. In an Aesop fable, "The Shepherd Boy and the Wolf," a boy shouts, "Wolf! Wolf!" to fool the villagers. Each time there is no wolf. Finally there is a wolf, but the villagers don't listen to the boy's cries. How is this poem like Aesop's tale?
2. In the end, Matilda swears never to lie again. Do you think she will keep that promise? Why?
3. Putney, Hackney Downs, and Bow are mentioned in the poem. Using context clues, tell what you think they are.

- **dreadful** (DRED ful) **awful; terrible**
- **in vain** (in VAYN) **without success**
- sear (SEER) **burn or scorch**
- smirk (SMURK) **tricky smile**

209

PUT YOUR BRAINS IN YOUR POCKET

by Arthur W. Hoppe

▶ Wouldn't it be wonderful to have all knowledge right at your fingertips? Before answering, consider what happened to Egbert.

At last the American ideal of true equality for one and all is in sight. I am speaking of the pocket calculator, which is now used everywhere.

Most school districts, for example, have approved buying pocket calculators. The next step is perfectly clear. Give students a pocket computer. This latest wonder machine will store billions of facts and solve every imaginable kind of problem.

Actually, just such a device was developed as long ago as 1938 by the famed electronics brain, Dr. Wolfgang von Houlihan. Realizing the great potential for human equality in his invention, Dr. von Houlihan decided to test it out first on his only son, Egbert.

Egbert was an ideal subject. It was not that he lacked the intelligence to do well in the school down the block. It was that he lacked the intelligence to *find* the school down the block.

But after weeks of patient instruction, his father was able to teach Egbert which buttons to push when. The change in him was startling.

With billions of facts at his fingertip, he naturally quit school. And, knowing everything, he naturally read nothing. And yet, unschooled and unread, he whizzed through life.

His employers were amazed by his incredible knowledge, his quick thinking, his perfect solution for every problem. At thirty-five,

- ideal (eye DEEL) **goal; standard of excellence**
- equality (ee KWOL i tee) **sameness in position or value**
- potential (puh TEN shul) **possibility**
- startling (START ling) **surprising**
- incredible (in KRED uh bul) **unbelievable**

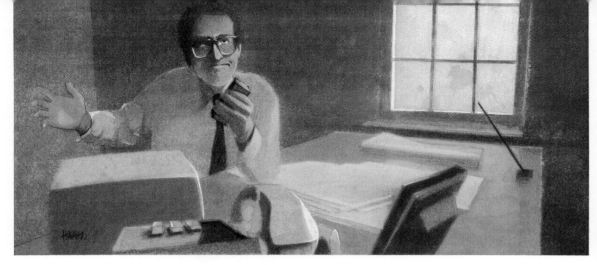

he became head of General Conglomerated, Inc.

"I got my brains from my father," he would say modestly when complimented. And then he would hum a few bars of his favorite song, "I've Got a Pocketful of Brains."

His quick mind made him a hit at parties. He always said the right thing, did the right thing, voted for the right candidate, and never ever once forgot his mother's birthday.

He was the perfect businessman, the perfect companion, the perfect citizen. And after he had computed the proper steps to sweep the beautiful Millicent Oleander off her feet, he was the perfect husband. While Millicent found Egbert strangely silent in the swimming pool, she was perfectly happy. After all, he was the perfect husband. He never ever once forgot their anniversary.

Needless to say, Egbert's father was overjoyed with the success of the experiment. "Just think!" he cried. "When all people carry their brains in their pockets, they will be not only equal but perfect!"

Dr. von Houlihan was at last ready to make public his wonder machine that would make all human beings perfect. Then THE CATASTROPHE struck. Afterward, he destroyed all his plans. And he was heard to say, "Equality's nice, but maybe we ought to just struggle along with what we've got."

Maybe you can guess what happened. One morning while her husband was in the shower, Millicent sent his trousers to the cleaners. And Egbert lost his mind.

- conglomerate (kun GLOM ur it) **a huge business made up of many smaller businesses**
- **compliment** (KOM pluh munt) **praise**
- catastrophe (kuh TAS truh fee) **sudden and great disaster**

ALL THINGS CONSIDERED _____

1. The author says that pocket calculators (a) solve all problems. (b) are widely used. (c) make everyone perfect.

2. He suggests a computer is better than a calculator because it (a) is more compact. (b) is less expensive. (c) does more things.

3. Egbert and Dr. von Houlihan probably are (a) real people. (b) made-up characters. (c) the author's friends.

4. Before getting a computer, Egbert is (a) very intelligent. (b) somewhat intelligent. (c) not very intelligent.

5. Then Egbert learns to (a) multiply and divide in his head. (b) push buttons on a computer. (c) write lyrics for songs.

6. Now Egbert knows everything because (a) his computer has all the answers. (b) he studies hard in school. (c) his father teaches him at home.

7. Because Egbert knows everything, (a) he doesn't need to read. (b) no one wants to marry him. (c) he invents a better computer.

8. Egbert is perfect when (a) his wife is nearby. (b) his father is present. (c) his computer is in his pocket.

9. Egbert is silent in the swimming pool because (a) he can't swim. (b) his computer isn't with him. (c) there is a rule against any talking.

10. Egbert loses his mind when (a) he loses his computer. (b) his father laughs at him. (c) he runs out of batteries.

THINKING IT THROUGH _____

1. What does Dr. von Houlihan mean when he says that pocket computers will make people equal?

2. Do you think a pocket computer could have been developed as early as 1938? Why?

3. How would you describe Millicent Oleander? Is she a good match for Egbert? Is the reader supposed to take either of them seriously? Explain.

4. At what point did the selection turn into a story? Until then, how would you describe the writing?

5. What is the theme, or message, of the story? Does the author make his point well? Explain.

Relationships

Cause and Effect

As you know, a cause is an event or an idea that leads to a certain result called an effect. A cause makes an effect happen.

Sentences telling cause and effect often use words and phrases such as *because, so that,* or *as a result.* But many sentences telling cause and effect do *not* use these words and phrases. The reader has to make the connection. This sentence is an example:

CAUSE   EFFECT
With billions of facts at his fingertips, he naturally quit school.

Sometimes the cause and effect are given in separate sentences:

CAUSE
His employers were amazed by his incredible knowledge.

EFFECT
He became head of General Conglomerated, Inc.

On your paper, write each of the following sentences. Then underline the <u>cause</u> once and the <u>effect</u> twice. Remember, the effect is sometimes told first. The first one has been done as an example.

1. His quick mind made him a hit at parties.

2. And, knowing everything, he naturally quit school.

3. Egbert's father was overjoyed with the success of the experiment.

4. The catastrophe struck. Afterward, he destroyed all his plans.

Composition

Follow your teacher's instructions before completing *one* of these writing assignments.

1. Write a sentence telling what you would do with a pocket computer. For example, you might store important phone numbers.

2. Write a paragraph telling the effect on the world of an invention such as the automobile, the airplane, or the computer. First tell what the invention does, and then tell how it changed the world.

THE BLACK PEARL OF KOWLOON

by Walter Dean Myers

▶ The Black Pearl of Kowloon* is missing! Who stole it? Will
the thief escape the careful eye of Dr. Aramy?

"It's gone! It's gone!" Mr. Uppley ran to the attic. He banged on Dr. Aramy's door. "It's gone! It's gone!" he cried.

Dr. Aramy had been asleep. He opened his eyes one at a time. He put on his fuzzy slippers. Then he opened the door. "What is gone, Mr. Uppley?"

"The Black Pearl of Kowloon, sir."

"The one they were to give to the queen?"

"The very one, Dr. Aramy. I just received the call from the Kowloon Hotel."

Dr. Aramy was a great detective. Mr. Uppley was his faithful friend. Together they set out for Kowloon. They rode their two-seater to the river, took the ferry to Kowloon, and soon were at the hotel.

The manager was quite upset. "Thank heaven you are here," he said. "I have locked the doors to the hotel. No one has left or come in."

"Is this where the pearl was kept?" Dr. Aramy held his magnifying glass near the display case. It was empty. He looked along the walls, on the floor, and under the corner of the rug. No pearl. Finally he discovered a clue. It was a shoe. In the shoe was a foot. The foot was attached to a person.

"Who are all these people?" Dr. Aramy asked, looking at the people in the room.

"This is Billy, the bellboy. This is Donald, the desk clerk. This is Charles, the chef. This is Garibaldi, the guard. This is Thomas, the tourist, and this is Duchess Doyle."

"Were they all here when the pearl was stolen?" Dr. Aramy asked.
"Yes."

"Only they and no one else?"

---

*Kowloon—section of Hong Kong

214

"That is correct."

"Then they are all suspects! Now tell me the facts." Dr. Aramy sat down in a large, stuffed chair. He adjusted the brim of his derby, and rested his hand on his cane.

"Well," began the manager, "the pearl was in the display case, which was covered by a velvet cloth. Suddenly there was a cry of fire."

"Zut! Fire, did you say?" Dr. Aramy jumped to his feet.

"Yes, but there is more."

"There is, my good man, no need for more. Who called out 'fire!'?"

"The desk clerk."

"He, then, is the thief." Dr. Aramy hit the desk with his cane. "He called out 'fire!' There was, of course, no fire. He just wanted everyone to run about so he could steal the pearl. Arrest him at once!"

"But there was a fire," said the manager.

"There was?"

"And when the call was made, he was at his desk."

"He was? Pity. Do go on."

"There was a cry of fire! Smoke was coming from the kitchen . . ."

"From the kitchen, you say?"

"Yes, but there is more."

"There is no need for more, dear fellow. We have our man. Arrest the chef!"

"The chef?"

"Of course. How clear it all is! He set the fire in the kitchen, knowing, of course, that the alarm would be given. When it was, there was confusion. Except for the man who set the fire. Then he crept out and stole the pearl. It's probably under his hat now!" Dr. Aramy knocked the chef's hat off. There was no pearl under the hat.

"But it was he who put *out* the fire," the manager said, picking up the hat.

"It was?"

"Yes," the manager said.

- **adjust** (uh JUST) arrange; put in order
- derby (DUR bee) **type of hat**
- **confusion** (kun FYOO zhun) **mixed-up state or condition**

"Pity. Go on with the story."

"Then the lights went out . . ."

"The lights?" asked Mr. Uppley.

"Yes," the manager said. "And when they came on again, I looked under the black velvet cloth. Which was, by the way, wet."

"Zut! Did you say that it was wet?"

"Well, just the corner," said the manager. "But there is more."

"Fool! How could you be so blind?" Dr. Aramy said. "We have found the thief!"

"Well done!" said Mr. Uppley.

"Well done!" they all said.

"Who is it?" asked the manager.

"It has to be the guard, of course. When everyone was looking the other way, he went into the kitchen and set the fire. Then he turned out the lights. He stole the pearl, then went back to his post. But it is a well-known fact that thieves have sweaty hands. He was standing near the case and wiped his sweaty hands on the velvet cloth."

So they searched the guard. They searched his turban and boots, his pockets, and even his beard. But they found no pearl.

"He doesn't have it," said the manager.

"He doesn't?" said Dr. Aramy. "Pity. But let me ask a few questions." Dr. Aramy pulled at his left ear. "Was everyone seated when the lights went on?"

"Yes," the manager said.

"Just as they are now?"

"Yes," said the manager.

"So—the pearl was stolen. And then the thief ran back to a chair. From where did the sounds come?"

"The sounds?" asked the manager. "What sounds?"

"The sounds of footsteps made by the thief."

"We heard nothing," the chef said.

"I did not ask you, my good fellow. You've caused enough trouble already."

"We heard nothing," said the manager.

"Surely the case cannot be this clear!" said Dr. Aramy.

• turban (TUR bun) **head covering made of cloth and wound around the head**

"Why, I do believe he's solved the case," said Mr. Uppley, waking from a short nap.

"The thief set a fire in the kitchen, ran and turned off the lights, ran to the display case and stole the pearl, wiped his sweaty hands on the cloth. But! And mind you well the 'but.' No steps were heard across the floor. And why not? Ah, it is quite simple. The thief was not wearing any shoes!"

"No shoes?" said Mr. Uppley. "Indeed!"

"Most of us wear shoes," said Dr. Aramy. "It is the habit of well-mannered people. But one of us—one of us in a long evening gown that touches the floor—has her feet hidden! Why? To conceal the fact that she wears no shoes."

"But surely you can't mean—?" Mr. Uppley gasped.

"But I do mean it," said Dr. Aramy. With that he leaped toward the duchess. He grasped the bottom of her gown, whose embroidered edges touched the floor. Then, after turning his eyes away, he lifted it almost to her knees.

"Oh!" and "Dear me!" the duchess cried.

"But she *is* wearing shoes!" the manager said.

"She is?" said Dr. Aramy.

"Save me!" said the duchess. And fainted dead away.

"Dear me," said Mr. Uppley. "The thief is still afoot. And, it would seem, the foot is shod."

"Did I tell you that we found a clue?" the manager asked as he fanned the duchess.

- **conceal** (kun SEEL) hide; keep out of sight
- **shod** (SHOD) **wearing a shoe or shoes**

217

"A clue?" said Mr. Uppley.

"We found a false mustache. It was in front of the display case."

"Tell me if it is red or black," said Dr. Aramy, standing on a chair.

"It is red," said the manager.

"Then we must be going," said Dr. Aramy, "after, of course, we collect our fee. For this case is solved. The crime happened like this. The thief set a fire in the kitchen. Then he came through the door yelling 'fire!' and turned off the lights. Then he tippytoed over to the pearl. But—he dropped his false mustache. The one clue that gave him away. Who here wears a mustache?"

"Thomas, the tourist," said Mr. Uppley. "But his is black."

"And as false as the red one," said Dr. Aramy. Then, faster than a bee's blink, Dr. Aramy grabbed Thomas's mustache and yanked it with all his strength.

"*Oooooweeeee!* You fool," said Thomas. "This mustache is real!"

"It is?"

"It is."

"Not false?"

"Not false."

"Pity. Then it is not a clue."

"There is another clue," said the desk clerk.

"What is it?"

"It is an order for a blueberry tart."

"Zut! Why was this not brought to my attention before?" Dr. Aramy turned very red. "Was the tart to be delivered to a room?"

"Why, yes," said the desk clerk.

"And who was to deliver it?"

"Billy, the bellboy."

"Kind sir! Kind sir!" the bellboy said.

"Beg not for mercy, wicked lad, for justice falls hard upon the bad."

"But, sir," said the bellboy, "when the call of fire came I was sitting. The duchess was so scared that she fainted, as you see she easily does. She landed upon my lap and stayed there. I could not move. I could not have taken the pearl."

"You could not have?"

"I am afraid not."

• tart (TART) **small pie**

218

"You are quite sure."

"Quite, sir."

"Pity."

"A genuine shame," said Mr. Uppley. "We have failed to solve the case."

"A shame? Yes," said Dr. Aramy. "But we have not failed to solve the case."

"And who do you accuse now?" asked the manager.

"Why, you, of course," said Dr. Aramy.

"Oh, how absurd," the manager said.

"Yes, is it not? May I have a cup of tea? And, perhaps, a blueberry tart?"

"But how did he do it?" asked Mr. Uppley.

"Simple," said Dr. Aramy. "First he stole the pearl, then he slipped into the kitchen. He hid the pearl and started the fire. Then he wanted to cause confusion, so he turned out the lights. In the darkness he dropped his false mustache and the order for the blueberry tart in which he had hidden the pearl! Which is why he had to wash his hands and later wipe them on the cloth. The one covering the display case."

Dr. Aramy reached into the tart, pushed about with his finger, then pulled out the Black Pearl of Kowloon.

"Gadzooks!" cried the manager. "I am caught! But you will never take me alive!" With that he ran toward the door. *Oooff!* Mr. Uppley grabbed him by the legs and sat upon him until the police arrived.

"Dr. Aramy, what put you on to him?" asked Mr. Uppley as they rode back to the ferry.

"Simple," said Dr. Aramy. "The cloth was wet on the left side. I noticed that the manager was left-handed. And I put two and two together."

"But the cloth was wet on the right side," said Mr. Uppley. "Not the left."

"Not the left?"

"I am afraid not."

"Pity," said Dr. Aramy. "It would have been such a good clue."

- **genuine** (JEN yoo in) **real; true**
- absurd (ab SURD) **foolish; silly**

219

ALL THINGS CONSIDERED _____

1. The setting of the story is a (a) school. (b) hotel. (c) bank.

2. Dr. Aramy and Mr. Uppley are called by the (a) hotel manager. (b) desk clerk. (c) police.

3. Someone has stolen (a) a pearl. (b) a million dollars. (c) the suitcase belonging to the duchess.

4. The doors are locked so that (a) the police cannot get in. (b) no one can leave. (c) the guests feel safe.

5. When Dr. Aramy hears that the desk clerk called "fire," he (a) wonders who started the fire. (b) asks who put out the fire. (c) accuses the clerk of being the thief.

6. When Dr. Aramy hears that the fire came from the kitchen, he accuses the (a) desk clerk. (b) chef. (c) guard.

7. Dr. Aramy accuses the duchess because she (a) looks like a thief. (b) could have been barefoot under her long dress. (c) is wearing the pearl.

8. When Dr. Aramy yanks at Thomas's mustache, (a) Thomas cries out. (b) the mustache comes off. (c) Thomas confesses to the crime.

9. Each time Dr. Aramy learns that he has wrongly accused someone, he says (a) "I don't believe you." (b) "Arrest him!" (c) "Pity."

10. Dr. Aramy finally finds the pearl and thief (a) because of perfect reasoning. (b) despite faulty reasoning. (c) with the help of Mr. Uppley.

THINKING IT THROUGH _____

1. A story is called a **spoof** when it makes fun of someone or something by imitating it in a silly way. Do you think the story you just read is a spoof? If so, who or what is being spoofed?

2. Did you notice anything curious about the names and roles of the suspects? Explain.

3. In the story, Dr. Aramy is called a great detective. Do you agree with this description? Why?

4. How does Dr. Aramy discover the thief? Would he agree with your answer? Explain.

Building From Details

Drawing Conclusions

It is the job of a detective to draw conclusions. It is also the job of a reader. **Drawing conclusions** means looking at facts and deciding what they mean.

In the story, Dr. Aramy says, "Now tell me the facts." The funny thing about Dr. Aramy is that he uses the facts to come to the *wrong* conclusions. For example, when he learns that the desk clerk yelled "fire," he concludes that he is the thief. His mistake is that he doesn't get all the facts before drawing a conclusion. It turns out there was a fire and *that* was the reason the clerk yelled.

As the reader, you probably came to some conclusions about the story. On a separate sheet of paper, answer the following questions. Write one fact from the story to support each answer.

1. Where is Dr. Aramy's bedroom?
2. Was the stolen pearl going to stay at the hotel forever?
3. Do Dr. Aramy and Mr. Uppley cross water to get to the hotel?
4. Is Dr. Aramy quick to make decisions or does he think things over for a long time?
5. Is the story meant to be funny or serious?

Composition

Follow your teacher's instructions before completing *one* of these writing assignments.

1. What does Dr. Aramy conclude from each of the following facts? Write your answers in complete sentences. (a) The clerk yelled "fire." (b) The lights went out. (c) The cloth was wet. (d) No sounds were heard. (e) Someone ordered a blueberry tart.
2. Write a one-paragraph newspaper story about the theft of the pearl. Tell *what* happened, *where* and *when* it happened (make up a date), *who* was involved, and *why* or how the case was solved. Write a headline for your news story.

221

WORD PLAY

▶ **Word play** means having fun with language. Sometimes a speaker or a writer means to make a "play on words." At other times it just happens. Read the tombstones below and judge for yourself.

WAYS OF KNOWING

1. A **pun** is a play on words that sound alike but have different meanings. Explain the pun on the first tombstone.
2. The writer of the second tombstone seems confused. First we are told that Thomas Vernon is dead. What word says the opposite?
3. What is wrong with the wording of the third tombstone? Tell how you would reword it.
4. If you hadn't been told, would you have known that Thomas Hinde was a clock and watch maker? Explain. Was the tombstone meant to be humorous? Do you think the writers of the other tombstones meant them to be humorous? Explain.

• horizontal (hor i ZON tul) **flat; level**

ARITHMETIC

by Carl Sandburg

▶ Arithmetic is an unlikely topic for a humorous poem. When the poem is written by Carl Sandburg, it adds up to great American humor.

Arithmetic is where numbers fly like pigeons in and out of your head.

Arithmetic tells you how many you lose or win if you know how many you had before you lost or won.

Arithmetic is seven eleven all good children go to heaven—or five six bundle of sticks.

Arithmetic is numbers you squeeze from your head to your hand to your pencil to your paper till you get the answer.

Arithmetic is where the answer is right and everything is nice and you can look out of the window and see the blue sky—or the answer is wrong and you have to start all over and try again and see how it comes out this time.

If you take a number and double it and double it again and then double it a few more times, the number gets bigger and bigger and goes higher and higher and only arithmetic can tell you what the number is when you decide to quit doubling.

Arithmetic is where you have to multiply—and you carry the multiplication table in your head and hope you won't lose it.

If you have two animal crackers, one good and one bad, and you eat one and a striped zebra with streaks all over him eats the other, how many animal crackers will you have if somebody offers you five six seven and you say No no no and you say Nay nay nay and you say Nix nix nix?

If you ask your mother for one fried egg for breakfast and she gives you two fried eggs and you eat both of them, who is better in arithmetic, you or your mother?

WAYS OF KNOWING

1. This poem consists of nine sentences. Three of them sound like silly word problems from an arithmetic book. Which three sentences are these? What do the other six sentences sound like?

2. Which sentence best tells what arithmetic means to you? Which sentence do you think is the most humorous? On a separate piece of paper, write two sentences of your own.

ALICE IN WONDERLAND

by Lewis Carroll

▶ In Alice's dream world, playing cards act like people and animals talk. The following scene from *Alice's Adventures in Wonderland* takes place in a rather unusual courtroom. The Jack of Hearts has been accused of stealing the queen's tarts.

The King and Queen of Hearts were seated on their throne with a great crowd about them. All sorts of little birds and beasts were there as well as the whole pack of cards. The Jack of Hearts was standing before them, in chains, with a soldier on each side to guard him. Near the King was the White Rabbit with a trumpet in one hand, and a pretty children's book in the other. In the very middle of the court was a table with a large dish of tarts upon it; they looked so good that Alice became quite hungry just looking at them.

Alice had never been in a courtroom before, but she had read about courts in books. She was quite pleased to find that she knew the name of nearly everything there. "That's the judge," she said to herself, "because of his great wig."

The judge was the King. As he wore his crown over the wig, he did not look at all comfortable. It was certainly not very becoming.

"And that is the jury box," thought Alice. "And those twelve creatures must be the jury." (She said "creatures," you see, because some of them were animals and some were birds.)

The twelve jurors were all writing very busily on slates. "What are they doing?" Alice whispered to the Griffin. "They can't have anything to write down yet, before the trial's begun."

"They're writing down their names," the Griffin whispered in reply, "for fear they'll forget them before the end of the trial."

"Stupid things!" Alice began in a loud voice. But she stopped herself hastily, for

- tart (TART) **small pie**
- **creature** (KREE chur) **living being**
- slate (SLAYT) **small writing board**
- griffin (GRIF un) **kind of imaginary animal with the head of an eagle and the body of a lion**
- **hastily** (HAYS ti lee) **in a hurried way**

224

the White Rabbit cried out, "Silence in the court!" The King put on his glasses and looked anxiously around to see who was talking.

Alice could see that all the jurors were writing down "stupid things!" on their slates. She could even make out that one of them didn't know how to spell "stupid." He had to ask his neighbor to tell him. "A nice muddle their slates'll be in before the trial's over!" thought Alice.

"Herald, read the accusation!" said the King.

The White Rabbit blew three blasts on the trumpet. Then he held up the book and read as follows:

The Queen of Hearts, she made some tarts,
  All on a summer day.
The Jack of Hearts, he stole those tarts,
  And took them quite away!

"Consider your verdict," the King said to the jury.

"Not yet, not yet!" the Rabbit interrupted. "There's a great deal to come before that!"

"Call the first witness," said the King. The White Rabbit blew three blasts on the trumpet, and called out, "First witness!"

The first witness was the Hatter. He came in with a teacup in one hand, and a piece of bread and butter in the other. "I beg your pardon, your Majesty," he

- muddle (MUD ul) **mix-up; confusion**
- herald (HER uld) **announcer**
- accusation (ak yuh ZAY shun) **the charge of doing wrong**
- verdict (VUR dikt) **opinion of a jury**
- hatter (HAT ur) **person who makes or sells hats**

225

began, "for bringing these in. But I hadn't quite finished my tea when I was sent for."

"You ought to have finished," said the King. "When did you begin?"

The Hatter looked at the March Hare, who had followed him into the court, arm-in-arm with the Dormouse. "Four-teenth of March, I *think* it was," he said.

"Fifteenth," said the March Hare.

"Sixteenth," added the Dormouse.

"Write that down," the King said to the jury. The jury eagerly wrote down all three dates on their slates, added them up, then changed the answer to dollars and cents.

"Take off your hat," the King said to the Hatter.

"It isn't mine," said the Hatter.

"*Stolen!*" the King exclaimed, turning to the jury, who instantly scribbled on their slates.

"I wear them to sell," the Hatter added as an explanation. "I've none of my own. I'm a hatter."

Here the Queen put on her glasses and began staring hard at the Hatter, who turned pale and fidgeted.

"Give your evidence," said the King. "And don't be nervous, or I'll have you executed on the spot."

"I'm a poor man, your Majesty," the Hatter began in a trembling voice. "I hadn't but just begun my tea—not more

than a week or so—and what with the bread and butter getting so thin—and the twinkling of the tea—"

"The twinkling of *what?*" said the King.

"It *began* with the tea," the Hatter replied.

"Of course twinkling begins with a T!" said the King sharply. "Do you take me for a fool? Go on!"

"I'm a poor man," the Hatter went on, "and most things twinkled after that. But the March Hare said—"

"I didn't!" interrupted the March Hare.

"You did!" said the Hatter.

"I deny it!" said the March Hare.

"He denies it," said the King. "Leave out that part."

"Well, at any rate, the Dormouse said—" the Hatter went on, looking anxiously round to see if the Dormouse would deny it too. But the Dormouse denied nothing, being fast asleep.

"After that," continued the Hatter, "I cut some more bread and butter—"

"But what did the Dormouse say?" one of the jury asked.

"That I can't remember," said the Hatter.

"You *must* remember," remarked the King, "or I'll have you executed."

The miserable Hatter dropped his teacup and bread and butter, and went

- dormouse (DOR mous) **kind of animal like a squirrel**
- fidget (FI jit) **be restless**
- interrupt (in tuh RUPT) **break in while a person is talking or in some other way busy**

down on one knee. "I'm a poor man, your Majesty," he began.

"I see," said the King. "If that's all you know about it, you may step down," continued the King.

"I can't go lower," said the Hatter. "I'm on the floor, as it is."

"Then you may *sit* down," the King replied. "And leave at once."

Holding his hat tightly on his head, the Hatter hurriedly left the court.

"And just take his head off outside," the Queen added to one of the officers. But the Hatter was out of sight before the officer could get to the door.

"Call the next witness!" said the King.

Alice watched the White Rabbit as he fumbled over the list. She was very curious to see what the next witness would be like. "They haven't much evidence *yet*," she said to herself. Imagine her surprise when the White Rabbit read out, at the top of his voice, the name "Alice!"

"Here!" cried Alice. And she jumped up in such a hurry that she frightened all the jurors, who jumped out of the jury box and lay sprawling about on the floor.

"Oh, I *beg* your pardon!" she exclaimed. She began picking them up again as quickly as she could.

"The trial cannot proceed," said the King in a very serious voice, "until all the jurors are back in their proper places—*all*."

Alice saw that in her haste she had put the Lizard in head downward. The

- fumble (FUM bul) **handle in a clumsy way**
- **evidence** (EV i duns) **facts needed to solve a case**

227

poor little thing was waving its tail about in a pitiful way, being quite unable to move. She soon got it out again, and put it right. "Not that it matters much," she said to herself. "I think it would be *quite* as much use in the trial one way up as the other."

As soon as their slates and pencils had been found and handed back to them, the jurors set to work to write out a history of the accident. Only the Lizard seemed too much overcome to do anything. It sat with its mouth open, gazing up at the ceiling of the court.

"What do you know about this business?" the King said to Alice.

"Nothing," said Alice.

"Nothing *whatever?*" persisted the King.

"Nothing whatever," said Alice.

"That's very important," the King said, turning to the jury.

They were just beginning to write this down on their slates, when the White Rabbit interrupted. "*Un*important, your Majesty means, of course," he said.

"*Un*important, of course, I meant," the King hastily said. Then he went on quietly saying to himself, "important—unimportant—unimportant—important" —as if he were trying to decide which word sounded best.

Some of the jury wrote down "important," and some wrote "unimportant." Alice could see this. "But it doesn't matter a bit," she thought to herself.

At this moment the King shut his notebook, for he saw it had only blank pages. "Consider your verdict," he said.

"There's more evidence to come yet, your Majesty," said the White Rabbit. "This envelope has just been brought in."

"What's in it?" said the Queen.

"I haven't opened it yet," said the White Rabbit. "It seems to be a letter,

There was a general clapping of hands at this. (It was the first really clever thing the King had said that day.)

"That *proves* his guilt," said the Queen.

"It proves nothing of the sort!" said Alice. "Why, you don't even know what the poem's about!"

"Read it," said the King.
written by the prisoner to—to somebody."

"It must have been that," said the King, "unless it was written to nobody, which isn't usual, you know."

"Whom is it addressed to?" said one of the jurors.

"It isn't addressed at all," said the White Rabbit. "In fact, there's nothing written on the *outside.*" He opened the envelope as he spoke, and added, "It isn't a letter after all. It's a poem."

"Is it in the prisoner's handwriting?" asked another of the jurors.

"No, it's not," said the White Rabbit. "And that's the oddest thing about it." (The jury all looked puzzled.)

"He must have imitated somebody else's handwriting," said the King. (The

• persist (pur SIST) **stay on a topic**

jury all brightened up again.)

"Please your Majesty," said the Jack, "I didn't write it, and they can't prove I did. There's no name signed at the end."

"If you didn't sign it," said the King, "that only makes the matter worse. You *must* have meant some mischief, or else you'd have signed your name like an honest man."

The White Rabbit put on his glasses. "Where shall I begin, your Majesty?" he asked.

"Begin at the beginning," the King said. "And go on till you come to the end. Then stop."

This is the poem the White Rabbit read:

They told me you had been to her,
*   And mentioned me to him:*
She gave me a good character,
*   But said I could not swim.*

He sent them word I had not gone
*   (We know it to be true):*
If she should push the matter on,
*   What would become of you?*

I gave her one, they gave him two,
*   You gave us three or more;*
They all returned from him to you,
*   Though they were mine before.*

My notion was that you had been
*   (Before she had this fit)*
An obstacle that came between
*   Him, and ourselves, and it.*

"That's the most important piece of evidence we've heard yet," said the King, rubbing his hands. "So now let the jury—"

"Can any one of them explain it?" asked Alice. "*I* don't believe there's an atom of meaning in it."

The jury all wrote down on their slates, "*She* doesn't believe there's an atom of meaning in it." But none of them attempted to explain the poem.

- fit (FIT) **sudden attack**
- obstacle (OB stuh kul) **something in the way**

229

"If there's no meaning in it," said the King, "that saves a world of trouble. We needn't try to find any. And yet I don't know," he went on, spreading out the poem on his knee, and looking at it with one eye. "I seem to see some meaning here. Consider ' . . . *said I could not swim.*' You can't swim, can you?" he asked, turning to Jack.

Jack shook his head sadly. "Do I look like it?" he said. (Which he certainly did *not,* being a playing card.)

"All right, so far," said the King. He went on reading the verses to himself: "*'I gave her one, they gave him two.'* Why, that must be what he did with the tarts."

"But it goes on, *'They all returned from him to you,'*" said Alice.

"Why, there they are!" said the King triumphantly, pointing to the tarts on the table. "Nothing can be clearer than *that.* Then again—*'before she had this fit'*—you never had fits, my dear, did you?" he said to the Queen.

"Never!" said the Queen furiously, throwing an inkstand at the Lizard as she spoke.

"Then the words don't *fit* you," said the King, looking around the court with a smile. There was silence.

"It's a pun!" the King added in an angry tone. Then everybody laughed. "Let the jury consider their verdict," the King said, for about the twentieth time that day.

"No, no!" said the Queen. "Sentence first—verdict afterward."

"Stuff and nonsense!" said Alice loudly. "The idea of having the sentence first!"

"Hold your tongue!" said the Queen, turning purple.

"I won't!" said Alice.

"Off with her head!" the Queen shouted at the top of her voice. Nobody moved.

"Who cares about you?" said Alice. "You're nothing but a playing card!"

At this the whole pack of cards rose up into the air, and came flying down upon her. She gave a little scream, and tried to beat them off. Then she found herself lying on the lawn beside her sister.

"Wake up, Alice dear!" said her sister. "Why, what a long sleep you've had!"

• triumphantly (try UM funt lee) **in a proud, victorious way**

ALL THINGS CONSIDERED

1. The King wears a crown over a wig because he is (a) cold. (b) the judge. (c) trying to look nice.

2. The jurors are (a) people. (b) playing cards. (c) animals and birds.

3. The King asks the jury to consider the verdict (a) before the evidence. (b) before Alice speaks. (c) after Jack defends himself.

4. The Hatter comes in with his teacup because (a) it is evidence. (b) he wants to give it to the King. (c) he hasn't finished his tea.

5. When the King says "Step down," the Hatter says (a) he won't. (b) "Where is that?" (c) "I can't go lower."

6. Alice is surprised when (a) Jack is accused. (b) she is called as a witness. (c) the King turns into a playing card.

7. When the King says "important—unimportant . . . ," some of the jurors (a) fall asleep. (b) ask what he means. (c) write "important" and some write "unimportant."

8. The King says that if the poem has no meaning, then (a) it proves that Jack stole the tarts. (b) it isn't a poem. (c) it isn't worth trying to understand.

9. The King says if the Queen does not have fits (a) she is not fit to be his wife. (b) she is not fit to be queen. (c) then the words of the poem do not fit her.

10. The Queen wants the sentence to be given (a) before the trial. (b) before the verdict. (c) at a card party.

THINKING IT THROUGH

1. Did you visualize as you read this story? Which character, event, or part of setting made the funniest picture in your mind?

2. What are some character traits of the King and Queen of Hearts? Give examples of things they do or say to support your answer.

3. In what ways is this story a spoof of a real trial?

4. There are several word plays in the story. Tell about one or two.

5. Like Dr. Aramy in "The Black Pearl of Kowloon," the King of Hearts seems to come to hasty and often incorrect conclusions. Give one example. First tell the evidence he is given. Then tell what he *incorrectly* concludes from that evidence.

Literary Skills

Fantasy

A story that is more like a dream than it is like real life is called a **fantasy.** The author uses imagination to create an unusual world. The characters may be strange. The setting may seem unreal. Even the events may be unusual.

Sometimes the effect of a fantasy is humorous. At other times it is scary. Either way, fantasies are fun because they let you explore a new world.

"Alice in Wonderland" is a fantasy. As you know, cards do not talk in real life, and silly poems are not read aloud in courts of law. In fact, you probably were not surprised at the end to learn that Alice had been dreaming.

On a separate piece of paper, tell three things about the story that made it seem like a dream. Do not use the examples mentioned above. Instead, look for other things that are silly, exaggerated, or strange. Tell about these things in complete sentences such as, "It is unusual for a rabbit to wear glasses," or "A person cannot talk to a griffin because griffins are not real."

Composition

Follow your teacher's instructions before completing *one* of these writing assignments.

1. Is "Alice in Wonderland" a good title for this fantasy story? Write a sentence saying whether you think it is or is not a good title. Then, in another sentence or two, give reasons for your answer.
2. Write a mini-fantasy. First, describe an imaginary place you'd like to visit. Then, tell about an unusual character you meet there. Finally, describe an experience you and the other character have. For example, you might describe meeting a creature in a cave and searching for hidden treasure.

VOCABULARY AND SKILL REVIEW ─────────────

Before completing the exercises that follow, you may wish to review the **bold-faced** words on pages 208–230.

I. On a separate sheet of paper, write the term from the list that means the same, or nearly the same, as the term in *italics.*

pun	conceal	evidence	genuine	dreadful
hastily	gallant	creature	confusion	adjust

1. The *living being* had pointy ears and a puffy tail.
2. He tried to *arrange* the hat so that it would be more comfortable.
3. In the *mix-up,* the thief escaped with the jewels.
4. The punishment served her right for telling such a *terrible* lie.
5. The child tried to *hide* the candy in his hand, but he dropped it.
6. It was a *true* disappointment when her chance for a promotion fell through.
7. You need more *facts* to support your claim that you were asleep at the time of the crime.
8. The firefighter was very *brave* to rescue the cat from the tall tree.
9. The *play on words* was very clever.
10. He spoke too *quickly* and wished he could take back his words.

II. Match the causes in Column A with their effects in Column B.

A	**B**
1. Alice had read about the courts.	a) The Hatter came in carrying his teacup.
2. The king wore his crown over a wig.	b) Alice stopped speaking.
3. The jurors were afraid they would forget their names.	c) Alice knew the name of nearly everything in the court.
4. The White Rabbit cried out, "Silence in the court!"	d) The king did not look comfortable.
5. The Hatter hadn't finished his tea.	e) The jurors wrote their names on their slates.

LOOKING AT LIMERICKS

▶ A **limerick** (LIM ur ik) is a five-line poem with a particular rhythm and pattern of rhyme. Practically every limerick is humorous with a comic twist in the last line. Here are a few examples.

A Tooter Tutor
A tutor who tooted the flute
Tried to tutor two tooters to toot.
   Said the two to the tutor,
   "Is it harder to toot or
To tutor two tooters to toot?"
      —Carolyn Wells

A Bear in Reverse
A cheerful old bear at the zoo
Could always find something to do.
   When it bored him to go
   On a walk to and fro,
He reversed it, and walked fro and to.
      —Anonymous

A Flea and a Fly in Flight
A flea and a fly in a flue
Were imprisoned, so what could they do?
   Said the fly, "Let us flee."
   Said the flea, "Let us fly."
So they flew through a flaw in the flue.
      —Anonymous

- **reverse** (ri VURS) the opposite; backward
- **flue** (FLOO) a passage for hot air, such as a chimney
- **flaw** (FLAW) fault; defect; crack

Willie and Millie

The bottle of perfume that Willie sent
Was highly displeasing to Millicent.
    Her thanks were so cold
    That they quarreled, I'm told,
Through that silly scent Willie sent Millicent.
                    —Anonymous

The Transparent Ghost

Wailed a ghost in a graveyard at Kew,
"Oh my friends are so fleeting and few,
    For it's gravely apparent
    That if you're transparent
There is no one who knows if it's you."
           —Myra Cohn Livingston

WAYS OF KNOWING

1. In the first limerick, what two words sound alike? How is this important to the humor of the poem?

2. Restate the question asked in "A Tooter Tutor" without using the words *toot, tutor,* or *tooters.*

3. How does the wording of "A Bear in Reverse" reflect the action of the bear?

4. What words sound alike in "A Flea and a Fly in Flight"? How is this important to the humor of the poem?

5. The humor of "Willie and Millie" depends a great deal on rhyming words. How many instances of rhyming words can you find in this limerick?

6. In the last limerick, who is transparent? What is the result? What word has a double meaning? How does the double meaning add to the humor?

- fleeting (FLEET ing) **soon gone**
- grave (GRAYV) **This word has two very different meanings: (1) a place for burying; (2) very serious.**
- apparent (uh PAIR unt) **clear; easily understood**

UNIT REVIEW

Write all your answers on a separate sheet of paper.

I. Match the terms in Column A with their definitions in Column B.

A	**B**
1. trickster tale	**a)** time and place of a story
2. setting	**b)** dream-like story
3. cause and effect	**c)** story with a quick-witted character
4. tall tale	**d)** story that imitates another
5. exaggeration	**e)** relationship between an event and its result
6. limerick	**f)** funny, exaggerated story
7. first person	**g)** angle a reader has on a story, either first person or third person
8. fantasy	**h)** five-line poem
9. point of view	**i)** point of view of a character in a story
10. spoof	**j)** stretching of the truth

II. Read the sentences below and think about how you would complete them. Then fill in your answers by writing each sentence on your paper. Each sentence allows you to express your opinion, so different answers are possible.

1. I think _____ is a good example of a trickster tale because _____ .

2. I think _____ is a good example of a tall tale because _____ .

3. I think _____ is a good example of a spoof because _____ .

4. I think _____ contains a good example of word play because _____ .

5. I think _____ is a good example of a story with a familiar setting because _____ .

6. I think _____ is a good limerick because _____ .

7. I think _____ is a good example of a fantasy story because _____ .

8. My favorite story or poem in this unit is _____ because _____ .

236

SPEAKING UP

A type of live variety show called **vaudeville** was a very popular form of entertainment in America. Vaudeville was mainly song, dance, and humor. A skit, or short funny act, was usually given by two people.

In this skit, there is a person who acts in a serious way, called the Straight, and a Comic. The Straight begins the dialogue and talks in a serious although somewhat forgetful manner. The Comic creates the laughs.

IZZY-WUZZY

CHARACTERS: Comic, Straight.

OPENING: *Comic and Straight enter, meet center stage.*

Straight: Well, hello. Hello, there—uh—uh. I'm afraid I forgot your name. Oh, no, I didn't. It's uh—what is your name? Now, don't tell me. Don't tell me. *(Busy thinking.)*

Comic: Huh! He doesn't know my name is Albert.

Straight: Now I remember: Albert. And you're from. . . . Let's see, now. Don't tell me. *(Busy thinking.)*

Comic: Can you imagine: He doesn't know I'm from Texarkana.

Straight: That's right. Little Albert from Texarkana. By the way, Albert, how's your sister?

Comic: Which one? Becky, Agnes, or Mabel?

Straight: Why, Becky, naturally. How is she?

Comic: Oh, she's fine. She's married and has twins.

Straight: You don't tell me.

Comic: But I just did.

Straight: Yes, you did. You did. Thank you.

Comic: "Thank you?" For what?

Straight: For telling me.

Comic: For telling you what?

Straight: For telling me—oh, skip it! But tell me, how old are the twins?

Comic: One is six. And one is four.

Straight: What are their names?

Comic: Izzy and Wuzzy.

Straight: Izzy and Wuzzy. Well, how are they?

Comic: Well, last week Izzy was sick. He's all right now. But when I left this morning Wuzzy was sick.

Straight: Oh, is he?

Comic: No, Wuzzy.

Straight: That's what I said: Is he?

Comic: No, Wuzzy. Izzy was sick last week.

Straight: Oh, was he?

Comic: No, Izzy.

Straight: I thought you said Wuzzy was sick.

Comic: Wuzzy was.

Straight: But now Wuzzy isn't, is he?

Comic: Of course Wuzzy isn't Izzy.

Straight: No, no. You don't understand me.

Comic: You don't understand English. I said Wuzzy was sick this morning.

Straight: Right. And now Izzy isn't, is he?

Comic: Are you trying to tell me Izzy isn't Izzy?

Straight: Look: Izzy was sick last week. Wuzzy was sick this morning. Right?

Comic: Right. Izzy was. Now Wuzzy was.

Straight: Right! Both was—Oh, no! Now you've got me talking that way!

Comic: What way?

Straight: Oh, never mind! Never mind! *(Both leave the stage very disgusted.)*

Writing Your Own Setting

What kind of mood, or feeling, do you get from this picture? How would you describe the house and its surroundings? What season do you think it is, and what time of day is it? Answering these questions will help you write a paragraph about the setting and the mood in this picture.

1. **Prewriting:** List five or six words that describe the setting. Make sure some of the words tell about mood, or feeling. Words that appeal to the *five senses* are good ones to use.
2. **Writing:** Use your plan to write a paragraph. Describe the setting in a way that lets a reader *visualize* it. Be sure to tell where things are located. For example, you might write this sentence: Bushes grow *beside* the house.
3. **Revising:** Reread your paragraph. Can a reader visualize the setting? Would your paragraph be more interesting if some short sentences were combined into longer ones? Would any long sentences be better if they were divided into shorter ones? Check your spelling, punctuation, and capitalization. Make corrections, and then rewrite your paragraph neatly.

GOING BEYOND

Do you shiver when an owl hoots? Do you shudder at a full moon? Do your nerves crackle at a sudden noise? If you answer *yes* to any of these questions, you'd better think twice before reading these selections.

This unit goes beyond the reality of everyday life. It reaches into the past for explanations of the unknown. It goes next door to find strange events. It leaps into the future for a look at the unimaginable.

So prepare yourself for new experiences, and beware. These selections may take you to places you have never been. Let imagination be your guide.

THE HATCH

by Norma Farber

▶ The speaker in this poem is hatching from an egg. This egg
is not a bird's egg. See if you can find out what it is.

I found myself one day
cracking the shell of sky,
peering into a place
beyond mere universe.

I broke from egg of here
into anotherwhere
wider than worldly home
I was emerging from.

I breathed, I took a step,
I looked around, and up,
and saw another lining
inside a further sky.

WAYS OF KNOWING

1. The speaker breaks "from egg of here into anotherwhere." What
   is the "anotherwhere" the speaker mentions? Is there one certain
   answer to this question, or do you think there can be several
   answers?
2. At the end of the poem, the speaker sees "another lining." What
   does this mean? What do you think the speaker might see on
   cracking through the next lining?

- peer (PEER) **look closely**
- mere (MEER) **common**
- emerge (ee MURJ) **come out**

THE BACKGROUND

Legends are stories that have been told over the years. They are often based on truth that has been stretched. You may know the legend of Davy Crockett. Davy Crockett (1786–1836) was known for his hunting and other outdoor skills. Life was tough on the American frontier, and people like Crockett were admired. Stories about him were told in homes and around campfires. Soon the facts became exaggerated, and the story of Davy Crockett became a legend.

In this unit, you will read the Mexican legend of La Llorona (la yor OH nah). Keep in mind that La Llorona was probably once a real person but that her story has been passed from person to person and from generation to generation. Now the legend has a life of its own, and the facts are less important.

Myths are also stories from the past. Myths tell the beliefs of a certain group of people. Myths are a way of explaining events in the world, especially in nature.

In this unit you will read a Native American myth that explains a custom of the Iroquois (IR uh kwoi) people. You will also read a Greek myth that explains the source of echoes. You will notice that gods, goddesses, and supernatural events are common in myths. As you read a myth, ask yourself, "What is this myth trying to explain? What does it say about the beliefs of the people?"

LA LLORONA

a Mexican legend

▶ It is said that on certain moonlit nights La Llorona—"the weeping woman"—wanders in search of her children. Who is this woman? What happens to people who meet her?

It is late at night. All is still. In the bright moonlight the backs of the mountains shiver.

Two men are sitting around a campfire. They are telling ghost stories, and the old man tells the young man the legend of La Llorona, the weeping woman. At the end of the tale, there is a long silence. The young man looks at the mountains around them. The moonlight has grown magical. It dances on the sides of the mountains like sparkling elves. The young man looks, and he shivers.

Suddenly, from out of the deep silence, comes a terrible shriek, then a long, mournful wail.

Could it be La Llorona?

The old man tells the young man to wait. The old man gets up and walks off. Where did the sound come from? It seems to have come from all directions. He walks on.

Then she appears. She is pale, dressed in white. Her hair is black and long. A breeze lifts it and settles it gently like a scarf around her shoulders.

The old man is frozen in his tracks. Then the woman moves, gliding silently like a mist. She moves without effort. Her feet do not seem to touch the ground.

"My little ones! My little ones!" she cries. Her words are icy fingers taking hold of the old man's heart. The shadows throw a veil over her face, but the man thinks she is the most beautiful woman he has ever seen. He follows her. He can't let her out of his sight. He is her servant.

- **mournful** (MORN ful) **sorrowful; sad**
- wail (WAYL) **loud cry**
- veil (VAYL) **a cloth worn over the face**

His feet make the sounds of stumbling against stones, yet the woman moves in silence. She leads him to a lake. She does not stop. She glides onward, moving over the water as easily as she had over the land.

The man cannot let her go. He wades out into the lake, following the beautiful woman. The water comes up to his knees, his waist, his neck. He keeps walking. The water closes over his head. All is still.

Meanwhile, the young man has fallen asleep. When he awakes, it is dawn, and the old man has not returned. The young man looks everywhere. He walks up into the mountains. He walks beside the lake. But there is no sign of the old man.

The next night the moonlight comes again. The young man gets up from his campfire to look for his lost companion. Now, in the moonlight, he sees clearly the footprints. They lead him from the campfire to the lake—and end there. The young man shivers in disbelief.

Suddenly, the stillness is again broken by the shriek and the wailing cry. "Oh, my little ones! My little ones!" La Llorona appears again. Like a cloud she drifts beside the lake.

But the young man is bold. He will not be silent. "How beautiful you are!" he calls. "Who are you?" There is no answer. "Please!" he calls. "Are you a ghost? Are you—are you La Llorona?"

The woman hovers over the water, her white gown moving like the mist. For a long while there is only silence. Then her voice comes in a hoarse whisper full of sorrow: "Look into the water. What do you see?"

The young man looks. His face grows pale in the moonlight. He trembles. "It's—it's—" He can't say it. Then the words burst out: "It's a pool of blood!"

La Llorona answers with a long moan. When the young man looks up, she is gone.

Who is La Llorona? No one knows for sure. Many believe that La Llorona is the ghost of a woman whose children were killed or stolen from her. They say her grief was so great that it did not die when she died. Some say she will haunt Mexico for a thousand years, but others say forever.

La Llorona is seen not only in the countryside, but also in the deserts and even in the cities of Mexico. She is seen wherever it is lonely, and especially when the night is clear and cold and the moon is full.

It is said that many who have met La Llorona have died mysteriously. The lucky ones she only fills with a terror they never forget.

Some say her cries can be heard only at a distance. Others say the cries are most piercing when one is near her. Even her face is a mystery. For every person who says it is beautiful, there is another who claims she shows the face of a horse or a grinning skull. Most of those who have seen her say she cries out, again and again: "My little ones! My little ones!"

So if you walk alone beneath a full moon and hear shrieks or wails or moans, or if you happen to see something white shimmering in the mountains, or floating beside a lake, do not follow, my friend. Do not look for La Llorona. You may find her.

- hover (HUV ur) **stay or wait without moving**
- **piercing** (PEERS ing) **sharp**

ALL THINGS CONSIDERED

1. The setting of the legend is the country on a (a) rainy night. (b) moonlit night. (c) moonless night.
2. The old man (a) follows La Llorona. (b) catches La Llorona. (c) searches for La Llorona.
3. The old man walks into the water and (a) saves La Llorona. (b) drowns. (c) saves the young man.
4. The next morning, the young man (a) saves the old man. (b) finds the old man dead. (c) finds no sign of the old man.
5. The next night, the young man (a) returns home. (b) looks for the old man. (c) stays by the campfire.
6. The young man (a) asks La Llorona about the old man. (b) refuses to look at La Llorona. (c) talks to La Llorona.
7. La Llorona tells the young man to look into the water and then she (a) disappears. (b) catches him. (c) shows him her children.
8. This legend started in (a) Texas. (b) Mexico. (c) Canada.
9. La Llorona is supposed to be looking for (a) her children. (b) the person who took her children. (c) gold at the bottom of a lake.
10. Many who see La Llorona (a) run from her. (b) die mysteriously. (c) become her friend.

THINKING IT THROUGH

1. Why do you think people tell scary legends like "La Llorona"?
2. Legends are based on real people and real events. However, real events become legends because people who retell the story tell more than just the facts. Why do you think people make up new events and details that become part of the legend?
3. Can you explain the death of the old man in the story as a natural event not related to La Llorona? If so, explain how it could have happened.

Vocabulary and Sentence Meaning

Figurative Language

In the first paragraph of "La Llorona" you find this sentence: "In the bright moonlight the backs of the mountains shiver." Obviously, the words do not *really* mean what they seem to say. The sentence is an example of **figurative language.**

One way to write figuratively is to compare one thing to another. A **simile** (SIM uh lee) compares two things by using the words *like* or *as.* In "La Llorona," you read that the moonlight "dances like sparkling elves."

A **metaphor** (MET uh for) does the same thing a simile does, but it does not use *like* or *as.* This makes the comparison stronger than in a simile. Instead of saying something is *like* something else, you are saying it *is* something else: "The moonlight is sparkling elves."

Read the following sentences from "La Llorona." Each one contains a simile or a metaphor. On a separate sheet of paper, mark them *S* (simile) or *M* (metaphor).

1. A breeze lifts her hair and settles it gently like a scarf around her shoulders.
2. Then the woman moves, gliding silently like a mist.
3. Her words are icy fingers taking hold of the old man's heart.
4. He is her servant.
5. Like a cloud, she drifts beside the lake.

Composition

Follow your teacher's instructions before completing *one* of these writing assignments.

1. Rewrite each simile to make it a metaphor.
   EXAMPLE: His smile is like a sunburst. (simile)
   His smile is a sunburst. (metaphor)
   a. Her hair is like a scarf around her shoulders.
   b. I felt like a leaf in the wind while on my hang glider.
   c. The wind stung my face like a thousand bees.
2. In one or two paragraphs, write about a time you were scared. Maybe you had a scary dream or saw a scary movie.

THE THUNDERS

a myth of the Iroquois people
as told to Alice Marriott by Malinda Peacock

▶ The League of the Iroquois was a union of five Native American nations in New York State. The nations had many traditions in common. One custom was that they never prepared the ground for spring planting until after the first thunder. The myth of "The Thunders" was a way of explaining this custom. It also taught young Iroquois the values and beliefs of their people.

Long ago, three young men went hunting together. They were brother-friends, each promising to protect the lives of the others as if they were his own. When they were far from home, one of them tripped on a rock and broke his leg.

"Don't leave me, my friends," the injured one begged. "You know what we have promised each other. Help me to get home to my mother. She has no one else to take care of her."

So the two young men who weren't hurt helped him. But as they went on, the lame man grew heavier and heavier on his friends' shoulders. They stopped sometimes and laid him down so he could rest. Each time the three men stopped, the two who were not hurt were more tired. They looked at each other over their injured friend's head. With their eyes, the two agreed to a plan.

At last, as they trudged along a high ridge, the three came to a deep ravine. There the two who were not hurt carried out their plan. They swung their brother-friend over the edge of the ravine and dropped him. Leaving him there to die, the two men turned away and hurried home. They entered the village with tears streaming down their faces, weeping and mourning.

"Oh, our poor friend!" they wailed. "As we went through the woods, enemies attacked us. We fought them off, but a last stray arrow struck our brother, and he is dead."

- tradition (truh DISH un) **long-standing practice of a group**
- **ravine** (ruh VEEN) **deep valley**
- stray (STRAY) **off course**

"Oh, my son!" wept his mother. "How can I rest? If he had died at home, his people could have buried him. I would know his soul was safe."

"We buried him deep and safe," the friends assured her. "No ugly spirits can reach him. No wild animals can dig him up."

The mother was a little comforted then. As time went on, she stopped mourning outwardly, but her heart was always sore.

The young man lay unconscious at the bottom of the ravine for many hours. When he opened his eyes, he saw an old man sitting beside him. The old man's gray hair hung long and loose on his shoulders. There was something strange about him.

"How did you come here?" the old man asked. "You could not have walked with a broken leg."

"My friends dropped me over the edge," the young man replied. "How could they treat me like that? I trusted them. We were like brothers to each other. Yet they threw me away to die."

"Stay with me and do what I tell you, and you won't die," said the old man.

"What do you want me to do?" the young man asked.

"I need someone to hunt for me," the old man told him. Promise to stay here and bring me whatever animals you kill, and I will save your life."

"I promise," said the young man.

So the old man took care of the young man, and soon the young man could hunt again. All winter long he brought food to the old man. But when the warm winds of spring came, he felt sad. He worried about his mother. He wondered how he could get out of the ravine.

One day the young man saw huge footprints on the ground. He followed them, up the ravine walls, across the flats, to the edge of the deep woods. There he came upon the biggest bear he had ever seen. And with a single arrow, right in the heart, he killed it. Suddenly, he heard voices speaking behind him. He turned and saw four men, dressed in strange, cloudlike robes.

"Who are you?" the young man asked.

"We are the Thunders," the four cloud-figures answered. "We were put here on earth to help everybody—all the people—whoever

• **assure** (uh SHUR) make certain

is in need. If there are cruel people or mean animals, we destroy them. Now we are looking for the old man who lives in the deep ravine. He is a very bad man."

"I work for him," the hunter said. "He saved my life, so I do whatever he tells me to do.

"Are you happy with this life?" the Thunders asked.

"No," answered the young man. "I want to go back to my own people. My mother needs me."

"This old man is taking all of your food and leaving you as thin as an eel in the springtime," said the Thunders. "If you will help us against him, we will take you home."

"I will help," the young man promised.

"Then go back and tell the old man that the bear is too heavy for one man to carry. Ask him to help you."

The old man was angry because his servant had left the ravine, but he was delighted when he saw the big fat bear. Together they skinned it and cut it up, ready to take home. "Put it all on my shoulders," the old man ordered. "More! More! Pile it on! I can hardly wait to get home and eat this fat meat."

As they walked along, the old man worried about rain. "Do you see any clouds?" the old man asked. He was bent over under the burden he insisted on carrying and could not look up.

● burden (BUR dun) **heavy load**

Soon there was a cloud to the northeast, but the young man didn't say anything. The cloud grew nearer and nearer and larger and larger. Then it stopped before them and the Thunders stepped out of its folds. The old man dropped his load and started to run away. He turned himself into a giant porcupine, and shot poisoned quills backward at his enemies. But the Thunders turned the quills aside with their power. They followed him, throwing lightning bolts ahead of them. Just as the old man-porcupine reached his cave, the lightning struck him. He fell to the ground dead.

"That old man made servants of people," the Thunders said. "He wore them out and killed them."

"Thank you, thank you!" the young man exclaimed. "How can I ever show you how grateful I am?"

"Perhaps some day you will do something for us," the Thunders assured him. "A time will come when you can make your return."

They gave the young man a cloud robe like theirs to wear. They showed him how to move the wings fastened to its shoulders. The young man hurried home. He took off his cloud robe and hid it away. Then he ran to his mother's house.

The mother held out her arms to him as if he were a little boy again. And so they hugged each other and cried with happiness.

When the Thunders saw how happy the young man and his mother were, they were very pleased. "Our work is finished for this year," said the Thunders. "We will be back again, many times. Keep the cloud robe. When we come again you can travel with us. Perhaps you can help us with our work."

The mother took care of the garden, and the young man hunted and fished. They lived well and were happy. When people in the village asked the young man where he had been, he only told them that he had been away and had come back. He would not say even one unkind thing about his friends.

In the spring, the Thunders returned. "Come and fly with us, friend," they said.

So the young man put on his cloud robe and flew with the Thunders. They were looking for an enemy who hid in the ground. He was hard to find.

One day the young man dropped down to earth and drank from

• quill (KWIL) **hard, sharp-tipped hair**

a pool. When he rose again and rejoined the Thunders, they saw that his lips were coated with something shiny, like oil.

"How did you get that shine on your mouth?" the Thunders asked.

"I drank from that little pool down there," the young man said, and he showed the Thunders which pool it was.

"That is the place we have been looking for!" the Thunders exclaimed. "That's the pool where our enemy lives. Now, you see, you have made your return. You found our enemy for us."

The Thunders all worked together. They made a great bolt of lightning and hurled it into the pool. The lightning was so strong it blasted the pool open, and in the bottom of it there was a great grub. It was like the cutworms that chew down young plants in the gardens, but it was a thousand, thousand times as big.

"He's dead!" cried the young man.

"Yes," said the Thunders. "From now on, the spring lightning will kill all the grubs in your gardens. If people will turn the earth in the spring so the lightning can get to it, we will make it clean. Go home now and tell your people this."

The young man hurried home to take the message to all the people. From that time on, the people honored the Thunders and respected them. They never broke ground until after the first thunder came in the spring.

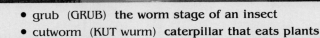

- grub (GRUB) **the worm stage of an insect**
- cutworm (KUT wurm) **caterpillar that eats plants**

ALL THINGS CONSIDERED ────────────────

1. The three young hunters are (a) brothers. (b) cousins. (c) very close friends.

2. One of the young men breaks his leg and (a) falls into a ravine. (b) is thrown into a ravine. (c) hides in a ravine.

3. The young man is saved by (a) an old man. (b) a bear. (c) his friends.

4. The young man (a) is paid by the old man. (b) is poisoned by the old man. (c) hunts for the old man.

5. The old man (a) makes people work for him. (b) feeds people to his animals. (c) locks people up in his cave.

6. The young man is saved by (a) his mother. (b) a bear. (c) the Thunders.

7. Back home, the young man (a) complains about his friends. (b) says nothing about his friends. (c) warns people about the old man.

8. The young man (a) tells the Thunders about his friends. (b) becomes the chief of his tribe. (c) flies with the Thunders.

9. The young man finds the giant grub, who is the (a) enemy of the Thunders. (b) one who makes the plants grow. (c) chief of the Thunders.

10. The young man (a) helps the Thunders plant in the spring. (b) takes the message of the Thunders to his people. (c) flies up to live in the sky.

THINKING IT THROUGH ────────────────

1. What does this myth try to explain? What does it say about the beliefs of the Iroquois people?

2. How are good actions rewarded in this myth? How are bad actions punished? Do you think the two friends should have been punished? Explain.

3. Do you feel that the myth is as important today as it was long ago? Why or why not?

Building From Details

Making Predictions

Are you good at making **predictions,** or guessing future events? We all make predictions, sometimes without knowing it. As we read, we predict what words and ideas will come next.

They were brother-friends, promising to care . . .

Did your mind predict the next word? Was it *for?* As you read a story, you should be asking questions. Here are some questions you might have asked while reading "The Thunders": Will the two brother-friends help the young man? Will the young man escape from the old man? How will the young man help the Thunders?

As you ask such questions about what will happen, your mind forms possible answers, or predictions. You continue reading to find out what the correct answers are. After finishing a story like "The Thunders," there are still some questions you might ask. So there are still some predictions you might make.

The following questions are about what happens after the end of "The Thunders." On a separate sheet of paper, write a prediction answering each question.

1. Will the young man continue to fly with the Thunders?
2. Will the two brother-friends feel bad for what they did to the young man? Will they be punished?
3. Will the Thunders ever defeat all their enemies in the world?

Composition

Follow your teacher's instructions before completing *one* of these writing assignments.

1. Write one or two sentences explaining some things young Iroquois would learn by listening to "The Thunders."
2. Make up a short myth about why you do a certain thing. Make the setting long ago. Briefly explain what caused your ancestors to start doing the particular thing that you still do today.

ECHO AND NARCISSUS

a Greek myth

adapted by Anne Terry White

▶ This Greek myth answers two questions: (1) Where do echoes come from? (2) Where does the flower called narcissus come from? To answer these two questions, two strange love stories are tied together into one story.

Of all the mountain nymphs, none was more charming than Echo. But she had one fault. She talked too much. It was chatter, chatter all day long. No matter what the topic, Echo always had the last word.

In Greek mythology, Zeus was the father of all gods, and Hera, his wife, was the mother of all gods. It happened that one day Hera became jealous. She thought Zeus was spending too much time with the nymphs. So Hera decided to punish the nymphs, and she came down to the mountainside to do so. All the nymphs fled like leaves before a gale—all except Echo. She stayed behind because she thought her voice could charm Hera and prevent her from chasing the other nymphs. It did, but Hera became furious. The mother goddess did not like being tricked by a nymph.

"You shall never get the chance to do that again," she told Echo. "That amusing tongue of yours shall lose its power. From now on it will never be able to start chattering. It will never do anything except the one thing you are so fond of—reply. Yes, indeed, you may have the last word, Echo. But that is all you will have! Never will you be able to speak *first!*"

Soon after this, Echo found out just how bad her punishment was. She fell in love. As luck would have it, she loved a young hunter who could not love anybody but himself. He was Narcissus, an exceptionally handsome youth. But he was as cold as he was handsome. No one could melt him.

- nymph (NIMF) **woodland goddess**
- **charming** (CHARM ing) **delightful**
- **mythology** (mi THOL uh jee) **collection of myths**
- **exceptionally** (ik SEP shun ul ee) **unusually**

Poor Echo trailed all over the mountains after Narcissus. How she longed to speak to him and win his love by gentle words! Alas, she did not have the power! Her words stayed locked up in her mind.

Then one day while Narcissus was hunting, it happened that he became separated from his companions.

"Who's here?" he shouted.

"Here!" Echo replied.

Narcissus looked around. He could see no one.

"Come!" he called.

Echo's answer shot back: "Come!"

Narcissus waited, but no one came. He called again, "Why do you not hear me?"

"Hear me!" Echo cried.

"Let us meet!" Narcissus called.

"Let us meet!" This time Echo's words danced back to him. And she ran to the spot, arms upraised and ready to throw around his neck.

Narcissus started back. "Do not touch me!" he cried. "I would rather die than have you love me."

"Love me!" Echo pleaded, but it was useless. The young man turned and left. Poor Echo remained, her heart broken.

Echo never showed herself again. Caves and mountain cliffs became her home. Her body wasted away with grief and longing until her flesh was gone. Her bones became rocks. Nothing was left of her but her sad voice. And her voice is still heard, as you know, for she still replies to anyone who calls.

Cruel Narcissus! Echo was not the only one whose heart he broke. But at last he got what he deserved. A maiden whom he had rejected asked the goddess of vengeance to take her part.

"Oh, may the time come," the girl prayed, "when Narcissus will feel what it is to love and get no love in return."

And the goddess heard . . . .

In the hills there was a most unusual spring. For some reason, shepherds never brought their flocks there. Neither did mountain goats nor any beasts of the forest ever drink from it. Fresh green grass grew all around, and rocks sheltered the spring from the sun. The water in the pool was as clear as polished silver. Not a dead branch, not a dead leaf polluted it.

- **vengeance** (VEN juns) **revenge**
- pollute (puh LOOT) **make dirty**

257

To this pool one day Narcissus came. Worn out with hunting, he was hot and thirsty. He stooped down to drink—and saw his lovely image in the water.

"It is the water-spirit," he thought, for he had never seen his own reflection before. Enchanted, he knelt down to look and could not tear his eyes away. He bent close and stretched out his arms to clasp the lovely being. At his touch the image dissolved into a thousand ripples. But even as he watched, it came back as clear as before.

"Beautiful being," Narcissus said, "why do you flee from me? Surely my face cannot displease you. Every nymph of the mountains is in love with me. You yourself look as if you feel exactly as I do. Your smile answers mine. When I stretch out my arms to you, you do the same. But then—"

Tears of longing rolled down his cheeks and splashed into the silver pool. At once the image fled again.

"Stay, oh, stay!" he pleaded. "If I may not touch you, let me at least gaze upon you!"

He was unable to tear himself away. Day after day he hung over the water, his eyes feasting on his own reflection. Love, which he had so often scorned, now consumed him. He lost his color and was no more than a pale image of himself. All he could do was sigh, "Alas! Alas!"

And Echo answered him, "Alas!"

- **enchanted** (en CHANT id) under a charm
- longing (LONG ing) great desire
- consume (kun SOOM) use up; eat or drink up; destroy

258

At last Narcissus faded away altogether and passed from the upper world. The nymphs who had given their hearts to him heaped wood into a funeral pile and would have burned his body, as the custom was. But his remains were nowhere to be found. Only a wax-white flower with a purple heart stood in the place where he had knelt and sighed. And to this flower the grieving maidens gave his name—Narcissus.

ALL THINGS CONSIDERED

1. Echo's problem is (a) talking too much. (b) being too shy. (c) always falling in love.
2. Hera punishes Echo because Echo has (a) fooled her. (b) bored her. (c) fallen in love with Narcissus.
3. Because of her punishment, Echo can only (a) whisper. (b) sing. (c) reply.
4. Narcissus rejects (a) Hera. (b) his own image. (c) Echo.
5. Echo wastes away until (a) she dies. (b) only her voice is left. (c) Hera ends her punishment.
6. Narcissus is punished by (a) a maiden. (b) Echo. (c) the goddess of vengeance.
7. Narcissus falls in love with (a) Echo. (b) the goddess of vengeance. (c) his own reflection.
8. When Narcissus reaches for his image, it (a) cries. (b) dissolves. (c) laughs.
9. Because his love is not returned, Narcissus (a) fights the goddess of vengeance. (b) fades away. (c) asks the goddess for help.
10. Narcissus becomes (a) a flower. (b) Echo's friend. (c) a mountain spring.

THINKING IT THROUGH

1. Reread the two questions asked in the introduction to this myth. The answers to these questions will help you find the themes of the myth. State these themes in your own words. Do other students agree with you?
2. What happens to Narcissus could serve as a lesson for a reader. What is this lesson? Do you agree with this lesson?
3. Echo and Narcissus had just about equal punishments. Did they deserve equal punishments? Why or why not?

Literary Skills

Topic and Theme

Writers always write about something. This "something" is the **topic.** "Echo and Narcissus" is really two myths combined into one. One tells of a nymph and explains echoes. The other tells of a young hunter and explains the narcissus flower. Both, however, have a topic in common—the topic of love.

The **theme** is what the writer says about the topic. It is the message—the meaning—that the writer hopes to give the reader. The theme in many stories is not directly stated. Readers may see the overall meaning in different ways. Sometimes people even disagree about the theme of a story. The theme of the Echo part of the myth can be stated like this: Love that is unreturned wastes away. In Echo's case, only a sad, lonely cry was left of her and her love.

What is the theme of the Narcissus part of this myth? Choose the best answer:
a. Being beautiful is a problem.
b. Love is not important.
c. It is wrong to love only yourself.
d. The narcissus is a beautiful flower.

Composition

Follow your teacher's instructions before completing *one* of these writing assignments.

1. Write the title of another story you read in this book. Then write a sentence telling the topic and another sentence telling the theme.

2. Imagine what would have happened if Zeus met Echo after she was punished by Hera. Write the story of this meeting. How does Echo explain what happened? What is Zeus's reaction? What does he do?

VOCABULARY AND SKILL REVIEW

Before completing the exercises that follow, you may wish to review the **bold-faced** words on pages 242 to 258.

I. On a separate sheet of paper, write the *italicized* term that best fills the blank in each sentence.

legends	*myth*	*mythology*	*assured*	*vengeance*
mournful	*ravine*	*piercing*	*charm*	*enchanted*

1. Stories that often are based on real people or events are _____.
2. A story that explains a culture's belief is called a _____.
3. Greek gods tried to get _____ after they had been wronged.
4. Many stories about gods make up Greek _____.
5. My parents _____ me that the bicycle would soon be mine.
6. Martha seemed to be _____ by the beautiful music.
7. The _____ was so deep you could not see to the bottom.
8. The family was _____ at the funeral.
9. The owl's screech is a _____ sound.
10. Thomas tried to _____ the audience with his smile.

II. Read each of the following sentences. On a separate sheet of paper, write *S* if the sentence contains a simile. Write *M* if the sentence contains a metaphor.

1. The big chair was like a throne on which my father sat.
2. The children were little mice sneaking up to the gifts.
3. Her hair lay plastered to her head like a bathing cap.
4. The dancer's arms were wings as she glided through the air.
5. His temper was a hot furnace ready to explode.
6. The silence washed over him like a wave.
7. The picture on the wall danced before his eyes.
8. The apple in the woman's hand looked like a big ruby.
9. Her singing made people float on clouds.
10. The girl's mind worked like a computer.

HOUSE FEAR

by Robert Frost

▶ It's dark and you've returned home to an empty house. Or is it empty?

Always—I tell you this they learned—
Always at night when they returned
To the lonely house from far away
To lamps unlighted and fire gone gray,
They learned to rattle the lock and key
To give whatever might chance to be
Warning and time to be off in flight:
And preferring the out- to the in-door night
They learned to leave the house door wide
Until they had lit the lamp inside.

NOT ME

by Shel Silverstein

▶ The bad things always happen to someone else, not you. Isn't that right?

The Slithergadee crawled out of the sea.
He may catch all the others, but he won't catch me.
No you won't catch me, old Slithergadee,
You may catch all the others, but you wo——

WAYS OF KNOWING

1. Why do the people in "House Fear" rattle the lock and key? What are they afraid they might find in the house?
2. Is the "Slithergadee" in "Not Me" real or imaginary? Why do you think the speaker is interrupted at the end?
3. How are the topics of the two poems similar? What is different about the way the two authors deal with their topics?

NINTH STREET BRIDGE

by Bill Cosby

▶ Sometimes our imaginations can get out of control. Then a normal situation can turn into something totally different. Find out what happened to Bill Cosby when his imagination was too powerful.

Old Weird Harold and I—Old Weird Harold, we called him that because he was six feet nine and weighed 50 pounds—we used to go to every horror picture in the world.

I'm telling you right now, we would go and we would see Frankenstein. We'd walk 100 miles to see Frankenstein.

And mind you, we never saw the monster once, never saw him once, 'cause we were too scared to look at him. And we had the best seats in the movie. We used to sit right up front. I mean right up front.

That's where you can see everything. You just look right up front there. And we'd say to each other, "You gonna look at the monster this time?"

"Yeah, yeah,"

"Now, don't lie now. If you're not gonna look at him, say that. You might as well get right on the floor now, if you're not gonna look at him. You didn't look at him the last time."

"Yes, I did."

"Don't lie. Look out now!"

That's the way we stayed for 12 days; used to come home with 100 black juji-fruits all on our backs.

We used to stay over and over trying to get to see the monster. But we couldn't do it, we were too scared.

And my mother used to come for us. "Will you come home? Get up off the floor and come home!"

You know, and the guys would razz us. "Hey, Cos, your mom came for you again. Ha ha ha!"

"You shut up!"

So my mother says one day, she says, "I'm not comin' for you.

• razz (RAZ) **make fun of**

That's all. You come home yourself. Walk under the Ninth Street Bridge by yourself in the dark, if you don't know how to come home."

"Aw, Mom, you'll come for us."

So, we were watching this one picture.

It was a heck of a picture. It was one of the greatest.

They had Frankenstein, Wolfman, Dracula, the Hunchback, the Mummy—everybody was in it.

And Harold and I stayed on that floor. Our eyes were closed. We never came up one time for air. Every time there was somebody on that screen, we didn't want to see. "The Mummy's on there now! We don't want to look. We don't want to look!"

And we sat through about 12 showings of the same picture.

"You gonna look this time?"

"No."

"Get up off the floor."

"No, I ain't gettin' up nowhere. He ain't gonna get me."

So, finally, during the cartoon, I got up and looked around and I said, "Hey, Harold, there's nothin' here but grown-ups."

And Harold says, "Yeah." 'Cause that's what he always says whenever I'm right. He's my closest friend, you know.

I said, "Ask that man what time it is."

"Hey, Mister! What time is it?"

"It's ten o'clock."

"Oh, Harold. Oh, Harold, we're in trouble. Ten o'clock, yeah. Ten o'clock, that's when the monsters come out and my mom didn't even come for us."

"Well, she said she wasn't."

"Yeah, but she supposed to come for us. She isn't supposed to let us walk home at ten o'clock when all the monsters come out and everything."

And we walk out of the movie crying.

Now, the walk home.

Ninth Street Bridge has no lights whatsoever, which is the only way to get home.

And we are *sick*. You talk about two scared kids just walking arm in arm, not even picking our feet up off the ground 'cause we want to be ready, if the monster touches us. We want to be ready to jump straight up to heaven.

When you pick one leg up, you take a chance on going sideways. You know. And we got our legs ready, sending our toes out six feet ahead of us like radar. *Too-doodle-poo-doo, too-doodle-doo, kids coming, too-doodle-doo, kids coming.*

And I'm telling you, really scared, ready to go any second. And I bumped into Harold. *Bump!*

I said, "Harold, did I bump into you?"

Harold said, "No."

I said, "Don't lie to me now, Harold. If I bumped into you, say that I bumped into you. Even if I didn't bump into you, *say* that I bumped into you. Because if I didn't, we're gonna get eaten alive. You know that, don't you?"

Harold says, "Well, you bumped into me."

I said, "Okay. Don't lie anymore."

Now, I don't know the name of the wino that came out of the alley that emptied onto the Ninth Street Bridge. I don't even *care* what the guy's name is, man.

All I know is, he was wrong. That's all I can say.

He was puredee wrong. You just don't walk out of an alley that empties onto Ninth Street Bridge without making some sort of an announcement, warning to little kids: "Look out, little kids coming home from the Astor movie after seeing a whole lot of horror monsters. This is nobody that can hurt you. It's just a little old wino."

And he came out. *B-b-b-l-l-aa-am-m!!!*

Now, I'm sure after filling out the accident report on this man, that the doctor said, "What happened?"

"I don't know. It was just four feet ran right up my chest, danced on my head for a half hour, and then ran straight down my back, doctor."

"But did they say anything?"

"Yes, they said, 'Aa-a-a-hh-h!!!!!!!'"

"Did you see them at all?"

"Yes, it was a little kid riding on top of a tall, skinny one, and he was beating him with a stick, saying, 'Faster, faster, you fool, you fool!'"

ALL THINGS CONSIDERED ───────────────

1. Cosby and Weird Harold loved (a) all movies. (b) horror movies. (c) cartoons.

2. They wanted to see the movie, but they were afraid (a) to go. (b) to watch. (c) of other kids there.

3. Cosby's mother (a) wouldn't let them go to the movies. (b) took them to the movies. (c) came to get them after the movies were over.

4. Cosby and Harold were afraid to (a) walk under the Ninth Street Bridge. (b) ride over the Ninth Street Bridge. (c) cross the Ninth Street Bridge because of traffic.

5. One time they (a) watched the movie on television. (b) told Cosby's mother they would walk home alone. (c) stayed at the movie until ten o'clock.

6. The boys knew it was late because (a) Harold had a watch. (b) the only people in the movie were adults. (c) the usher told them.

7. They thought that at ten o'clock (a) they would watch the movie. (b) the monsters came out. (c) the movie would be over.

8. As they walked, they kept their feet on the ground to (a) make noise. (b) be ready to run if the monster touched them. (c) keep from falling.

9. Under the bridge, an old man came out of an alley and (a) they bumped into him. (b) Harold ran back to the movie. (c) Cosby fainted.

10. What happened after the collision is told through the eyes of (a) Cosby. (b) Weird Harold. (c) the old man.

THINKING IT THROUGH

1. Cosby uses *exaggeration* to make the story funnier. List five examples of exaggeration in the story.
2. Can you relate Cosby's experience to any of your experiences?
3. How do people's fears change with age and with experience? Give examples.

Oral Interpretation

Performing a Monologue

Bill Cosby has told "Ninth Street Bridge" to many audiences. The piece is a **monologue** (MON uh lawg), or a talk by one person. Read the selection imagining Cosby in front of an audience and hearing the way he might say the words.

Think about how *you* would perform this monologue. What type of voice would you use when Cosby's mother is speaking? What kind of voice would you use when the boys talk together in the movie? What kind of voice would you use for the boys when they are walking home? And at the end, how do you think the old man would sound?

Practice reading the selection by yourself—in front of a mirror, if possible. You'll find it gets to be a lot of fun.

Composition

Follow your teacher's instructions before completing *one* of these writing assignments.

1. Write three sentences telling about a time when your imagination built something up to be greater than it was.
2. Write a *funny* monologue about a time when your imagination tricked you. If other people were involved, include their reactions. See if you can use exaggeration as Bill Cosby did. For example, "The wall I had jumped over seemed 100 feet high."

PLAYMATE

by Leslie Croutch

▶ Father and Mother and Bobby are living quiet, ordinary lives. Then Bobby brings home a new playmate, and something extraordinary happens.

I was in the kitchen when Bobby came bouncing through the door, letting the screen bang. Without even seeming to breathe, he asked, "Hey, Mom, can I have Rickie over for supper tonight?"

Betts paused as she was about to pop a pie into the oven.

"Who's Rickie, dear?" she asked.

Bobby, slyly helping himself to a cookie, answered carelessly, "He's the new boy who moved in next door, Mom."

"Is he a nice boy?"

"Sure he's a nice boy." I sensed the scorn in Bobby's voice.

"What's he like, son?" I asked.

"Oh, I dunno—he's—well, he's just different."

We let it go at that.

It was comfortable on the porch. There was a small breeze blowing. I was sitting there, feet up on the rail, half asleep. Betts came out and picked up a magazine. Only the slight sound of her flipping the pages disturbed the peace of a hot summer afternoon.

"Hey, Mom! Where's the oil can?"

Bobby came tearing around the side of the house, yelling his request in an impatient tone. He mounted the steps and asked again before we had had a chance to answer.

"I think there's one in the cupboard under the kitchen sink." I supplied the information.

"Got to be thin oil," he said.

I grinned. "Three-in-one. Is that thin enough?"

He pushed through his hair with a grimy hand. "I guess so. Rickie needs it."

Betts smiled. "What does Rickie need it for?" she asked.

His voice came back to us as he vanished into the house.

"It's for Rickie. *He squeaks!*"

Later I went to the garage, which doubled as my workshop. I thought I might tidy up a little.

I was working, shirt sleeves rolled up, when I heard voices. It was Bobby, and apparently he had brought Rickie with him.

"Pop's got a bench back here. We can fix you there, maybe," I heard him say.

I grinned. I found Bobby's odd use of words amusing. I wondered, briefly, what might be broken.

I was bending down for a rake when I heard Rickie speak.

• **scorn** (SKORN) look down upon

"Heck, no," Rickie exclaimed. "Not that one. It's too large."

"No, it's not," Bobby's voice replied.

"It is too. It'll stick out and get in the way."

"Pop uses bolts that are too long. He cuts 'em off and polishes the end."

"Well—maybe. All right. Be careful though. I won't be able to pick anything up if it isn't just right."

Then I heard the various tiny clickings of tools in use. Then the thin rasp of a hacksaw.

I didn't believe in interfering with the activities of boys at play. I went on with my work and quickly forgot the incident.

The roast certainly smelled good. But then, Betts is a wonderful cook. She carried it to the table.

"Where's Bobby?" she asked, setting it down.

"Oh, somewhere about. Down in the basement, I think."

"Will you call him, dear?"

I did, and soon I could hear his footsteps and those of his new friend clattering up the stairs. The faucet went on, splatteringly.

"Get another towel, Bobby," Betts called.

"Phooey!" Bobby answered. "Only need one. Rickie doesn't wash!"

Betts frowned and headed toward the kitchen.

"Oh, dear," I heard a second later.

When I turned, she was standing at the table, a funny look on her face. It wasn't a frightened one. It was sort of amazed—speechless. She looked at me and gave the strangest shrug.

Then Bobby and his friend came in.

I had carved the roast and was passing the plates before I got a chance to look closely at the new boy. I'd thought there was something a little out of the ordinary about him when he had come in. His walk had been rather stiff, as though his knees wouldn't bend properly.

When I saw his face I was astounded. Never had I seen one like it before.

It had human lines, yes. The texture of the skin appeared normal, only there was a hardness, a harshness, that was altogether alien. That is the only term I can use—alien. The mouth opened, but it wasn't soft like a human mouth. It was supposed to be that, I know, but it was something else.

I watched him as we ate. He drank his milk as Bobby did, only differently. That is, he didn't seem to swallow it, he just appeared to pour it down. He'd place the glass to his lips, tip it, and the fluid would pour down, steadily, quickly, and the whole glassful would disappear in one smooth flow.

Exactly as though he didn't have to swallow, I thought to myself.

He didn't chew his food, either, as far as I could see. He didn't place the food in his mouth, move his jaws, and pause

- **astound** (uh STOUND) amaze; greatly surprise
- **texture** (TEKS chur) smoothness or hardness
- alien (AYL yun) foreign; strange

269

now and then. He fed himself like a machine. He ate each piece of meat, each forkful of potatoes, each bite of bread with the evenly spaced movements of a machine. And this went on until his plate was empty. There was not the slightest sign of hesitation.

It may seem I was a very imperfect host to have watched a guest in such a fashion. But I think that if you had just met Rickie, you would have watched him too.

When the main course was finished, we had ice cream. This I have to eat with some care, as the cold hurts my teeth. Betts can eat ice cream without a thought in the world. But even she doesn't gulp it the way Rickie did. He shoveled it in the way you'd shovel dirt into a wheelbarrow.

Finally the meal was over. Bobby was impatient to get away. His friend seemed just as eager. As they left the room, I again noted his stiff, yet somehow graceful stride.

I looked at Betts. She was staring at me with eyes big and round.

"What's the matter, dear?" I asked.

"That boy. He isn't normal."

"That's putting it mildly," I told her.

"Oh, I know what you mean. The way he eats. But that isn't all."

I lifted my eyebrows.

"When I went to the kitchen to see about his washing up, what do you think I saw? I saw him oiling himself!"

I opened the newspaper. After a full meal, I like to relax a bit.

"Did you hear me?" she went on. "I said he was oiling himself!"

"Oh, sure, he was oiling himself. What's wrong with that?"

I stood and began to clear the table. Then the meaning of her words struck me. I did a quick double-take. "He was—*what?*"

- **hesitation** (hez i TAY shun) a short delay; a pause
- **double-take** (DUB ul TAYK) delayed reaction to a startling event or statement

"Oiling himself."

"Are you sure? Maybe you ate too much—maybe the heat—"

"Heat, nothing. He was leaning against the table. He had a can of oil, and he was squirting it in his hands and rubbing it on his neck and wrists."

I sat down and stared at her.

"I'm just telling you what I saw," she said.

I rose. "Come on. We'll find Rickie and get to the bottom of this."

The boys were building something in the back yard. It looked like a house. They had two or three old piano crates and some scrap lumber from the garage. They were nailing it all together.

Bobby was busily banging away with a hammer. I imagined the nails he was wasting, with his habit of using ten where one or two would do. I could hear his friend hammering away on the other side, out of sight.

"How're you doin', Rickie?" Bobby yelled as we came up.

"Fine," Rickie replied.

"Are you using the hammer?"

"Nope. It's faster without."

"Doesn't it hurt your hand?"

"Nope."

"I wish I could drive nails with my hand."

"It's easy. You just double up your fist and give the nail a whack on the head—"

We didn't hear the rest. We moved around the packing cases and stared.

Rickie was standing there, nails sticking out of his mouth. He'd take one in his

left hand, hold it to the wood, and bang! bring his fist down on it and drive it home. No hammer—no nothing. Just his bare hand doubled into a fist. He was driving those nails home with the regularity of a machine.

Betts turned and ran into the house. When I caught up with her we held a consultation. Then we went over to our new neighbors—the Robesons—and knocked on the door. I think we half expected some strange creature to answer. But the door opened, and we saw a perfectly ordinary-looking woman.

We introduced ourselves. "We live next door—" I began.

"Oh!" She seemed to be expecting us.

"Please come in."

• consultation (kon sul TAY shun) conference; meeting

271

She led us into a nicely furnished front room and called to her husband.

Upon seeing us, he drew in his breath. I could see lines of weariness about his mouth.

"We've been sort of expecting you," he said, sitting down. "But not so soon."

My eyebrows raised.

"I guess," he patted his wife's hand where it rested on his shoulder, "I guess you've met our son."

"Yes," Betts answered. "Our little boy had him to our home for supper."

Mrs. Robeson sat down and started to wring her hands.

"Oh, dear. So now you know! We've had to move so often—people just can't understand."

I started to feel uncomfortable. I ran my finger around inside my collar. Maybe we should have left well enough alone.

"Oh, I'm so sorry," Betts said. "But really, he seems to be such a nice boy. He is so quiet and well mannered. We—er—" she stumbled.

"Yes, I know just what you mean," Mr. Robeson said and rose to his feet. He paced up and down the small room. "You can imagine what we feel like, living with him for almost seven years. Even we know very little about him."

"Perhaps a doctor—" I muttered and was sorry immediately.

"Doctor!" He smiled slightly. "I had the same idea a long time ago. We took him to the best and found out nothing. After looking him over for a time, they wanted to put him on display before other scientists. They wanted to experiment on him. We could't allow that. After all, he *is* our son."

"He was born to us in a normal way," Mrs. Robeson took up. "He seems to grow. But we don't understand how. Nothing seems to hurt him. He never gets cut. He's never been ill, and he eats anything he wants."

Robeson laughed, somewhat bitterly. "Don't forget the oil, my dear."

She smiled. "Oh, yes, the oil. I forgot—if he doesn't oil himself quite frequently, especially during wet weather, he stiffens up so that he can hardly move. He doesn't need as much as he used to, though."

"No, not since he started eating more fats and oily foods," her husband added.

"What did the doctors say?" I asked.

"Oh, they used a lot of long words that meant nothing to us. What it all boiled down to was that they didn't know either."

"But haven't you any idea of what he might—er—be, or what might be the matter with him?"

Mr. Robeson shook his head. "There is nothing wrong with him. If anything, he is too perfect. Consider that he has never been ill. He never has a cold. He never has any pains. Apparently he can't be hurt. He can't be shocked, I know that. I've seen him do things around electricity that would kill an ordinary person. He is strong. His flesh seems too hard to give.

• **bitterly** (BIT ur lee) **with hurt feelings**

Why, I've seen him drive nails with his fists. He is smart. He's a regular prodigy. So you tell me what is wrong with him!"

He stopped. Running his fingers through his hair, he suddenly smiled.

"I'm sorry. Guess you think I'm a little nuts. But we've had to move a lot of times just because people got nosy and started saying things. It bothers a person after a while."

I figured it was time to leave.

"Don't worry about it," I said as I shook hands with him at the door. "We won't say anything. We have a son, too, you know, so we understand. Our boy seems to like him, and that's enough for us."

That night, at bedtime, Betts and I went in to say goodnight to Bobby. He was sitting up, looking out of the window at the moon. It was big and silvery, just coming up out of the east.

He turned as we entered.

"What are you thinking about, son?" I asked, mussing his hair.

"I was just thinking about Rickie, Pop."

"And what about Rickie?" Betts asked.

He looked at us, his eyes big, his face a little sad.

"I was thinking how Rickie was so lucky. He can't ever get hurt, or be sick. He told me today he won't die for hundreds and hundreds of years because he's not like us. He's got no tonsils to get sore. His teeth won't ever get bad. He knows millions and millions of things I don't know. Oh, he's awfully lucky and awfully smart, Pop. I wish I could be like him."

- prodigy (PROD i jee) **young person with great talent or ability**

"What is he like, Bobby?" I asked.

He looked thoughtful. "I guess I can tell you," he said. "He asked me not to tell people, but I guess it's all right to tell you and Mom. It *is* all right, isn't it, Pop?"

"If you think it is, son," I said. "If you feel it's all right, then it's all right."

He thought this over. Finally he sighed.

"Well," he began, "Rickie hasn't got insides like us, Pop. He's different. He says he's got wires and plastic and water— only it isn't water, it's all kinds of colors— instead of blood. He doesn't have to eat, but he says he likes to because he likes the taste of things."

I felt Betts's hand close over mine and grip tight. Was this another childish game, another bit of make-believe?

"Rickie says he can tell only some kinds of kids about himself, because he says most kids are like grown-ups. They don't believe him. They think he is crazy and try to shut him up. But he says some kids are different, and those he can tell. He says when they grow up, they will be his friends. Then he won't be alone. Then he can do things for people with their help."

"Are there others like—well, like Rickie?" I heard Betts ask.

"Oh, yes. Rickie says there are lots more. He says he knows ten right in this city."

"How did he meet them?" I asked.

"He didn't meet them!" was the somewhat surprising response. "Rickie doesn't have to meet them. He says he just thinks, and one of them thinks back at him. They just talk—inside here," he touched his forehead. "He says when he gets bigger, he can think longer and meet more like him. But he says he knows there are lots more like him because sometimes he dreams about them."

Bobby lay down. Facing the moon, he said, "I wish I were like Rickie. Then I could do all kinds of wonderful things. Rickie says when he gets big he will rule the world, and he and his people will not let there be any more war or let people kill each other or be bad. Gee, Pop, why can't I be like him?"

His eyes closed. We waited for a few moments. Then we left the room and closed the door softly behind us.

In the hall we stood silently looking at each other.

"What do you think?" Betts asked.

"I don't know, Betts. If it's all made up, then the answer is simple. If he's right, then somewhere a new kind of humanity is springing up. What is creating it I don't know. And whether it is good or bad is equally uncertain."

She sighed. "I prefer to think it's just a game he is playing?"

. . . But as I lay in bed that night I wondered. And in the many nights since then I've begun to worry. It's not that I'm afraid. Or maybe I am—I don't know. It's the uncertainty. The fear of something you cannot understand—something you know you are powerless to stop.

You see, Rickie continues to play with Bobby. Just the other day I saw them by the garage. They were building something. And Bobby was pounding the nails in with his fist. . . .

ALL THINGS CONSIDERED ─────────────

1. This story is told by (a) Bobby. (b) Bobby's mother. (c) Bobby's father.
2. Bobby is probably about (a) four years old. (b) eight years old. (c) sixteen years old.
3. To help Rickie, Bobby needs (a) water. (b) medicine. (c) oil.
4. Rickie also needed a new (a) eye. (b) bolt. (c) watch.
5. Instead of washing, Rickie (a) oils himself. (b) goes swimming. (c) hides his hands.
6. When Rickie drinks milk, he (a) gets sick. (b) doesn't swallow. (c) spills it.
7. Rickie hammers nails with (a) his fist. (b) a rock. (c) a hammer.
8. The Robesons have had to move because of (a) Mrs. Robeson's health. (b) Mr. Robeson's job. (c) Rickie.
9. Rickie began his life as (a) an adult. (b) a normal baby. (c) a machine.
10. At the end of the story, Bobby seems to be (a) becoming like Rickie. (b) helping Rickie become human. (c) turning against his parents.

THINKING IT THROUGH ─────────────

1. What are the first clues that suggest Rickie is not quite human?
2. Bobby accepts Rickie without asking any questions. Why do you think he is so accepting when his parents are so suspicious?
3. Are there other people like Rickie in the city where he and Bobby live? If so, does Rickie know these people? Explain your answer.
4. Bobby says that Rickie knows "millions and millions of things I don't know." How do you think Rickie learned these things?
5. What do you think Rickie will be like when he grows up? Will he be a good influence on the world? Or, will he be a danger? Give reasons for your answer.

Literary Skills

Author's Purpose

Every writer has a **purpose,** or a reason for writing. The writer has an audience of readers. The writer wants to affect the audience in some way.

There are three general types of author's purpose:

- To explain or teach

- To persuade or prove a point

- To entertain

Think about Bill Cosby's story, "Ninth Street Bridge." The purpose of the story is to entertain. There is some explaining in the story, but it is used only to let the audience see the action better.

"Playmate" is also entertaining. But there is another purpose, one that is common to science fiction stories. The author is trying to explain or teach about possibilities in the future. The story makes the reader think about ideas that are out of the ordinary.

What would be the author's main purpose for writing the following?

1. A letter to the mayor about an issue
2. A magazine article about a writer's travels in a foreign country
3. A "how-to" book on home repair

Composition

Follow your teacher's instructions before completing *one* of these writing assignments.

1. Imagine you are Rickie. Write a paragraph explaining how you can pound a nail into wood with your hand. Tell about other things you can do that most people cannot.
2. If you were Bobby's parents, what would you do about Rickie? Write a letter to the editor to persuade your neighbors to (a) do something about Rickie, or (b) leave the Robesons alone.

Isaac Asimov (Born 1920)

Isaac Asimov saw his first science fiction magazine in his father's store in Brooklyn. Young Isaac had to convince his father to let him read the magazine. His father finally agreed. Ever since then, Isaac Asimov has been fascinated by science fiction and science fact.

Asimov has written more than 250 books, most of them on science. When he writes about science fact, he calls himself "an explainer." He is one of the best at explaining science to the everyday reader. When he writes science fiction, he is one of the most imaginative and popular writers we have.

Asimov's interests and talents also go beyond science. He has written books on literary classics and on the Bible. He has written mysteries and books for young people.

How can Asimov do all these things? Aside from an eager mind that questions everything, he likes to work. He writes 12 hours a day, types 90 words per minute, and rarely takes a day off. This is why he has averaged a book every six weeks since 1950.

However, long hours and fast typing do not tell the whole story. Asimov's books are successful because they touch their readers in a special way. When Asimov describes a scene, you can really see it. You can really tell what his characters are like. And his science fiction always seems real.

THE FUN THEY HAD

▶ In the twenty-second century everything will be different—even school. There will be electronic teachers and telebooks, and school buildings might no longer exist. But will school be more fun than today? The opinion of the future students in this story might surprise you.

Margie even wrote about it that night in her diary. On the page headed May 17, 2157, she wrote, "Today Tommy found a real book!"

It was a very old book. Margie's grandfather once said that when he was a little boy *his* grandfather told him that there was a time when all stories were printed on paper.

They turned the pages, which were yellow and crinkly, and it was awfully funny to read words that stood still instead of moving the way they were supposed to—on a screen, you know. And then, when they turned back to the page before, it had the same words on it that it had had when they read it the first time.

"Gee," said Tommy, "what a waste. When you're through with the book, you just throw it away, I guess. Our television screen must have had a million books on it and it's good for plenty more. I wouldn't throw *it* away."

"Same with mine," said Margie. She was 11 and hadn't seen as many telebooks as Tommy had. He was 13.

She said, "Where did you find it?"

"In my house." He pointed without looking, because he was busy reading. "In the attic."

"What's it about?"

"School."

Margie was scornful. "School? What's there to write about school? I hate school."

Margie always hated school, but now she hated it more than ever. The mechanical teacher had been giving her test after test in geography and she had been doing worse and worse until her mother had shaken her head sorrowfully and sent for the County Inspector.

He was a round little man with a red face and a whole box of tools with dials and wires. He smiled at Margie and gave her an apple, then took the teacher apart. Margie had hoped he wouldn't know how to put it together again, but he knew how all right, and, after an hour or so, there it was again, large and black and ugly, with a big screen on which all the lessons were shown and the questions were asked. That wasn't so bad. The part Margie hated most was the slot where she had to put homework and test papers. She always had to write them out in a punch code they made her learn when she was six years old, and the mechanical teacher figured the mark in no time.

The Inspector had smiled after he was finished and patted Margie's head. He said to her mother, "It's not the little girl's fault, Mrs. Jones. I think the geography sector was geared a little too quick. Those things happen sometimes. I've slowed it up to the ten-year level. Actually, the over-all pattern of her progress is quite satisfactory." And he patted Margie's head again.

Margie was disappointed. She had been hoping they would take the teacher away altogether. They had once taken Tommy's teacher

away for nearly a month because the history sector had blanked out completely.

So she said to Tommy, "Why would anyone write about school?"

Tommy looked at her with very superior eyes. "Because it's not our kind of school, stupid. This is the old kind of school that they had hundreds and hundreds of years ago." He added loftily, pronouncing the word carefully, "*Centuries* ago."

Margie was hurt. "Well, I don't know what kind of school they had all that time ago." She read the book over his shoulder for a while, then said, "Anyway, they had a teacher."

"Sure they had a teacher, but it wasn't a *regular* teacher. It was a man."

"A man? How could a man be a teacher?"

"Well, he just told the boys and girls things and gave them homework and asked them questions."

"A man isn't smart enough."

"Sure he is. My father knows as much as my teacher."

"He can't. A man can't know as much as a teacher."

"He knows almost as much, I betcha."

Margie wasn't prepared to dispute that. She said, "I wouldn't want a strange man in my house to teach me."

Tommy screamed with laughter. "You don't know much, Margie. The teachers didn't live in the house. They had a special building and all the kids went there."

"And all the kids learned the same thing?"

"Sure, if they were the same age."

"But my mother says a teacher has to be adjusted to fit the mind of each boy and girl it teaches and that each kid has to be taught differently."

"Just the same they didn't do it that way then. If you don't like it, you don't have to read the book."

"I didn't say I didn't like it," Margie said quickly. She wanted to read about those funny schools.

They weren't even half-finished when Margie's mother called, "Margie! School!"

Margie looked up. "Not yet, Mamma."

- sector (SEK tur) **part**
- superior (suh PEER ee ur) **being better than**
- loftily (LOF tuh lee) **in an impressive manner**

"Now!" said Mrs. Jones. "And it's probably time for Tommy, too."

Margie said to Tommy, "Can I read the book some more with you after school?"

"Maybe," he said. He walked away whistling, the dusty old book tucked beneath his arm.

Margie went into the schoolroom. It was right next to her bedroom, and the mechanical teacher was on and waiting for her. It was always on at the same time every day except Saturday and Sunday. Her mother said little girls learned better if they learned at regular hours.

The screen was lit up, and it said: "Today's arithmetic lesson is on the addition of proper fractions. Please insert yesterday's homework in the proper slot."

Margie did so with a sigh. She was thinking about the old schools they had when her grandfather's grandfather was a little boy. All the kids from the whole neighborhood came, laughing and shouting in the schoolyard, sitting together in the schoolroom, going home together at the end of the day. They learned the same things, so they could help one another on the homework and talk about it.

And the teachers were people. . . .

The mechanical teacher was flashing on the screen: "When we add the fractions ½ and ¼— —"

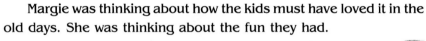

Margie was thinking about how the kids must have loved it in the old days. She was thinking about the fun they had.

ALL THINGS CONSIDERED ————————

1. The setting for this story is (a) the present. (b) about 50 years from now. (c) more than 150 years from now.

2. The books that Margie and Tommy read are *not* written (a) on paper. (b) in words. (c) by people.

3. The old book that Tommy finds surprises Margie because (a) it is fun to read. (b) the pages turn themselves. (c) the words stand still.

4. Margie says that she (a) likes her teacher. (b) hates school. (c) loves school.

5. Margie's teacher is (a) her mother. (b) a college student. (c) a machine.

6. Margie's teacher marks homework (a) immediately. (b) with a funny pencil. (c) by sending it to the County Inspector.

7. Margie says that a person (a) makes the best teacher. (b) is not smart enough to be a teacher. (c) needs a helper to teach.

8. Margie is surprised to learn that students in the old days (a) had mechanical teachers. (b) enjoyed television. (c) went to school together.

9. Margie thinks that one good thing about going to school together is that students could (a) help each other. (b) do less homework. (c) help their teacher.

10. Margie thinks that in the old days school was (a) boring. (b) interesting. (c) fun.

THINKING IT THROUGH ————————

1. What advantages does Margie's school seem to have over yours? What advantages do you think your school has over hers?

2. What kind of school would you prefer—your own or Margie's? Why?

3. Margie doubts that a person could be a good teacher. Which do you think might be smarter—a person or a computer? Explain your answer.

Vocabulary and Sentence Meaning ⎯⎯⎯⎯

Pronoun Reference

Pronouns are words that refer to people and things. They point ahead or back to the people or things that are mentioned elsewhere. The most common pronouns are these:

I, me	we, us	it
she, her	they, them	you
he, him		

Study the pronouns *he* and *her* in the following sentence from "The Fun They Had." Notice the person to which each pronoun refers.

The Inspector smiled after *he* was finished and patted Margie's head. *He* said to *her* mother. . . .

The two *he*'s refer back to *the Inspector.* The *her* refers back to *Margie.*

Once in a while a pronoun refers to a person or thing mentioned later. In the next sentence, *he* refers ahead to *the Inspector.*

After *he* was finished, *the Inspector* smiled.

Read the following paragraph. Number a separate sheet of paper 1 through 4. Write down the *italicized* pronouns found in each sentence. Next to each pronoun, write the word to which it refers.

(1) Margie had hoped the Inspector wouldn't know how to put the teacher together again, but *he* knew how all right, and, after an hour or so, there *it* was again. . . . (2) The part *she* hated most was the slot in *it* where she put homework and test papers. (3) *She* wrote *them* out in punch code. (4) When *they* were dropped in the teacher, *it* calculated her marks in no time.

283

Composition

Follow your teacher's instructions before completing *one* of these writing assignments.

1. Rewrite the paragraph below by replacing *nouns* (people or things) with *pronouns* whenever you can. Use a pronoun *only* when it clearly refers to a person or thing; if the reference is not clear, do *not* use a pronoun.

> Tommy told the Inspector that Tommy had given Tommy's homework to the teacher, but the teacher never gave Tommy a grade for Tommy's homework. The teacher seemed funny to Tommy. The Inspector told Tommy not to worry because the Inspector could fix the teacher.

2. Write a paragraph telling the kind of school you would like better— your school or Margie's school. Give reasons supporting your choice.

VOCABULARY AND SKILL REVIEW

Before completing the exercises that follow, you may wish to review the **bold-faced** words on pages 263 to 280.

I. On a separate sheet of paper, mark each sentence *correct* or *incorrect.* If it is *incorrect,* rewrite the whole sentence to make it correct.

1. Several *astounding* plays made the game very boring.
2. His voice sounded *bitter* as he told the story of lost love.
3. The *texture* of my suit is dark brown.
4. Gena's *hesitation* always kept her moving ahead quickly.
5. Thinking of how well her new calculator worked, Juana looked at the paper and pencil with *scorn.*

II. On a separate piece of paper, answer the following questions. Explain each of your answers.

1. Is the author's purpose in "House Fear" to explain fear of the unknown or to tell about a haunted house?
2. Is the author's purpose in "Not Me" to describe a horrible sea creature or to explain the dangers of being too sure of yourself?
3. Is the author's purpose in "Playmate" to make readers scared of other people or to make readers think about how people might change?

STARS AND PLANETS

by Frank Stilley

▶ How many planets are in the universe? How many planets like *ours* are in the universe? Are there intelligent beings on any of them? These are questions that scientists are asking today. Questions that may be answered in your lifetime!

On a clear night many stars seem so near that you can almost reach out and touch them. But of course they are much farther away than they appear.

Stars may look alike, too, but this again is far from the truth. The chances are that they are very different in age, size, brightness, color, and temperature. Such things as these determine whether or not a star can have a system of planets around it.

As a matter of fact, astronomers generally rule out the possibility of planets for all but a tiny percentage of stars. That would seem to make any effort to discover planets a waste of time and money.

But what would appear such a small possibility isn't really that way. It is the opposite. That is because of the enormous number of stars in the universe.

It has been estimated that on a good night for star-gazing the average person can see some 6,000 to 9,000 stars with the unaided eye. An average pair of binoculars will turn up thousands more. With the use of our big-eyed telescopes the number explodes into countless billions.

We know that there are certain conditions during the formation of a star that are needed to form planets. We know these conditions because we find them right at hand—in our own solar system.

Among the incredible number of stars in just our Milky Way, our sun is not unusual. Indeed it is a very ordinary ball of fire, as stars go. It isn't among the largest, or smallest, or brightest, or dimmest.

- **system** (SIS tum) **parts making up a whole**
- **percentage** (pur SEN tij) **part of a whole; part of 100**
- **solar** (SOH lur) **having to do with the sun**
- **incredible** (in KRED uh bul) **unbelievable**

285

What it has going for it is that it has planets with it. It also has had the necessary conditions for intelligent life to live on one of those planets. So our solar system itself provides us with a ready laboratory for research on things elsewhere.

Astronomers conclude that there must be hundreds of billions of other stars with conditions like those of our sun. As a result, it is possible that there could be a million earthlike planets in our Milky Way galaxy alone.

It is quite possible for a star-sun to have many planets, yet no life of any kind on any of them. As far as we have been able to learn, there is not even a tiny sign of life on any of the other eight planets around our sun. Mars is a possible exception. Some experiments conducted after the Viking landings on Mars in 1976 hinted at the possibility of life in the past if not at the present time.

It is believed that for anything like human life to exist on a planet several key conditions must be met:

(1) The planet must not be too far from its star. If it is, the temperature will be far too cold. Neptune, Uranus, and Pluto are examples of planets that are too cold to support life.

(2) It cannot be too close to its star. If it is, it will be so hot that liquids will boil away. Mercury is such a planet.

(3) The planet must have a nearly circular orbit around its star. If the planet moved too far from the sun at some point, it's temperature would vary too greatly between the extremes of cold and hot. The earth's orbit is very nearly circular.

(4) The planet must be a particular size. An atmosphere is certainly a necessity. It is thought that too small a planet would not have enough gravity to hold an atmosphere and liquids. Similarly, the gravity on too large a planet would be too crushing. A planet about the size of earth is just about right.

(5) A fairly rapid rotation is required. This evens out the extremes between the cold of night and heat of day.

- condition (kun DISH un) **necessary ingredient**
- intelligent (in TEL uh junt) **ability to learn or understand**
- **vary** (VAYR ee) **change back and forth**
- atmosphere (AT mus feer) **the gases that surround the earth**
- require (ree KWYR) **need**

How many planets meet these criteria? No one knows, of course. But there are billions upon billions of stars. So astronomers reason that there must be millions of planets not very different from our own earth.

ALL THINGS CONSIDERED ─────────────────

1. Stars look alike but differ in (a) brightness and color. (b) what makes them up. (c) shape.

2. Most stars (a) have planets. (b) do not have planets. (c) are planets.

3. The universe contains (a) thousands of stars. (b) millions of stars. (c) billions of stars.

4. Without a telescope, we can see (a) most stars. (b) no stars. (c) a small percentage of stars.

5. Our sun has (a) one planet that supports life. (b) three or four planets that support life. (c) many planets that support life.

6. Scientists estimate that (a) no stars are like our sun. (b) thousands of stars are like our sun. (c) billions of stars are like our sun.

7. There is a possibility of life on Mars (a) in the past. (b) now. (c) in the future.

8. If a planet is very far from its star, it will be (a) too hot. (b) too cold. (c) just right.

9. To support life, a planet needs a circular orbit so (a) it stays warm enough. (b) it stays cold enough. (c) temperatures do not vary too much.

10. A planet that is small would not have (a) any gravity. (b) an atmosphere. (c) a sun.

THINKING IT THROUGH ─────────────────

1. The Milky Way is our galaxy. How many earthlike planets do scientists think exist in the Milky Way? What do you think about this?

2. Have you ever looked through a telescope at the sky or simply stood and looked up at the stars? What did you see and how did you feel?

> • criteria (cry TEER ee uh) **standards**

Building From Details

Paragraph Structure

As you know, when you write a long report you divide it into paragraphs. The paragraphs make the paper look better, and help to organize your information.

But how do you put a paragraph together? What goes into a good paragraph? Read this sample from "Stars and Planets":

Among the incredible number of stars in just our Milky Way, our sun is not unusual. Indeed it is a very ordinary ball of fire, as stars go. It isn't among the largest, or smallest, or brightest, or dimmest.

The *italicized* sentence is called the **topic sentence.** It gives the main idea that the paragraph will be about. The other two sentences in the paragraph give **supporting details.** The sentences are related to the topic, and explain something about it to make the topic more complete. The supporting details in the paragraph explain what the writer means when he says that our sun is "not unusual."

On a separate sheet of paper, write the topic sentences of two paragraphs in "Stars and Planets." Be ready to discuss how the other sentences in the paragraph provide supporting details.

Composition

Follow your teacher's instructions before completing *one* of these writing assignments.

1. Write two or three questions you would like to ask a being from another planet.
2. Go to the library and ask the librarian for the *Reader's Guide to Periodical Literature.* (This is an index of magazine articles.) Look for the headings "Stars" and "Planets." Choose one or two articles on the subject. Read the articles you chose, and write one or two paragraphs reporting what you find. Be sure each paragraph has a topic sentence and supporting details.

THE DIFFERENT ONES

a play for television

by Rod Serling

▶ In this future society, a boy is driven to hide because he is "different." Is there any place where he will be accepted? Any place at all?

CHARACTERS

Mr. Koch	**Another Woman**	**First Girl**
Victor Koch	**Official**	**Second Girl**
Mrs. Koch	**Man**	**Third Girl**
Woman		

Scene 1

Fade in on Victor Koch's *bedroom—day. The small room is dark—shades drawn so that only little slivers of sunlight intrude; nothing in the room, including* Victor *himself, is identifiable at this moment. From outside comes the chant of children.*

Children's voices: Ugly, ugly, ugly . . . bird-head, bird-head . . . freak, freak, freak!!

Mr. Koch's voice *(closer by; shouting)***:** Get out of here, you kids! Get out of here before I call the police!

(The chant is broken up. There are giggles, squeals, and harsh laughter, then the sounds of running footsteps on concrete that disappear, and one last defiant piping little voice shouts out.)

Child's voice: Victor's an ugly bird-head freak!

(Then distant squeals of laughter, then silence. Camera pans from shades to a corner of the room where we see Victor—*or, at least his outline—a gangly teenager about seventeen, with a stocking cap pulled down over his head and almost covering his eyes. He sits huddled in the corner of the room, motionless.)*

- **defiant** (di FY unt) **openly resistant**
- **gangly** (GANG glee) **tall and thin**

Scene 2

Koch *living room—day. A small, neat, modestly furnished room.* Mrs. Koch *sits near the window, fingers clenched in front of her, staring at the floor. She hears her husband's voice in one last burst.*

Mr. Koch's voice: And don't come back, you crummy kids!—or you'll be sorry!

(Sound of a screen door closing, then the entering footsteps of Mr. Koch *as he comes into the living room.* Mrs. Koch *looks up, her face full of pain and fear, her voice very soft.)*

Mrs. Koch: Sometimes . . . sometimes it's best that you just ignore them——

Mr. Koch: Ignore them!? A pack of wild little animals calling our kid a freak—and we're supposed to ignore them?

Mrs. Koch *(looks ceilingward):* Sometimes I think he's grown used to it. . . .

Mr. Koch: Oh, for Pete's sake, Doris—*how* could he grow used to it? Could *you* get used to it—three times a day, seven days a week—those monsters screaming at you at the tops of their lungs? And we're supposed to just sit here, read the evening

290

paper, and make believe it's some kind of a blessing?

(Mrs. Koch just closes her eyes and doesn't respond. Mr. Koch moves over to her, his voice much softer now.)

Mr. Koch: Doris . . . we've got . . . we've got some decisions to make. . . . He's seventeen. He's not a child anymore——

(Her face jerks up.)

Mrs. Koch *(with startling anger)*: *I won't have him sent away . . . !*
Mr. Koch *(shakes head slowly)*: Honey—I don't think we have any choice. He can't live the rest of his life huddled in a corner of his bedroom. It's destroying him—it's destroying *us.*
Mrs. Koch *(brokenly)*: Where . . . where would they send him?
Mr. Koch: I don't know. But much more of this . . . we wouldn't have a son anyway. We'd have just a . . . just a silent piece of scar tissue who hides in dark corners——

(His own voice breaks now. He turns away from her abruptly, moves across the room over to the hallway at the foot of the stairs. She follows him there.)

Mrs. Koch: Paul—must it be now?

(Mr. Koch says nothing, but whirls soundlessly, rushing in misery up the stairs. Mrs. Koch stands at the foot, staring forlornly after him.)

Scene 3

Victor Koch's *bedroom—day.* Victor *stands by the closed shades, his back to camera. There's a knock at the door, then the door opens.* Mr. Koch *enters, closing the door behind him.*

Mr. Koch: Vic? I'd like to talk to you, son.
Victor *(softly)*: All right.

• **forlorn** (for LORN) abandoned, miserable

Mr. Koch: Your mother and I . . . well . . . we've been discussing this. . . .

(Victor turns to him. We see only the outline of him—the stocking cap, the thin, drawn face—but nothing more.)

Victor: What have you been discussing?

Mr. Koch: I know . . . we both know . . . how miserable it is here for you. We think it's imperative that——

Victor *(as Mr. Koch hesitates)***:** You want to send me away.

Mr. Koch *(almost in agony)***:** Son—there are places . . . perhaps . . . where boys like yourself——

Victor *(cuts in, flatly)***:** There aren't any "boys like myself." I'm unique. Didn't you know that? I'm a one-of-a-kind collector's item! *(Shrugs)* Do whatever you want.

Mr. Koch: That's not the point. I want to do what *you* want. But just to stay here—hiding in your room—that's no kind of life. . . .

Victor: Give me an alternative kind of life. Or I'll give you some. If there were still freak shows—I could be the star attraction. Or pickle me and stick me in a jar . . . *(Voice rising)* Or why don't you rent me out for parties and conventions——

Mr. Koch *(outshouting him)***:** Vic! No *more!*

(There is a silence. The boy turns away.)

Victor: You're quite right, Dad. No more. Please get out.

(Mr. Koch stands there a moment, then opens the door, exits.)

Scene 4

The Koch living room—day. Mr. Koch comes down the stair, pauses at the foot, then, after a deep breath, turns and moves to a kind of small telephone-television set. He stands in front of a small, dark screen, lifts a receiver,

- imperative (im PER uh tiv) **urgent**
- agony (AG uh nee) **terrible mental or physical pain**
- **unique** (yoo NEEK) **one of a kind; having no like**
- **alternative** (ol TUR nuh tiv) **something else to choose**

dials a number. There are several beep-beep sounds; then the image of a Woman *appears on the screen.*

Woman: Information.

Mr. Koch: I'd like . . . I'd like the government office that . . . that's involved in population——

Woman: There are several sublistings under "Population," sir. What particular department did you have in mind?

Mr. Koch: Whatever the outfit is that——*(Hesitates)*

Woman *(impatient)***:** Go on, sir.

Mr. Koch *(voice softer)***:** Whoever is involved with deformed children.

(The Woman *nods, punches several buttons, reads some information off a computerized scanning device.)*

Woman: That would be the Office of Special Urban Problems. Just a moment, sir, I'll connect you.

(There are more beep-beep sounds, lines crisscross the screen, and then Another Woman *appears.)*

Another Woman: Special Urban Problems, how may I help you?

Mr. Koch: My . . . my son——*(Wets lips)* Well . . . my son has a deformity——

Another Woman: Your name and sector, sir.

Mr. Koch: Koch. Paul Koch. Southeast Sector . . . residential 2-B.

Another Woman: And your son's name?

Mr. Koch: Victor.

Another Woman: Age?

Mr. Koch: Seventeen . . . seventeen-and-a-half.

Another Woman: And the deformity, sir—birth or accident?

(We see the shadow of Victor *on the wall as he stands listening behind a corner.* Mr. Koch *is unaware of his eavesdropping.)*

- deformity (di FOR mi tee) **misshaped part of the body**
- eavesdrop (EEVS drop) **listen in private**

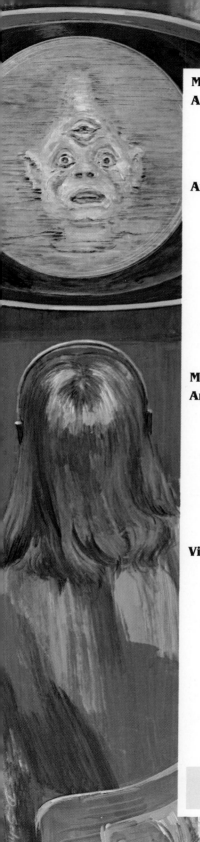

Mr. Koch: Deformed at birth.
Another Woman: And the nature of the deformity?

(Mr. Koch closes his eyes, unconsciously takes a step sideways.)

Another Woman: You're moving offscreen, sir. I can no longer see you. Would you step back into my vision, please?

(We now see Mr. Koch from the Woman's point of view. She is in the Special Urban Problems Office. There is a line of perhaps eight women sitting in front of television-phones, their voices supplying a background hum to the scene. In front is the Woman talking to Mr. Koch. We see his face as he steps back into frame on her TV screen. He is pale, perspiring.)

Mr. Koch: What was it you asked——?
Another Woman: The nature of the deformity, sir. If you could just give me some general idea——

(She gasps as Mr. Koch is suddenly thrust aside and, in his place, filling her TV screen is a big, blown-up close-up of Victor, who whips off his stocking cap. We are looking at a distorted horror—a funnel-shaped head with a third, dead, listless eye in the middle of the forehead.)

Victor *(with tears rolling down his cheeks)***:** Get a good look for yourself, ma'am. Now, appearing on your screen—Victor Koch. Ugly, ugly, ugly . . . bird-head, bird-head, bird-head . . . *(Head drops forward; one quaking, spasmodic sob; then)* . . . freak, freak, freak——

Scene 5

Federal office—day. An antiseptic-looking room with low-slung futuristic furniture, mostly in whites and blacks. An Official sits behind a free-form desk. In front of him sits Mr. Koch. Mr. Koch is nervous, and with difficulty is

- distorted (di STOR tid) **badly shaped**
- **antiseptic** (an tuh SEP tik) **overly clean and bright**

forcing himself to do what he feels he must. The Official
*leans back, toying with a metal pencil, tapping it on his
fingers.*

Official: . . . So, I'm afraid, Mr. Koch, there is very little this office
can do. At least, in the area of placement.

Mr. Koch: There are no . . . institutions?

Official *(with a shrug)*: Not for a case like your son's.

*(He half turns in his chair, pushes a button so that shades
over the window slide closed just a little bit, cutting out
the light. At the same time, the artificial light in the room
becomes slightly brighter.)*

Official: The Federal Conformity Act of 1993 covered cases of mental incompetence. But, of course, were his condition changea-
ble, medically speaking——

Mr. Koch: We've been to a dozen doctors. They tell us there isn't
anything that can be done surgically——

Official: Which is unfortunate . . . and leaves us pretty much back
where we started.

Mr. Koch *(intensely)*: He's a bright boy. He has an exceptionally
high IQ and he's . . . he's a nice kid too——

Official: I've no doubt. But you've pretty much reached the proper
conclusions on your own . . . .

Mr. Koch *(nods gloomily)*: I know he can't stay with us anymore.
But there *must* be some place——

Official *(impatient tinge)*: I've already told you there are no private
or government sectors that institutionalize this kind of case.
(Long silence; turns back toward Mr. Koch*)* . . . which leaves us
with the only remaining alternative. *(Long pause)* And there's no
sense in our tiptoeing around it, is there?

Mr. Koch: Kill him, you mean.

Official: That would be in the nature of an old-fashioned value
judgment, Mr. Koch. Hardly applicable in this day and age—to
put someone to sleep for humanitarian reasons is certainly not
an act of murder. . . .

- incompetence (in KOM puh tuns) **lack of ability or intelligence**
- humanitarian (hyoo man i TAYR ee un) **helping attitude**

Mr. Koch: Beautiful! I just love *your* value judgments: Merciful! ". . . humanitarian." You take a human life, mister—and you can spray that act with pretty words like they were perfume—but it's still taking a human life. *My son's life!*

(As the Official *spins about in his chair and faces* Mr. Koch, *his voice and facial expression are ice cold.)*

Official: Suit yourself, Mr. Koch. You have the alternatives. He can remain with you for the rest of his life or you can do the right thing . . . really the most charitable thing——

(But Mr. Koch *is no longer listening. He rises, moving blindly toward the door.)*

Mr. Koch *(mumbles tonelessly)***:** Thank you for your trouble.

(He opens door to leave. Just then a red light goes on, a bell rings. Reacting, the Official *holds up his hand.)*

Official: Just a moment, Mr. Koch——*(Flicks a switch)* Yes?
Voice: Are you handling a case involving a deformity—seventeen-year-old boy—File Number 783-T9-66B?
Official: Koch. That's correct.
Voice: Check latest bulletin in your Relocation rulings, 74X9C.
Official: Immediately. *(Flicks off switch)* Apparently, Mr. Koch, there are some new courses of action still open to us.

(Mr. Koch is standing at the door, his hand on the knob, watching as the Official *flicks another switch, then pushes a button. From a slot in his desk comes an official-looking paper. The* Official *takes it, reads it, nods, then looks across the room at* Mr. Koch.)*

Official: Sit down, won't you?

(Mr. Koch retraces his steps to the chair, sits. The Official *studies the paper for a moment, then looks up, his expression brightening.)*

• charitable (CHAR i tuh bul) **caring for another**

Official: As you know, we have Exchange Programs with several of the populated planets——*(Clears throat a little nervously as* Mr. Koch *stares at him)* In most cases, these are *cultural* exchanges . . . *scientific* exchanges . . . usually for prescribed periods. I'm reminded—*(Points to paper)*—of a new arrangement with a planet called Boreon. Tiny little world just beyond Mars. Unknown to us ten years ago. . . . We've had no mutual visitations with the planet, but considerable voice communication. In our last exchange, they told us that they were extremely anxious for people to move there. *Males* especially. Seems the place is seriously underpopulated. . . . Additionally, they've indicated that they would place no restrictions of any kind on whomsoever we wanted to send. That is to say—well—here they are, inviting any and all kinds of people——

Mr. Koch *(softly)*: Like my son.

Official *(shrugs)*: Like anyone. They simply want more people. *(Consults papers)* Their planet is roughly one fiftieth the size of Earth. But its atmosphere is almost identical. Its people are humanoid . . . reasonably advanced. And altogether anxious, it would seem, to welcome anyone we might send. So anxious, in fact, that they're willing to finance the entire operation. Now, how does that strike you? Isn't that the sort of thing that—that *Victor* might find . . . exciting and to his liking?

> • **humanoid** (HYOO mun oid) like a human

297

Mr. Koch: You tell me. You send a kid a million miles into space—dump him on some faraway planet—like a garbage run. Would *you* find that . . . "exciting" . . . and "to your liking"?

(The Official *leans forward, elbows on the desk.)*

Official *(speaks softly but with firmness)***:** If the alternative, Mr. Koch, were death—yes, I think I should prefer the former. . . .

Scene 6

Victor Koch's *bedroom—night. A single bed lamp provides the only light. The room is full of darkness and shadows, and we see* Victor *just finishing packing a small suitcase that is open on the bed. There is a knock at the door.* Mr. Koch *enters.*

Mr. Koch: 'Bout ready, son?

*(*Victor *closes the suitcase, nods.* Mr. Koch *hesitates.)*

Mr. Koch *(blurting)***:** Vic—your mother and I . . . your mother and I want you to know that——

*(*Victor *turns to him. He still wears the stocking cap.)*

Victor *(quiet; gentle)***:** Tell Mom . . . and this is for you too—no guilts . . . no blaming yourselves . . . and no long good-bys.

Mr. Koch *(voice shaking)***:** If we knew what the place was like . . . if we were just certain in our own minds that——

Victor *(with a smile)***:** Want to know something? It can be desert, frozen tundra, or a pit where the sun never shines . . . *and it would be better than this!* (Picks up suitcase) . . . Let's go, huh?!

Scene 7

The rocket port—night. The rocket's engines flame into life; the rocket hurtles toward the night sky, vanishing.
In the departure area, Mr. Koch *and his wife stand looking through a wire mesh gate, faces filled with an inexpressible sadness, looking up toward the sky.*

Scene 8

*A long, dark room on Boreon. The walls are curved—
something in the nature of a metal tunnel with a light at
the far end. A door opens.* Victor *walks down the length of
the corridor. He stops about halfway down the corridor,
removes his stocking cap, looks around. A figure emerges
from behind camera and walks to him.*

Man: Did you just get off the ship? *(As Victor nods)* From Earth?

Victor: That's right. *(Then, studying the Man intently)* Are you . . .
are you the Welcoming Committee?

Man *(back to camera)*: Not really. I'm taking off on the ship. I'm
going to Earth on the return leg. . . . I've been waiting years to
get permission.

Victor: You're not from——

Man *(nods emphatically)*: Yes, I'm from here.

(Camera shows Man. *He is extremely handsome, roughly*
Victor's *age, but completely normal. He carries a small
traveling bag.)*

Man: This is the first exchange we've made—your planet and mine.
(Pause) I wish you luck.

Victor: You too.

(The Man *starts to walk past* Victor *in the direction of the
light. As an afterthought,* Victor *checks him.)*

Victor: Could I ask you something? *(As the* Man *stops)* Why are you
leaving?

Man: Look at me.

Victor *(staring)*: What's . . . what's wrong?

Man: Are you kidding? What's wrong? You don't have to be kind. I'm
used to being this way . . . any I'm used to the reactions. *(Pause)*
Well—I hope it works out all right for you. *(He continues down
the corridor.)*

First Girl's Voice: Victor Koch—from the planet Earth?

(The First Girl *standing before* Victor *is exactly like* Victor—
*the pointed head, the third eye. She holds out her hand,
smiles.)*

First Girl: I'm very pleased to welcome you, Mr. Koch, to the planet Boreon.

(She looks over her shoulder, beckons. Several more people come out of the darkness, each a carbon of the other—the same head, the same third eye. They smile at Victor *with obvious warmth. Two other girls stare at* Victor, *then whisper with a little giggle.)*

Second Girl: He's gorgeous!

Third Girl: Shhh—he'll hear you!

(Victor looks around from face to face. One of the men takes his bag, the two girls lock arms with Victor *as they start to walk in the opposite direction.)*

First Girl: We hope you'll like it here. The climate is very comfortable. And in terms of language and art—I think you'll find it almost identical to Earth—the cultures are very similar. . . .

Victor *(He pauses, looks back along the corridor)***:** I think . . . I think I'll be very happy. I already feel as if . . . as if I belong!

(Then they move out of camera range, leaving just the darkness of the corridor. We hear the sound of the rocket blasting off for its return trip to the distant planet Earth. Fade out.)

● carbon (KAR bun) copy

ALL THINGS CONSIDERED ────────────────

1. The play begins with Victor (a) outside playing with other children. (b) in the corner of his dark room. (c) asking his father to help him.

2. Mr. Koch says Victor's problem (a) is destroying the whole family. (b) can be corrected. (c) is something they can learn to live with.

3. Victor says angrily that (a) his parents don't love him. (b) the kids hate him. (c) there is no one else like him.

4. Victor's problem is his (a) lack of friends. (b) deformity. (c) fear of the outdoors.

5. Mr. Koch wants the government to (a) pay for Victor's operation. (b) take Victor away. (c) help Victor.

6. The government official at first suggests (a) putting Victor "to sleep." (b) operating on Victor. (c) leaving Victor alone.

7. The people on Boreon want to (a) learn about people on Earth. (b) have young men move to their planet. (c) get rid of all their strange people.

8. Victor tells his parents that (a) he doesn't love them. (b) they could have done something else to help him. (c) they should not feel guilty.

9. The man leaving Boreon as Victor arrives, is ugly according to (a) Boreon standards. (b) Earth standards. (c) the standards of both planets.

10. Victor will probably (a) go back to Earth. (b) forget about his treatment on Earth. (c) be very happy on Boreon.

THINKING IT THROUGH ────────────────

1. Why is the play called "The Different Ones" instead of "The Different One"? Is this small difference very important? Explain.

2. Do you think that Mr. Koch wants to do the best thing for Victor, or does he want to do the best thing for himself? Support your answer with actions or speeches from the play.

3. What are the standards that make a person beautiful or ugly? Do these standards change from time to time? Do they change from place to place?

Literary Skills

Recognizing Theme

The topic of this play is given in the title—"The Different Ones." The topic tells what the play is about. When you know the topic, you can look for the theme—the message that the story gives about the topic.

In some stories, such as fables, the theme is stated. In others like "The Different Ones," the reader has to discover the theme. One way to find the theme is to see how the conflict of the story is resolved. Usually, the main character is somehow changed by the conflict. Other times, the character's situation is changed so that the conflict is no longer there. If you compare the situation after the conflict is resolved to the situation before, you should be able to find the theme.

To uncover the theme of "The Different Ones," answer the following questions.

1. Who is the main character in the play?
2. What is the conflict that the character faces?
3. How is the conflict resolved?
4. How is the character's situation changed?
5. Now compare the character before and after the conflict is resolved. What message can you draw from this comparison?

Composition

Follow your teacher's instructions before completing *one* of these writing assignments.

1. Write a paragraph predicting the reaction of the boy who is leaving Boreon when he lands on Earth.
2. Imagine that the boy leaving Boreon is greeted on Earth by Mr. Koch, with whom he will be living. Write a dialogue in which the boy tells Mr. Koch why he left Boreon, and Mr. Koch explains how he feels now about the "exchange." Write your dialogue in the form of lines from a play.

VOCABULARY AND SKILL REVIEW

Before completing the exercises that follow, you may wish to review the **bold-faced** words on pages 285 to 300.

I. On your paper, mark each sentence *correct* or *incorrect.* If it is *incorrect,* rewrite the sentence to make it correct.

1. A cat seems to be *humanoid.*
2. The *percentage* of students from my school at the rally is very high.
3. It is *incredible* that two plus two should equal four.
4. The temperature *varies* from hot to cold.
5. Our sun is like other suns, so we call it *unique.*
6. The term *solar* refers to the earth.
7. Surrounded by his friends, Rob was *forlorn.*
8. A *defiant* yell rang out from the other team.
9. Pamela likes to have several *alternatives* from which to choose.
10. My cut became infected because the doctor's office was very *antiseptic.*

II. Below are statements about topic and theme for three selections in this unit. On a separate sheet of paper, indicate whether you *agree* or *disagree* with each statement. If you *disagree,* explain why.

1.   **a.** The topic of "The Fun They Had" is a future girl's thoughts about school.
   b. The theme of "The Fun They Had" is that schools are always getting better.

2.   **a.** The topic of "Stars and Planets" is the search for other planets like earth.
   b. The theme of "Stars and Planets" is that with so many stars in the universe, there is a good chance that some of them have planets.

3.   **a.** The topic of "The Different Ones" is space travel.
   b. The theme of "The Different Ones" is that space travel is dangerous.

H.G. Wells (1866-1946)

Was H. G. Wells the first science fiction writer? In the 1890s he wrote about the end of the earth, an invasion from Mars, and other futuristic ideas. He believed in the power of science to make society better. He wrote many books and articles to spread his ideas. Two of his most famous books are *The War of the Worlds* and *The Time Machine.*

Wells wrote endlessly about many subjects, and he was always popular. But many critics looking back on his work agree that his best writing showed the reality and humor of the lives of everyday people.

The following story has an interesting mixture of the natural and supernatural. It shows Wells's eye and ear for everyday detail as well as the power of his imagination to carry the reader into a world of strange events.

THE MAGIC SHOP

by H. G. Wells

▶ A father takes his son into a store that sells magic tricks. But everything is much more magical than the father is ready to believe. Why does the father have such a hard time accepting it? Why does the boy have such an easy time?

I had passed the magic shop once or twice before. A window displayed little objects—magic balls, magic hens, disappearing coins, packs of cards that *looked* all right, and all that sort of thing. But never had I thought of going in until one day, almost without warning, my boy Gip hauled me by my finger right up to the window. His big eyes told me that there was nothing to do but take him in.

I had not thought the place was there, to tell the truth. There was only the window on Regent Street between the picture shop and the place where the birds run about. But there it was sure enough. I had imagined it was down near the Circus, or round the corner in Oxford Street, or maybe even in Holborn. Always over the way and a little hard to find it had been, with something unreal about it. But here it was now quite certainly, and the fat tip of Gip's finger made a noise upon the glass.

"If I was rich," said Gip, his finger pointing at the Disappearing Egg, "I'd buy myself that. And that," which was

called "The Crying Baby, Very Human," "and that," which was a mystery, but a neat card said, "Buy one and astonish your friends."

"Anything," said Gip, "will disappear under one of those cones. I have read about it in a book."

"And there, Daddy, is the Vanishing Penny. Only they've put it this way up so's we can't see how it's done."

Gip, dear boy, inherits his mother's breeding, and he did not suggest we enter the shop or worry in any way. Only, you know, quite unknowingly he tugged my finger doorward.

"That," he said, and pointed to the Magic Bottle.

"What if you had that?" I said.

"I could show it to Jessie," he said, thoughtful as ever of others.

"It's less than a hundred days to your birthday, Gibbles," I said, and laid my hand on the door handle.

Gip made no answer, but his grip tightened on my finger. So we came into the shop.

It was no common shop this. It was a magic shop, and Gip showed proper respect for it. He left the burden of the conversation to me.

It was a little, narrow shop, not very well lit, and the doorbell pinged with a sorrowful note as we closed it behind us. For a moment or so we were alone and could glance about. There was a plaster tiger on the glass case—a kind-eyed tiger that waggled his head in a thoughtful manner. There were several crystal spheres, a china hand holding magic cards, a stock of magic fishbowls in various sizes, and a magic hat that carelessly displayed its springs. On the floor were magic mirrors. One drew you out long and thin. One swelled your head and cut off your legs. One made you short and fat like a dwarf. While we were laughing at these, the shopman, as I suppose, came in.

At any rate, there he was behind the counter—a curious colorless man with one ear larger than the other and a chin like the toe of a boot.

"What can we have the pleasure?" he said, spreading his long, magic fingers on the glass case. And so—with a start—we were aware of him.

"I want," I said, "to buy my little boy a few simple tricks."

"Card tricks?" he asked. "Animal? Household?"

"Anything amusing," said I.

"Um!" said the shopman, and scratched his head for a moment. Then, quite casually, he drew from his head a glass ball. "Something in this way?" he said, and held it out.

The action was unexpected. I had seen the trick done at entertainments many times before, but I had not expected it here. "That's good," I said, with a laugh.

"Isn't it?" said the shopman.

Gip stretched out his hand to take this object and found merely a blank palm.

"It's in your pocket," said the shopman. And there it was!

"How much will that be?" I asked.

"We make no charge for glass balls," said the shopman politely. "We get them—" he picked one out of his elbow as he spoke—"free." He produced another from the back of his neck, and laid it beside the two on the counter. Gip regarded his glass ball thoughtfully. Then he looked questioningly at the two on the counter. Finally he brought his round-eyed gaze to the shopman, who smiled. "You may have those too," said the shopman. "And, if you *don't* mind, one from my mouth. So!"

Gip studied me silently for a moment. Then, in a deep silence, he put away the four balls, took back my dependable finger, and readied himself for the next event.

"We get all our smaller tricks in that way," the shopman remarked.

I laughed in the manner of one who understands a joke. "Better than going to the wholesale shop," I said. "Of course, it's cheaper."

"In a way," the shopman said. "Though we pay in the end. But not so heavily—as people suppose. . . . Our larger tricks, and our daily specials and

all the other things we want, we get out of that hat. . . . And you know, sir, if you'll excuse my saying it, there *isn't* a wholesale shop, not for Genuine Magic goods, sir. I don't know if you noticed our full name on the door—the Geniune Magic Shop." He drew a business card from his cheek and handed it to me. "Genuine," he said with his finger on the word, and added, "There is absolutely no deception, sir."

He seemed to be carrying out the joke pretty thoroughly, I thought.

He turned to Gip with a down-to-earth friendly smile. "You, you know, are the Right Sort of Boy."

I was surprised at his knowing that, because, in the interest of good upbringing, we keep it rather a secret even at home. But Gip heard the expression in silence, keeping a steady eye on him.

"It's only the Right Sort of Boy gets through that doorway."

And, as if by way of illustration, there came a rattling at the door, and a squeaking little voice could be faintly heard. "Nyar! I wanna go in there, Daddy. I wanna go in there. Ny-a-a-ah!" Then the tired voice of an overworked father: "It's locked, Edward," he said, trying to comfort the boy.

"But it isn't," said I.

"It is, sir," said the shopman. "It's always locked for that sort of child." As he spoke, we had another glimpse of this other youngster. A spoiled brat, to be sure, with a face twisted in anger and pale from too many sweets and hands that pawed at the enchanted pane. "It's no good, sir," said the shopman, as I moved forward to help the child. And presently the spoiled child was carried off howling.

"How do you manage that?" I said, breathing a little more freely.

• deception (di SEP shun) **trick; act of deceiving**

"Magic!" said the shopman, with a careless wave of the hand. And behold!—sparks of colored fire flew out of his fingers and vanished into the shadows.

"You were saying," he said, addressing himself to Gip, "before you came in, that you would like one of our 'Buy One and Astonish Your Friends' boxes?"

Gip, after a gallant effort, said, "Yes."

"It's in your pocket."

And leaning over the counter—he really had an extraordinarily long body—this amazing person produced the article in the usual magician's manner. "Paper," he said, and took a sheet out of the empty hat with the springs. "Strings," and behold his mouth was a string box from which he drew an unending thread. He tied the parcel and bit off the string and then, it seemed to me, swallowed the whole ball of string. Then he lit a candle at the nose of one of the ventriloquist's dummies, stuck one of his fingers (which had become sealing-wax red) into the flame, and so sealed the parcel.

"Then there was the Disappearing Egg," he remarked, and brought one from within my coat and packed it. And then he did the same with The Crying Baby, Very Human. I handed each parcel to Gip as it was ready. He clasped them to his chest.

Gip said very little. His eyes and the clutch of his arms showed his feelings. He was the playground of unspoken emotions. These, I thought, were *real* Magics.

Then, with a start, I discovered something moving about in my hat—something soft and jumpy. I whipped it off, and a pigeon dropped out and ran on the counter, and went, I guessed, into a cardboard box behind the plaster tiger.

"Tut, tut!" said the shopman, skillfully relieving me of my hat. "Careless bird, and—as I live—nesting!"

He shook my hat. Out into his extended hand came two or three eggs, a large marble, a watch, about half-a-dozen of those glass balls, and then crumpled, crinkled paper, more and more and more. All the time he talked of the way in which people neglect to brush their hats *inside* as well as out. He spoke politely, of course, but with a certain personal application. "All sorts of things build up, sir. . . . Astonishing what they carry about with them. . . ." The crumpled paper rose and billowed on the counter more and more and more, until he was nearly hidden from us. Then he *was* hidden, but still his voice went on and on. "We none of us know what the outer appearance of a human being may conceal, sir. Is each of us then no better than a painted surface, the outside of a Magic Box—"

His voice stopped—the same as when you snap off the radio, the same instant silence. Even the rustle of the paper stopped. Everything was still. . . .

"Have you done with my hat?" I said, after a while.

There was no answer.

* ventriloquist (ven TRIL uh kwist) **a person who can "throw" his or her voice**

I stared at Gip, and Gip stared at me. There were our altered shapes in the magic mirrors looking very odd and grave and quiet. . . .

"I think we'll go now," I said. "Will you tell me how much all this comes to? . . .

"I say," I said, on a rather louder note, "I want the bill—and my hat, please."

There might have been a sniff behind the paper pile. . . .

"Let's look behind the counter, Gip," I said. "He's making fun of us."

I led Gip round the head-wagging tiger, and what do you think there was behind the counter? No one at all! Only my hat on the floor, and a common white rabbit looking as stupid and crumpled as only a magician's rabbit can do. I picked up my hat, and the rabbit hopped a clumsy hop or so out of my way.

"Daddy!" said Gip, in a whisper.

"What is it, Gip?" said I.

"I *do* like this shop, Daddy."

"So should I," I said to myself, "if the counter wouldn't suddenly stretch out to shut us off from the door." But I didn't call Gip's attention to that.

"Kitty," Gip said, with a hand out to the rabbit as it came hopping past us. "Kitty, do Gip a magic!" And Gip's eyes followed it as it squeezed through a door I had certainly not noticed a moment before. Then this door opened wider, and the man with one ear larger than the other appeared again. He was smiling still, but his eye met mine with something between amusement and hostility.

Gip tugged my finger forward. I glanced at the counter and met the shopman's eye again. I was beginning to think the magic a little too genuine. "We haven't *very* much time," I said. But somehow we were inside the showroom before I could finish that.

"All goods of the same quality," said the shopman, rubbing his hands together. "And that is the best. Nothing in the place that isn't genuine Magic. Excuse me, sir!"

I felt him pull at something that clung to my coat sleeve. Then he held a little, wriggling red demon by the tail. The little creature bit and fought and tried to get at his hand, but he tossed it carelessly behind the counter. No doubt the thing was only a piece of twisted rubber, but for the moment—! And his gesture was exactly that of a man who handles some little biting pest. I glanced at Gip, but Gip was looking at a magic rocking horse. I was glad he hadn't seen the thing. "You haven't many things like *that* about, have you?" I asked in a whisper.

"None of ours! Probably brought it with you," said the shopman—also in an undertone, and with a more dazzling smile than ever. "Astonishing what people *will* carry about with them unawares!"

And then to Gip, "Do you see anything you fancy here?"

There were many things that Gip fancied there.

He turned to this astonishing shopkeeper with growing confidence. "Is that a Magic Sword?" he said.

"A Magic Toy Sword. It neither bends, breaks, nor cuts the fingers. It makes its owner unconquerable in battle against anyone under eighteen. Half-a-crown to seven and sixpence,* according to size. These suits of armor on cards are for young knights and very useful—shields of safety, sandals of swiftness, helmet of invisibility."

"Oh, Daddy!" gasped Gip.

I tried to find out what they cost, but the shopman did not listen to me. He had got Gip now. He had got him away from my finger. He had begun his explanation of all his confounded merchandise, and nothing was going to stop him. Presently I saw with a bit of distrust and something very like jealousy that Gip had hold of this person's finger as usually he has hold of mine. No doubt the fellow was interesting, I thought. No doubt he had an interestingly faked lot of stuff, really *good* faked stuff, still—

I wandered after them, saying very little, but keeping an eye on this fellow. After all, Gip was enjoying it. And no doubt when the time came to go we should be able to go quite easily.

• hostility (hos TIL uh tee) **anger; unfriendliness**

*sixpence—English money

CHECKPOINT _____

Answer these questions before going on. They will help you follow the story. If you don't know an answer, you may look back.

1. Among the objects in the window of the magic shop are (a) magic wands. (b) white rabbits. (c) disappearing coins.

2. The father is (a) surprised to find the shop on Regent Street. (b) expecting to find the shop on Regent Street. (c) avoiding the magic shop.

3. The shopman calls Gip (a) The Right Sort of Boy. (b) The Birthday Boy. (c) The Crying Baby.

4. The shopman says his tricks are (a) science experiments. (b) genuine magic. (c) good fake stuff.

5. At this point in the story, Gip has (a) taken his father's hand. (b) left the shop. (c) wandered away from his father.

It was a long rambling place, that showroom. A gallery was broken up by stands and stalls and pillars, with archways leading off to other departments where the oddest looking assistants loafed and stared, it seemed, at me. Everywhere there were puzzling mirrors and curtains. So puzzling, indeed, were these that I was soon unable to make out the door by which we had come.

The shopman showed Gip magic trains that ran without steam or electricity. He showed Gip some very, very valuable boxes of soldiers that all came alive when you took off the lid and said——. I myself haven't a very quick ear and it was a tongue-twisting sound, but Gip got it in no time. "Bravo!" said the shopman, stuffing the soldiers back into the box and handing it to Gip. "Now," said the shopman, and in a moment Gip had made them all alive again.

"You'll take that box?" asked the shopman.

"We'll take that box," said I, "unless you charge its full value. In which case we would need to rob a bank."

"Dear heart, no!" and the shopman swept the little men back again, shut the lid, waved the box in the air, and there it was, in brown paper, tied up and—*with Gip's name and address on the paper!*

The shopman laughed aloud at my amazement.

"This is the genuine magic," he said. "The real thing."

311

"It's a little too genuine for my taste," I said again.

After that he fell to showing Gip tricks, odd tricks, and still odder the way they were done. He explained them. He turned them inside out, and I watched my dear little boy nodding his busy bit of a head in the wisest manner.

I could not pay attention as well as I should have. "Hey, presto!" said the magic shopman. Then would come the clear, small "Hey, presto!" of the boy. But I was distracted by other things. It was becoming clear to me just how tremendously odd this place was. I was, so to speak, overwhelmed by a sense of oddness. There was something a little odd about the lamps even, about the ceiling, about the floor, about the casually placed chairs. I had a strange feeling that whenever I wasn't looking at them straight they moved about, playing a noiseless game behind my back. The molding high on the wall had a strange twisting design with masks—masks altogether too expressive for plaster.

Then suddenly my attention was caught by one of the odd-looking assistants. He was some way off and apparently unaware of my presence. I saw a sort of three-quarter length of him over a pile of toys and through an arch. He was leaning against a pillar in an idle sort of way and, you know, making the most horrid expressions with his face. The particular horrid thing he did was with his nose. He did it just as though he were idle and wanted to amuse himself. First of all, it was a short, blobby nose. Then suddenly he shot it out like a telescope. Then out it flew and became thinner and thinner until it was like a long, red, flexible whip. Like a thing in a nightmare it was! He whirled it about and flung it forth as a fisher flings his line.

My instant thought was that Gip mustn't see him. I turned about, and there was Gip quite taken up with the shopman. They were whispering together and looking at me. Gip was standing on a stool, and the shopman was holding a sort of big drum in his hand.

"Hide and seek, Daddy!" cried Gip. "Try and find me!"

And before I could do anything to prevent it, the shopman had placed the big drum over him.

I saw what was up. "Take that off!" I cried. "This instant! You'll frighten the boy. Take it off!"

The shopman did so without a word. He held the big drum towards me to show its emptiness. The little stool was also vacant! In that instant my boy had utterly disappeared? . . .

You know, perhaps, that sinister something that comes like a hand out of the unseen and grips your heart. You know it takes your common self away and leaves you tense and expectant, neither slow nor hasty, neither angry nor afraid. So it was with me.

I came up to this grinning shopman and kicked his stool aside.

"Stop this folly!" I said. "Where is my boy?"

"You see," he said, still showing me the drum's empty interior, "there is no deception—"

I put out my hand to grip him, and he escaped me by a skillful little movement. I snatched again. He turned from me and pushed open a door to escape. "Stop!" I cried, and he laughed and disappeared in a puff of smoke. I leaped after him— into utter darkness.

Thud!

"Oops! Bless my heart! I didn't see you coming, sir!"

I was in Regent Street, and I had collided with a decent looking man. A yard away, perhaps, and looking a little confused with himself, was Gip. There was some sort of apology. Then Gip had turned and come to me with a bright little smile, as though for a moment he had missed me.

And he was carrying four parcels in his arm!

He secured immediate possession of my finger.

For the moment I was rather at a loss. I stared round to see the door of the magic shop, and, behold, it was not there! There was no door, no shop, nothing, only the dividing wall between the shop where they sell pictures and the window with the birds! . . .

I did the only thing possible in my state of mental confusion. I walked straight to the curb and held up my umbrella for a cab.

I helped Gip in, recalled my address with an effort, and got in also. Something unusual made itself known in my back pocket. I felt and discovered a glass ball. Annoyed—no, more angry than annoyed—I flung it into the street.

Gip said nothing.

For a space neither of us spoke.

"Daddy!" said Gip, at last. "That *was* a proper shop!"

That brought me round to the problem of just how the whole thing had seemed to Gip. He looked completely undamaged—so far, good. He was nei-

---

• sinister (SIN i stur) **threatening; dark; evil**

ther scared nor troubled. He was simply tremendously satisfied with the afternoon's entertainment, and there in his arms were the four parcels.

Confound it! What could be in them?

"Um!" I said. "Little boys can't go to shops like that every day."

He received this with his usual calm. For a moment I was sorry I was not his mother so I could there, in public view, kiss him. After all, I thought, the thing wasn't so very bad.

But it was only when we opened the parcels that I really felt relieved. Three of them contained boxes of soldiers. They were ordinary toy soldiers, but of so good a quality as to make Gip altogether forget that originally these parcels had been Magic Tricks of the only genuine sort. The fourth contained a kitten, a little living white kitten, in excellent health and appetite and temper.

I saw this unpacking with relief. Still, I hung about in Gip's room for quite a long time. . . .

That happened six months ago. And now I am beginning to believe it is all right. The kitten had only the magic natural to all kittens. And the soldiers seem as steady a company as any colonel could desire. And Gip—?

The intelligent parent will understand that I have to go cautiously with Gip. But I went so far as this one day. I said, "How would you like your soldiers to come alive, Gip, and march about by themselves?"

"Mine do," said Gip. "I just have to say a word I know before I open the lid."

"Then they march about alone?"

"Oh, *quite,* Daddy. I shouldn't like them if they didn't do that."

I showed no special surprise. Since then I have made it a point to drop in on him once or twice, without announcing myself, when the soldiers were about. So far I have never discovered them acting in anything like a magical manner. . . .

It's so difficult to tell.

There's also a question of paying the bill. I have been up and down Regent Street several times, looking for that shop. I am inclined to think, indeed, that in that matter honor is satisfied. Surely Gip's name and address are known to them, so I may very well leave it to these people, whoever they may be, to send me their bill in their own time.

ALL THINGS CONSIDERED ————————————————

1. Gip's father goes into the magic shop because (a) he wants to buy a gift. (b) Gip urges him to go in. (c) the shopman tricks him.

2. The shopman gives Gip (a) money. (b) advice. (c) glass balls.

3. Gip shows he depends on his father by (a) asking questions. (b) acting afraid of the shopman. (c) holding his father's finger.

4. Gip wants a magic box and the shopman says, (a) "Take it." (b) "It's in your pocket." (c) "No one can have it."

5. Gip becomes so interested in the magic shop that he (a) wants to become a magician. (b) spends all his money. (c) takes the shopman's finger.

6. Finally the shopman makes (a) Gip disappear. (b) the father disappear. (c) the toy soldiers disappear.

7. The father goes after the shopman and (a) catches him. (b) turns into a kitten. (c) finds himself outside on the street.

8. The father (a) enjoys the magic. (b) learns to do magic himself. (c) does not like the magic shop.

9. The father never sees Gip (a) go to the shop. (b) make the soldiers come alive. (c) play with the magic gifts.

10. The father never (a) lets Gip do magic again. (b) finds the magic shop again. (c) talks to Gip about the magic gifts.

THINKING IT THROUGH ————————————————

1. What does the shopman mean when he says that his magic is "genuine," with "no deception"?

2. Why does there seem to be a struggle between the father and the shopman? Use examples from the story to support your reasons.

3. At the end, Gip says his soldiers "come alive . . . and march about by themselves." Do you think the father believes this?

4. The theme of "The Magic Shop" probably concerns the differences between a father and his son. The father sees magic as something evil. How does the son see magic? (a) If the father stands for old-fashioned ways of looking at things, what does the son stand for? (b) Will the father and son ever agree?

UNIT REVIEW

I. Match the terms in Column A with their definitions in Column B.

A	B
1. legend	**a)** sentence that tells the main idea of a paragraph
2. myth	
3. predicting	**b)** message or meaning of a story or other piece of writing
4. pronoun	
5. theme	**c)** talk by one person
6. monologue	**d)** expression that compares two things by using like or as
7. author's purpose	
8. simile	**e)** someone's reason for writing
9. topic sentence	**f)** story that explains events and tells the beliefs of a group of people
10. metaphor	
	g) word that refers to a person or thing mentioned elsewhere
	h) guessing at future events
	i) expression that compares two things without

II. On your paper, indicate whether each of the following sentences has a pronoun reference, a metaphor, or a simile.

    1. The stone headed toward the window like a speeding arrow.
    2. Mr. Alloway was glad that he was a grocer.
    3. Paula couldn't find the book she needed for the report.
    4. A computer is a dumb monster.
    5. Apologizing for her lateness, Mary hurried into the room.

III. The selections in this unit have topics that "go beyond" reality. Write the selections listed below in order from closest to reality to farthest beyond reality. Then write several sentences telling why you put the selections in this particular order.

      "Ninth Street Bridge"   "The Different Ones"

      "La Llorona"   Playmate"

Speaking Up

One topic that interests scientists is life on other planets. Life as we know it has not yet been discovered anywhere else in the universe. But scientists keep searching. All kinds of scientists. . . .

IS THERE LIFE ON OTHER PLANETS?

by Marion Lane

CHARACTERS
Chief Scientist
Five Scientists

Setting: *A conference room.* Chief Scientist *and other* Scientists *are seated at conference table, their backs to audience.*

Chief Scientist: *(Rising with back to audience)*: Ladies and gentlemen. Please come to order. I have called you here today to make an important announcement. I am sorry to tell you that after years of studies, we are forced to conclude that there cannot be any life on the planet nearest us.

First Scientist: But what about the changes in color from white to green that have been seen on the planet's surface? Don't these show weather changes and some kind of atmosphere?

Chief Scientist: All tests show that there is some atmosphere on the planet, but it is not enough to support life as we know it.

Second Scientist: Then how do you account for the ditches or canals that have been seen with our telescopes?

Chief Scientist: Latest viewings show that these are merely natural ground formations, and there is no proof whatever that they are made by any living beings.

Third Scientist: Then we must conclude that the flying saucer stories are all hoaxes?

Chief Scientist: No, of course not. Most of these sightings have perfectly logical, scientific explanations, and the rest are the direct result of mass hysteria.

Fourth Scientist: Then all the strange sounds picked up on radio receivers come from our own transmitters or are produced by atmospheric pressures?

Chief Scientist: I'm afraid so.

Fifth Scientist: I, for one, am extremely disappointed. I've always been sure we had neighbors on other planets, or at least on the one nearest to us. Perhaps not life as we know it, but some kind of intelligent life, totally unknown to us.

Chief Scientist: Ladies and gentlemen, I am going to adjourn this meeting. I can see no point in discussing this matter further. The tests have been so conclusive that any intelligent person must accept the fact that there is no life on—

All *(Turning to audience to reveal weird masks or makeup):* Earth! *(Curtain)*

- hoax (HOHKS) **fake**
- logical (LOJ i kul) **reasonable; following rules of thinking**
- mass hysteria (mas hi STAIR ee uh) **senseless excitement among crowds**

318

WRITING YOUR OWN SKETCH

A sketch is a picture in words. Write a sketch about this picture. Combine what you learned about describing people (page 73), actions (page 159), and settings (page 239). You may want to look back at those pages to help you write this sketch.

1. **Prewriting:** List a few words that describe the setting and the mood. Next, list words that describe the people. In this case, think of them as characters in a story. Finally, make notes about what happens first, second, and last.
2. **Writing:** Use your plan to write an opening paragraph about the setting. Make sure it sets the mood. Then name and describe the characters in one or two paragraphs. In a final paragraph, describe the action.
3. **Revising:** Reread your sketch. Check to see that your descriptions are clear and interesting. Check your spelling, punctuation, and capitalization. Be sure all sentences have subjects and verbs. Make corrections and rewrite your paragraphs neatly.

UNIT 5

STANDING TALL

Do you know people who seem to stand taller than all others? Do you know men and women who, in the words of Robert Louis Stevenson, "stand above the common herd"? If you do, you know the sort of people who are heroes. Heroes can be famous, but they don't have to be. A hero is any person who uses wisdom and courage to meet life head-on.

There are many heroes in this unit. Some may remind you of yourself at times. As you read, consider what it takes to stand tall.

LIFEBOAT IN SPACE

by Gurney Williams III

▶ How do people show courage when they face a life-or-death situation? How would you act if you were one of the astronauts in this true story?

The spaceship carrying three men to the moon shuddered as if it had bumped into something.

The shudder made no sense. There was nothing to bump into, 205,000 miles away from earth in space. Astronaut Fred W. Haise was floating between two cabins in the ship when he felt the bump. He pulled himself quickly into the main cabin, also called the command module. The ship continued to shake up and down. Haise's heart was beating twice as fast as usual.

There was no gravity in space, so Haise appeared to be floating through the air. Quickly, he pulled himself to his seat. Another astronaut, John L. Swigert, slammed the door that sealed off the cabin.

Now all three were sitting in a small compartment, about as big as a three-person tent. It was a little after 9:00 P.M.

on Monday, April 13, 1970, somewhere between earth and the moon.

In their cramped quarters, the crew tried to figure out what had happened. They read the dials in front of them. The whole ship was wobbling now, like a car with a flat tire. Their eyes raced over the lighted boards.

A few of the dials were behaving wildly. Some showed the ship was losing electrical power. Captain James A. Lovell tried to stop the wobbling by firing small rockets outside the ship. It didn't work. Then suddenly he hit on the problem. One of the instruments was like a fuel gauge on a car. It showed how much fuel—which in this case was oxygen— was left in one of the large tanks. The fuel was used to make electrical power to run the ship. Just as important, oxygen was a vital part of the air the astronauts breathed. Without fuel, the ship and the

- shudder (SHUD ur) **shake; shiver; tremble**
- module (MOJ yool) **part of a spacecraft that is designed to do a particular job and has everything necessary for that job**
- **cramped** (KRAMPT) **crowded; having little space to move**
- gauge (GAYJ) **instrument that measures something**
- **vital** (VY tul) **necessary for life; very important**

people running it would die.

Lovell radioed the earth about what he had found. "Our oxygen number two tank is reading zero," he said.

Then Lovell got out of his seat and glided to a window so he could see the outside of Apollo 13. He turned to the section of the ship called the service module. That was a large cylinder containing the fuel tanks and the main rocket engine. The service module was connected to one end of the command module where the men lived. In the black night of space, Lovell saw a ghostly cloud coming out of the side of the service module.

Lovell got back on the radio. He flashed the news to the mission control room in Texas. "It looks to me like we are venting something," he said.

Apollo 13, pride of America, had taken off from earth two days before. Now, like an old boat, it was leaking, or "venting." One of its fuel tanks had exploded, blasting a hole right through the side of the service module. Fuel was disappearing into space. Every two seconds the ship moved a mile closer to the moon and farther from earth.

Dozens of people on the ground tried to figure out what to do. What they needed was a lifeboat—another rocket ship with its own supply of oxygen and its

own rocket engine—to bring the men home.

In a way, Apollo 13 had a lifeboat. Its name was Aquarius. Aquarius was a small but complete rocket ship. It was attached to the command module where the men lived. It had been designed to break away from the command module and carry two crew members to the surface of the moon. Then it could take them back to the command module. It had its own air supply. It had its own rocket engine.

What it didn't have was space. There was no room to sit down in Aquarius. It had about as much space as a small closet. Aquarius also did not have

- cylinder (SIL in dur) **anything shaped like a tube with closed ends**
- mission (MISH un) **a special job, such as a space flight**
- mission control—**the group of people on the ground in charge of the people in space**

323

strength. It was built to land on the moon—not on the earth. If the astronauts tried to ride it all the way home into the earth's air, it would burn up. The command module was the only part of Apollo 13 that was designed to survive the fiery plunge back to earth.

The people on the ground argued and sweated over what to do. Finally, they agreed on a plan. They radioed the idea into space. Turn off everything in the command module to save what fuel is left. Climb into Aquarius. Use the Aquarius air supply and the Aquarius rocket to get home. Then when you get close to earth, climb back into the command module to protect yourselves when things get hot during the landing.

Haise was the first to enter Aquarius. There were no lights except his flashlight. He floated into the dark little cabin. Closer and closer he moved toward the instruments covering the walls. He moved closer to the two triangular windows that had been designed for a view of the moon's surface. There were no seats. Haise turned on some of the switches. Soon the cramped lifeboat was filling with its own supply of oxygen.

Lovell joined Haise. Swigert stayed behind in the command module for a few minutes. He turned everything off to save the little fuel left for the earth landing. Then he followed the other two into Aquarius. There was no chance now that Aquarius would land on the moon. It now had a new mission, a more important one—to keep three men alive.

Apollo 13, its crew huddled in one end, sped on toward the moon. The ship curved around the back side of the moon, out of sight of the earth. The gray lunar surface unrolled beneath the ship. Then the earth, a blue-green ball, appeared again. It was time to see whether the small rocket on Aquarius could blast the whole ship into a good course back home to earth. If the course adjustment failed, Apollo could miss the earth completely. The crew wouldn't survive long. Then the ship would carry their bodies on an endless trip through space.

"Mark!" said a man in Texas. That told Lovell he had forty seconds to go before firing. Lovell put his hand on the firing button. "Five . . . four . . . three . . . two . . . one." At exactly the right time, the rocket began to fire. No one could hear the explosion. Sound couldn't pass through empty space. But the astronauts could feel the movement. The little rocket on Aquarius kept pushing the whole ship into line. It kept firing for four minutes. Then a computer took over. It turned the rocket off at precisely the right moment.

The men in space and the people on the ground anxiously checked the

- fiery (FY uh ree) **flaming; on fire**
- lunar (LOON ur) **having to do with the moon**
- course (KORS) **particular path or direction**
- precisely (pruh SYS lee) **exactly**
- **anxiously** (ANGK shus lee) **in a worried way**

course. The rocket had done its job. The ship was aimed for a landing in the Pacific Ocean, a quarter of a million miles away. At least the ship was headed in the right direction. Whether it would splash down safely, no one knew.

Other problems crowded in on the men in the crippled ship.

Since fuel was low, there was not enough energy to keep Aquarius warm. The temperature was rapidly dropping. And there were no winter clothes on Apollo 13.

Fuel had been used to make water, so now water supplies were low, too. Like desert explorers, the men had carried some of the water from the main supply in the command module to Aquarius in plastic juice bags. But the supply was still low. Their constant thirst was making it hard for the men to concentrate.

The air was bad. Back in the command module, a machine cleaned the air of dangerous gases. Aquarius had no such machine. Scientists on the ground suggested that the men try to build an air cleaner out of scraps aboard the ship—plastic bags, a hose, some cards, and tape. No one knew whether the contraption would work.

By now, millions of people on earth were worried about the voyagers. Concern had spread around the world. Thirteen countries offered to help in recovering the ship if it made it back to earth.

People gathered on streets to watch TV reports and in churches and synagogues to pray.

In space, it was cold and quiet. By early Wednesday morning, the temperature in Aquarius had dropped to fifty-five degrees. No one aboard could sleep. The men stayed awake—thirsty, tired, and cold.

"You got up kind of early, didn't you?" the ground radioed. The men said it was impossible to sleep. Temperatures were headed for the forties.

The air got worse. Before noon on Wednesday, a yellow light in Aquarius warned suddenly that it wasn't safe to breathe. Lovell turned on the taped-up

- **constant** (KON stunt) **always the same; not changing**
- concentrate (KON sun trayt) **give very careful attention**
- contraption (kun TRAP shun) **machine or gadget; thing put together to do a job**

contraption. It began to suck air through the filter.

Clean air flooded the cabin. The light went off. They would be okay as long as the makeshift air cleaner worked.

The thirst and cold were making it more and more difficult to think clearly. A sharp mind was now critical. The ship sped toward earth. The men had to begin moving back into the command module to prepare to land. Landing was complicated because most of Apollo 13 had to be thrown away in space before it was safe to come down. The command module had a shield on its bottom to help it survive the heat when it plunged into the earth's air. Aquarius had no such protection.

One of the astronauts' first jobs was to separate the command module from Aquarius and the service module. The service module was spinning away into space when Lovell spotted the damage caused by the fuel tank explosion. "There's one whole side of that spacecraft missing," he said.

Haise saw it too. "It's really a mess," he reported. The service module shrank to a dot in the blackness.

As it disappeared in the distance, the crew aboard Apollo began to worry about something more dangerous than anything that had happened. The fuel tank explosion had damaged the service module just a few feet from the heat shield that would protect the men during the last few minutes of the flight. Suppose the explosion had also damaged the heat shield. Would the command module stand the shock of reentering earth's atmosphere? No one talked about the possibility. The earth seemed to grow steadily, a big blue ball out the spaceship's window.

Lovell was the last to leave Aquarius. He eased his way back into the command module. The men switched over to the remaining oxygen in the command module. Then they blasted away from their lifeboat.

They were falling now, in the command module, at about 15,000 miles an hour. In less than an hour, they would either land or burn up.

No one was talking much. People on the ground were figuring out the course. There was little that could be done now. The command module was picking up speed—17,000, then 18,000 miles an hour. In a few minutes it reached 20,000 miles an hour. That meant the end of radio contact was near. The ship-to-ground radios couldn't work through the fire that would soon surround the command module. The ground crew talked nervously with the astronauts about a

- makeshift (MAYK shift) **put together for the time being to act as a substitute for something else**
- critical (KRIT uh kul) **necessary for success; very important**
- complicated (KOM pli kayt id) **very difficult; not easy to deal with**
- **shield** (SHEELD) **something used for protection**

party they would have after the mission was ended. Swigert said he wished he could be there for it.

About 400,000 feet above the earth, the capsule began heating up. Soon flames whipped around it and the radio went dead. Ground scientists expected radio contact to be broken for about three and a half minutes.

At the end of three and a half minutes, there was still no word. Another half-minute ticked by. Apollo 13 remained silent. And then another half-minute. Some people began to lose hope.

"Okay, Joe." The voice was Swigert's. He was on the air again. Within minutes, white-and-orange parachutes rose like giant party balloons over the little command module. It splashed into the sea and the men were picked up from their ship. They had survived.

ALL THINGS CONSIDERED ————————————————

1. At the beginning, the spaceship was (a) headed toward the moon. (b) lost in space. (c) returning to earth.

2. The first sign of danger was (a) a fuel gauge that read zero. (b) warnings from mission control. (c) the shaking of the spaceship.

3. The most serious thing the astronauts had to worry about was (a) not getting to the moon. (b) not having enough oxygen to stay alive. (c) getting lost on the moon.

4. The "lifeboat" was (a) a special spaceship made to save the astronauts from danger. (b) a rocket ship made to carry the astronauts to the moon from their spaceship. (c) an extra spaceship that mission control sent up.

5. Aquarius could not take the astronauts all the way back to earth because it (a) had to be returned to the moon. (b) was too small. (c) was not built to withstand the heat of reentry.

6. Aquarius helped the astronauts by (a) providing air and saving fuel. (b) giving them a chance to reach another spaceship. (c) acting as mission control.

7. To head the astronauts back toward earth, rockets were fired by (a) mission control. (b) an astronaut in the command module. (c) an astronaut in Aquarius.

8. The astronauts had to put together a special machine to give themselves (a) fresh water. (b) more heat. (c) clean air.

9. After they returned to the command module, a new worry was that (a) Aquarius might crash into them. (b) the heat shield would not protect them. (c) the fuel tank might explode.

10. At the end, Swigert's words, "Okay, Joe," were a sign that (a) radio contact had been restored. (b) the parachutes wouldn't open. (c) the astronauts needed air.

THINKING IT THROUGH ————————————————

1. The astronauts were in very great danger, but they stayed calm. How do you think they really felt? Do you think they would have survived if they had panicked?

2. How was quick thinking important to the astronauts? Give at least two examples of quick thinking by them or by others.

3. What can we learn about space travel from this story? Tell two things you learned about spaceships and their mission.

Literary Skills: Review

If you wish to review the meaning of any term in *italics* in this exercise, refer to the Glossary of Terms (pages 394–396).

I. Write complete sentences on a separate sheet of paper to answer these questions.

1. Who are the *main characters* in this story?
2. Is this story *fiction* or *nonfiction*? (Explain how you can tell.)
3. What is the *setting* for "Lifeboat in Space"?
4. Which of these sentences best describes the *plot* of the story?
   a. Astronauts get lost trying to land on the moon, so they return to earth.
   b. Some astronauts are braver than others.
   c. Astronauts work to save their lives when their equipment fails.

II. Choose the correct ending for each of these statements.

1. The main *conflict* in this story is (a) between people. (b) between people and machines. (c) within one person.
2. The *climax* of the story comes when (a) the astronauts realize they have no oxygen. (b) the astronauts enter Aquarius. (c) the capsule reenters the earth's atmosphere.
3. The *topic* of the story is (a) traveling to Mars. (b) solving problems in space. (c) ten uses of oxygen.

Composition

Follow your teacher's instructions before completing *one* of these writing assignments.

1. Would you like to travel in space? Give at least three reasons for your answer. Begin your composition by writing "I would (or would not) like to travel in space because . . ."
2. Think of a problem that you or someone you know solved by keeping calm and thinking clearly. Write one or two paragraphs about the problem and how it was solved.

A NATION'S STRENGTH

by Ralph Waldo Emerson

▶ Ralph Waldo Emerson (1803–1882) was one of America's great writers. Emerson thought and wrote a lot about his country. Here is his idea of what makes a nation stand tall. Do you agree with him?

Not gold, but only men can make
   A people great and strong;
Men who, for truth and honor's sake,
   Stand fast and suffer long.

Brave men who work while others sleep,
   Who dare while others fly—
They build a nation's pillars deep
   And lift them to the sky.

WAYS OF KNOWING

1. What does Emerson believe is the most important thing to make a nation strong? Do you think he is right? Why or why not?

2. Emerson used the word "men" in this poem. Do you think he meant "women" as well? Give some examples of both women and men today who fit the description he gives.

3. What does "Men who . . . Stand fast and suffer long" mean? What does "Who dare when others fly" mean? Put each of these lines into your own words.

4. Can you visualize people building "a nation's pillars deep" and lifting them "to the sky"? What would the picture look like?

- **fast** (FAST) **firmly; loyally**
- fly (FLY) **run away**
- pillar (PIL ur) **column that helps support a building**

LINEAGE

by Margaret Walker

My grandmothers were strong.
They followed plows and bent to toil.
They moved through fields sowing seed.
They touched earth and grain grew.
They were full of sturdiness and singing.
My grandmothers were strong.

My grandmothers are full of memories.
Smelling of soap and onions and wet clay
With veins rolling roughly over quick hands
They have many clean words to say.
My grandmothers were strong.
Why am I not as they?

WAYS OF KNOWING

1. What examples does the speaker give of her grandmothers' strength? Which of the ways tell of physical strength? Which describe the inner strength of people who stand tall in quiet ways?

2. What memories does the speaker have of her grandmothers? Which of the five senses form parts of these memories?

3. Look at the question in the last line of the poem. Why do you think it is asked? Might the speaker be wrong about herself?

- lineage (LIN ee ij) **the people who came before you in your family; ancestors**
- toil (TOYL) **hard work; physical labor**
- sturdiness (STUR dee nes) **strength**

331

NO MEDALS FOR MARY

by Eve Pownall

▶ There are many people who live quiet lives, and few people know of them. These unsung heroes and heroines may stand very tall. Do you know anyone like Mary Blattman?

Many settlements were established in New South Wales, Australia, by the 1860s. Hills and gullies had long known the rumble of wagon wheels and teams of horses making the long trek into the land of the west. But in each decade, other districts opened up. These new areas required work equal to that of the early pioneers.

Mary Blattman, married at 17, helped John, her husband, clear and fence a small farm in the mountains around Jenolan Caves.

They built a little four-roomed wooden house, plastered and whitewashed it inside and out, hung shutters at the windows, and thatched the roof with grass from the creek bank.

There were children in the cottage, magpies in the gum trees, and geese on the creeks near the house. Mary baked crusty bread in the camp oven, churned butter, made cheese, and sewed for the family by hand. After 12 or 13 years, the little farm looked well with its crops and a few cows and horses grazing about it.

Then John was brought home one day badly hurt. "An accident with horses," says the family.

Before her 30th birthday, Mary was a widow. She was now the owner and manager of the little farm that must support herself and her six young children. Life became one never-ending round of duties. She worked in the fields by day, washed, baked bread, cured bacon, and did the dairy work late at night. Her eldest daughter, aged 11, worked beside her until sleep slowed her hands and set her young head nodding. The eldest boy chopped wood, fed stock, car-

- **establish** (eh STAB lish) set up; build
- **trek** (TREK) ?
- magpie (MAG py) ?
- stock (STOK) ?

Notice that some vocabulary words are not defined. As you read, use context clues to figure out their meanings. Definitions will be given later.

ried buckets of water from the creek, and helped where he could. Eight years old is young to shoulder a man's work.

Mary drove a heavy old-fashioned cart to Oberon, 10 miles away, for groceries and supplies. In winter, when carts bogged down in swollen creeks, she went on horseback. She rode along the tracks (there were no roads), picking her way over creeks (there were no bridges), and dismounting to open and close the gates.

The farm pigs became fat on potatoes, turnips, and boiled rye. A neighbor killed and butchered them, but Mary herself did the curing. This was her method:

"She stabbed the rind with a bootmaker's awl, then, with a little board, rubbed coarse salt into the holes. The pieces were then turned over and salt sprinkled on the fleshy side. Covered with a cloth, it was left for two days. Then the process was repeated three times altogether. It was then hung in the kitchen to dry. It kept a long time and was good bacon." (*From a letter by Mrs. E. Arrow of Bathurst, daughter of Mrs. Blattman.*)

In the large dairy she made cheese. Rennet tablets placed in fresh milk formed thick curds after an hour or two. They were crumbled by hand, tipped into a vat lined with thin cloth, pressed tightly,

- shoulder (SHOHL dur) **take on a responsibility; accept something difficult**
- bog down (BOG DOUN) **?**
- awl (AWL) **sharp pointed tool**
- rennet (REN it) **liquid used for making cheese**
- curds (KURDZ) **?**

and the cover weighted. Next day the cheese was turned out and set on shelves to dry, covered with white cloth, and turned over once a day for several days. When thoroughly dried it was ready for market— a mild cheese that always sold well.

Three or four times a year Mary harnessed a spring cart and drove forty miles to Bathurst, with eggs and poultry, her home-cured bacon, and cheese. When she returned, there were goods to unpack—a new saucepan, perhaps, a butter churn, tools or supplies for the farm, boots for the family, and material for clothes which she made up by hand in the time she miraculously squeezed from the day.

Working round the clock allowed no time for self-pity. Never a holiday in twenty years, rising early to pull on the elastic-sided boots she liked because there were no laces to tie. A slight figure, dressed mostly in cotton skirts and blouses and a sunbonnet, she was out early in the paddocks.

The children must be off to school (half a day only; the teacher divided his time between two schools five miles apart). There were the lamps to fill, wicks to trim, melted fat to pour into candle molds, cooking, making bread, housework, sewing—that was the day gone. Winter winds sweeping from the mountains, spring returning with the wattle to the hills, the children growing and helping—the years were flying by.

Mary, used to the old sorrow of a lost mate, now had a new one to set beside it—an ailing child whom she took to Bathurst but could not save. It was a long drive homeward down the lonely road with only a small son and her own thoughts for company. But that was life and the busy years were going. They had gone, like last year's snow on Oberon's hills. The boys grew and built their own homes. The daughter, who had worked sleepy-eyed beside her mother, became a bride and moved away.

Mary was tired and the little farm had served its purpose. It was sold and Mary turned her back on the thatched roof and the wattle-

- **miraculously** (mi RAK yuh lus lee) **amazingly; seeming to be caused by a miracle**
- paddock (PAD uk) **closed-in field used for horses and other animals**
- wick (WIK) **thick thread in a candle**
- wattle (WOT ul) **kind of bush with yellow or white flowers, found in Australia**

clad hills, and moved to Bathurst. She died in her sleep in her daughter's home, aged 90, joining the many who rate no place in the nation's remembrance, no banners, no medals for a life of uncomplaining service.

Farewell, Mary! May the wattle glow brightly wherever your dust is drifting.

ALL THINGS CONSIDERED

1. The story begins in (a) 1800. (b) the 1860s. (c) the 1900s.
2. Mary set up the farm (a) by herself. (b) with her children. (c) with her husband.
3. The first serious trouble Mary had was when (a) she married. (b) her husband died. (c) her child died.
4. She got help on the farm from (a) her young children. (b) her nearest neighbors. (c) a hired worker.
5. At the time of this story, there probably were no (a) towns nearby. (b) places to buy things. (c) cars and trucks.
6. Two things that Mary sold were (a) horses and candles. (b) bacon and cheese. (c) bread and vegetables.
7. The children went to school half a day because (a) Mary needed them to help her on the farm. (b) the five-mile trip was too long. (c) the teacher taught at another school the other half a day.
8. Mary's daughter (a) got married and moved away. (b) ran away from home. (c) became a teacher in a school near the farm.
9. When Mary grew old she (a) lived on the farm by herself. (b) gave the farm to her children. (c) sold the farm and moved to town.
10. From the way the story is written, you can tell that the author (a) thinks Mary wasted her life. (b) admires Mary very much. (c) believes Mary should have married again.

THINKING IT THROUGH

1. Do you think that Mary Blattman is the kind of person Emerson described in "A Nation's Strength"? Why or why not?
2. Mary is a pioneer. So are the astronauts in "Lifeboat in Space." What makes all of them pioneers?

- clad (KLAD) dressed; decorated

335

Vocabulary and Sentence Meaning: Review

I. Five words in the story are listed at the bottoms of the pages but are not defined. Use *context clues* to help you figure out their meanings. On a separate sheet of paper, match the words in Column A with their meanings in Column B.

A	B
1. bog down	**a.** farm animals
2. curds	**b.** kind of bird
3. magpie	**c.** difficult journey
4. stock	**d.** get slowed by mud
5. trek	**e.** thick milk for making cheese

II. In each sentence below, replace the <u>underlined</u> word with an *antonym.*

1. Mary drove a heavy <u>old-fashioned</u> cart.
2. Rennet tablets were placed in <u>fresh</u> milk.
3. She was out <u>early</u> in the paddocks.
4. She was used to the <u>sorrow</u>.
5. <u>Before</u> her 30th birthday, Mary was a widow.
6. Her daughter <u>worked</u> beside her.
7. The pigs became <u>fat</u> on potatoes.
8. The rind was left <u>covered</u> for two days.
9. Mary bought a <u>new</u> saucepan.
10. <u>Farewell</u>, Mary!

Composition

Follow your teacher's instructions before completing *one* of these writing assignments.

1. Pick one paragraph from the story with three or more sentences. Rewrite it in your own words.
2. Use one or two of the following words in a paragraph. The paragraph can be about Australia or about anything you choose.

    clad   establish   miraculously   shoulder

WINTER

by Nikki Giovanni

▶ Meeting life's challenges can be as exciting as standing up
to a once-in-a-lifetime event, or as simple as preparing for
the next season.

Frogs burrow the mud
snails bury themselves
and I air my quilts
preparing for the cold

Dogs grow more hair
mothers make oatmeal
and little boys and girls
take Father John's Medicine

Bears store fat
chipmunks gather nuts
and I collect books
for the coming winter

WAYS OF KNOWING

1. What animals does the poet mention? How does each prepare for
winter? How does each animal's activities help that animal live
through the winter?

2. What do the humans in the poem do to prepare for winter? Are
they the same kinds of things that the animals do? For example,
does gathering nuts serve a similar purpose for a squirrel that
collecting books does for a person? Why do you think the poet
put these ideas in the same stanza?

3. What are the most important things that you do to prepare for a
new season or a change such as the start of a school vacation?

- **burrow** (BUR oh) **dig**
- Father John's Medicine—a cough medicine

_____

Before completing the exercises that follow, you may wish to review the **bold-faced** words on pages 322–337.

I. On a separate sheet of paper, write the *italicized* word that best fills the blank in each sentence. Each word should be used only once.

burrow	*anxiously*	*constant*	*cramped*	*establish*
fast	*miraculously*	*shield*	*trek*	*vital*

1. It was a long _____ through the forest to the new home.
2. She held _____ to the rope and was pulled to shore.
3. Worms like to _____ into the earth of our garden.
4. We _____ awaited the results of the test.
5. He held up the _____ to protect him in battle.
6. It was very _____ with 15 people in the small room.
7. _____, everybody was saved when the airplane crashed.
8. It is _____ to carry a supply of water in the desert.
9. They grew tired of the _____ sound of the waves on the shore.
10. The town wants to _____ a school for young children.

II. Match the terms in Column A with their definitions in Column B. If you wish to review the meaning of any word in Column A, refer to the Glossary of Terms (pages 394–396).

A	**B**
1. characters	**a.** story that is true
2. plot	**b.** story that is made up
3. setting	**c.** people in a story or a play
4. topic	**d.** word that means the opposite of another word
5. theme	
6. antonym	**e.** where and when a story takes place
7. context clues	**f.** what a story is about
8. fiction	**g.** high point of a story or a play
9. nonfiction	**h.** series of actions or events
10. climax	**i.** hints that help the reader decide what a word means
	j. what the writer says about a topic

Matsuo Basho (1644-1694)

At the time Matsuo Basho was born,
Japan was at peace after many years
of civil war. Basho was born in to a
family of samurai, or warriors. But since
there were no wars to fight, he was sent
to serve a lord in a castle.

He began writing haiku when he was a
teenager. Basho was in his early 20s when
the lord he worked for died. He left the
castle to live among Buddhist monks, but
he continued to write haiku. After a while,
he began to teach others to write haiku.

Basho is believed to have given the
haiku form some of its rules. It was Basho
who encouraged others to suggest
pictures or ideas instead of describing
them. Many people consider him the first
of the great Japanese haiku poets.

THREE HAIKU

by Matsuo Basho

▶ As you read each of these poems, try to form a picture in
your mind. Think about how the world of nature stands tall
in the poet's mind.

An old silent pond . . .
into the pond a frog jumps
splash! silence again.

The still snow we watched
has it covered the same hill
again this winter?

So cold are the waves
the rocking gull can scarcely
fold itself to sleep.

WAYS OF KNOWING

1. Which season is brought to mind by each of these poems? Explain your answers.
2. In the frog poem, how much of the picture is a picture you can
   see? How much is a "picture" you can hear?
3. Is there any real answer to the poem about the snow? Can you
   ask the question in a different way?
4. Do you think "fold" is a good word to use in the poem about the
   gull? Why or why not?
5. These poems have been translated from Japanese into English.
   What problems might there be in writing a translation?

• gull (GUL) gray-white bird that lives in water

WINGS OF SUMMER

by Ray Bradbury

▶ Sometimes having the right thing to wear makes you feel that you are standing taller. Did you ever feel the way Doug feels?

CHARACTERS

Narrator
Doug, *a teenage boy*
John, *another teenage boy*
Dad, *Doug's father*
Mr. Sanderson, *owner of a shoe store*

This play is meant to be read aloud, not acted out. Characters rise and sit, as directed, to show that they are in or out of the scene. All, except the narrator, are seated as the play opens.

Narrator: You do not hear them coming. You hardly hear them go. The grass bends down, springs up again. They pass like cloud-shadows downhill . . . the boys of summer, running.

Doug *(rises and steps forward)***:** Hey! John Huff! Charlie Woodman! Wait for me.

John *(stands)***:** Doug—come on! Doug!

Narrator: It's no use. . . .They're gone.

John: Doug! Come on, Doug! (John *sits.*)

Narrator: The running boys fade.

Doug *(still standing)***:** I'm alive. But what's the use? They're more alive than I am. How come? How come?

Narrator: You know the answer, Douglas Spaulding. Standing alone there, you know. Look down, Doug. Stare down at your motionless feet . . . .

Doug: It's these shoes. . . .

Narrator: Late that night, Douglas Spaulding, going home from the movie with your mother and father and brother Tom, you see

• **narrator** (NAR rayt ur) **person who tells a story**

the tennis shoes in the bright store window. Your ankles are seized, feet suspended. The earth spins. Mom and Dad and brother walk quietly forward. You, Douglas, trudge backward, watching the shoes in the midnight window.

Doug: Dad . . . back there in the window, those creamy-sponge Para Litefoot shoes . . .

Dad (*rises*)**:** Suppose you tell me why you need a pair of sneakers. Can you do that?

Doug: Well . . .

Narrator: Tell him, Doug. Tell him how they feel like running through summer grass without any shoes on. Like sticking your feet out of hot covers to let cool breezes slip soothingly across them. Tell him how tennis shoes feel like it always feels the first time each year, wading in the slow waters of the clear creek.

Doug: Dad—it's kind—kind of hard to explain.

Dad: But what's wrong with last year's shoes? Dig *them* out of the closet.

- suspended (suh SPEND id) **hanging in air**
- **trudge** (TRUJ) **walk in a heavy way**

342

Narrator: The people that make tennis shoes seem to know what boys need and want. They must have watched a lot of winds blow the trees and a lot of rivers going down to lakes. Whatever it is, it is in the shoes, and it is summer. Douglas, try to say all this in your words.

Doug: Don't you see, Dad? I just can't use last year's pair . . . .

Narrator: They were great last year. But now . . . why, Mr. Spaulding, now they're all dead inside!

Dad: Well . . . we'll see, Doug. *(meaning "no")* We'll see. (Dad *sits.*)

Doug: I just gotta, Dad. I just gotta. Why, with those shoes I could do anything . . . anything at all! (Doug *sits.*)

Narrator: The next morning, old Mr. Sanderson moves through his shoe store as the proprietor of a pet shop must move through his shop where are kenneled animals from every place in the world, touching each one on his way. Brush the shoes in the window . . . some dogs, some cats . . . touch each pair with concern, adjusting laces, fixing tongues . . . .

There is the sound of thunder! One moment the door to Sanderson's shoe emporium, empty. Next, Douglas Spaulding standing clumsily in the opening. The thunder had stopped when his shoes stopped. (Doug *stands.* Mr. Sanderson *rises.*)

Sanderson: Don't say a word, Douglas.

Narrator: Douglas freezes. All the night before—before he had gone to bed—dreaming of cream-sponge Para Litefoot tennis shoes, he had carefully stacked the nickels, dimes, and quarters of his piggy-bank. He had said to himself . . .

Doug: Whatever you want, you got to make your own way.

Narrator: Now he stands frozen in the doorway, in the bright sunlight of the shoe emporium—frozen, staring down at his leather shoes as if these heavy things could not be pulled up out of the cement.

Sanderson *(moving forward)***:** First, I know just what you want to buy.

Narrator: Mr. Sanderson's voice reaches Douglas's ears . . . but he cannot respond. He cannot move.

- proprietor (pruh PRY i tur) **owner**
- kenneled (KEN uld) **kept in kennels or cages**
- emporium (em POR ee um) **large store**

Sanderson: Second, I see you every afternoon at my window. You think I *don't see?* You're wrong. Third, to give it its full name, you want the ROYAL CROWN CREAM-SPONGE PARA LITEFOOT TENNIS SHOES. "Like menthol on your feet!" Fourth, you want credit!

Doug *(moves forward):* No! I got something better than credit to offer! Before I tell, Mr. Sanderson, you got to do me one small favor. Can you remember when was the last time you yourself wore a pair of Litefoot sneakers?

Sanderson: Oh, ten, twenty, say thirty years ago. Why?

Doug: Oh? . . . Well . . . don't you think you owe it to your customers to at least *try* the tennis shoes you sell, so you'd know how they feel?

Sanderson: You may not have noticed, but I'm wearing shoes.

Doug: But not sneakers, sir. How can you rave about them if you haven't worn them for thirty years?

Sanderson: Well, now I . . .

Doug: Mr. Sanderson, you sell me something, and I'll sell you something just as valuable.

Sanderson: Is it absolutely necessary to the sale that I put on a pair of the sneakers, boy?

Doug: I sure wish you would, sir.

Sanderson: Well . . . *(He sighs and shrugs resignedly.)*

Narrator: A minute later, seated, panting quietly, Mr. Sanderson laces the tennis shoes to his long narrow feet. They look detached and alive down there next to the dark cuffs of his business suit.

Doug: How do they feel?

Sanderson: "How do they feel?" he asks. They . . . they feel just fine.

Doug: Oh, sir! Please don't sit down; kinda rock back and forth, sponge around while I tell you the rest.

Narrator: Better sit back, Mr. Sanderson. Sink deep into your shoes, flex your toes. You can't stop this flow of words. A dam

---

- menthol (MEN thawl) **kind of medicine that feels cool on the skin**
- rave (RAYV) **speak with enthusiasm; praise a great deal**
- resignedly (ri ZY nid lee) **giving in; not offering a protest**
- detached (di TACHT) **not attached or connected; separated**
- flex (FLEKS) **bend**

has burst. Limber your arches. All the flood will come out in one gigantic gush of words. So sit back, test your ankles . . . feel the softness on your feet.

Doug: Mr. Sanderson, I'll give you my money; you give me the shoes. I still will owe you a dollar. But, Mr. Sanderson—soon as I get those shoes on, you know what *happens?*

Sanderson: What?

Doug: Bang! I deliver your packages, pick up packages, bring you lunch, burn trash, run to the post office, library . . . you'll see twelve of me in and out every minute. Feel those shoes . . . see how fast they'd take me? Feel all that running inside? You stay in the nice cool store while I'm jumping all over town! But it's not me, really; it's the shoes. They go like mad down alleys, cutting corners . . . there they go! Whoooooooooosh! . . .

Narrator: Feel those shoes, Mr. Sanderson. Douglas is right. Feel how they hush themselves deep into the carpet, sink as in jungle grass, in loam and resilient clay. You should look in a mirror, Mr. Sanderson. How many years has it been since *that* light shown in your face, in your eyes?

Sanderson: Boy! In five years, how'd you like a job selling shoes in this emporium?

Doug: Gee, thanks, sir! I don't know what I'm going to be, yet.

Sanderson: Anything you want to be, son—you'll be it. No one will ever stop you. Find your size and lace 'em up. There's a dozen things you have to do for me today. Finish them, we're even-steven, and you're fired.

Doug: Thanks, Mr. Sanderson. I'm on my way!

Sanderson: Stop! . . . How do they feel, boy?

Narrator: The boy looks down at his feet in deep rivers, in fields of wheat in the wind, already rushing him out of town. He looks up at the old man; his eyes flame; his mouth moves . . . but no sound comes out.

Sanderson: Antelopes, son? Gazelles?

Narrator: Douglas hesitates, nods a quick yes and vanishes. (Doug *sits.*) With a whisper he spins around and is gone. The door stands empty. The sound of tennis shoes drifts away on the jungle air. From a long time ago a memory comes back to old Mr. Sanderson.

Sanderson: I remember when I was a boy . . . I remember the sound. Beautiful creatures leaping under the sky, gone through brush, under trees, away. Only the soft echo of the running left behind. Antelopes. Gazelles.

Narrator: Mr. Sanderson stoops to pick up the boy's abandoned winter shoes, heavy with forgotten rains and long melted snows. (Mr. Sanderson *sits.*)

- loam (LOHM) **rich soil**
- resilient (ri ZIL yunt) **elasticlike; capable of springing back easily**
- gazelle (guh ZEL) **kind of small antelope that runs swiftly and gracefully**
- hesitate (HEZ i tayt) **pause because one is not sure**

ALL THINGS CONSIDERED ───────────────

1. The first voice in the play is the voice of (a) Doug. (b) John. (c) the narrator.

2. The narrator says that Doug does not feel alive because (a) he is sad. (b) his shoes are wrong. (c) he doesn't run enough.

3. When Doug asks for new tennis shoes, his father says (a) "No, absolutely not." (b) "Well . . . we'll see." (c) "You've got to make your own way."

4. The character who first explains how boys feel in new tennis shoes is (a) the narrator. (b) Doug's father. (c) Mr. Sanderson.

5. The tennis shoes that Doug wants are called (a) Para Litefoot. (b) Menthol-lined. (c) Resilient Crown-Sponge.

6. When Mr. Sanderson sees Doug in the store, he (a) tells him he has sold all the shoes. (b) says he knows what Doug wants. (c) asks Doug if he wants a job.

7. Doug offers to (a) pay part of the price of the sneakers and work for the rest. (b) pay for the sneakers after he gets a job. (c) have his father come in later with the money.

8. Mr. Sanderson admits that he (a) doesn't like sneakers. (b) hasn't sold many pairs of sneakers lately. (c) hasn't worn Litefoot tennis shoes in many years.

9. Mr. Sanderson says that in five years Doug (a) may have enough money to buy the shoes. (b) can have a job in the store. (c) probably won't wear sneakers anymore.

10. In the end, Doug gets the shoes (a) as a gift from his parents. (b) on credit. (c) by working for Mr. Sanderson.

THINKING IT THROUGH ───────────────

1. What does the narrator add to the story? Would you understand the story as well without the things the narrator says?

2. Do you ever feel the way Doug does about a new pair of sneakers? Do the right clothes make you feel better about yourself? Explain. Do you think that many people feel the way you do?

3. What did the offer to exchange work for goods tell you about Doug?

4. What does the title mean? What are the "Wings of Summer"?

Relationships: Review

On a separate sheet of paper, rewrite the following sentences in the correct *time sequence.*

1. Doug puts on his new pair of sneakers and vanishes.
2. Doug sees sneakers in a shop window.
3. Doug makes a deal with Mr. Sanderson.
4. Doug asks his father to buy him new sneakers.

Oral Interpretation: Review

Select part of the play to practice reading out loud. Here are some things you may want to do as part of your practice. Rewrite them in the order in which you think they should be done.
a. Speak clearly and distinctly.
b. Look up the words you don't know.
c. Choose the right tone of voice for the part.
d. Make sure you understand the sentences in the selection.
e. Practice the part until it sounds right.

Composition

Follow your teacher's instructions before completing *one* of these writing assignments.

1. Choose a story in this book. Find a small section in which people speak to each other. There should be at least two speakers and each should speak at least twice. Rewrite what they say in the form of a play. In parentheses ( ), put any instructions on how the characters should act.

2. Pretend that you are trying to sell someone a pair of shoes. Choose a name for the shoes. Write a short speech that tells someone what is special about the shoes and why the person should buy them. Then practice saying the speech out loud. Try to sound convincing.

CANIS MAJOR

by Robert Frost

▶ Canis Major, or the Great Dog, is the name of a group of stars. One of its stars is Sirius, the Dog Star, the brightest star in the sky. How does the speaker in this poem feel next to Canis Major?

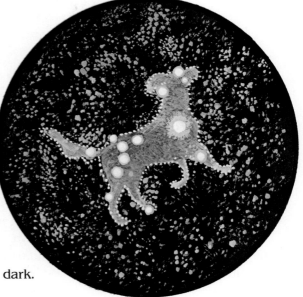

The great Overdog.
That heavenly beast
With a star in one eye,
Gives a leap in the east.

He dances upright
All the way to the west
And never once drops
On his forefeet to rest.

I'm a poor underdog,
But tonight I will bark
With the great Overdog
That romps through the dark.

WAYS OF KNOWING

1. What is the Overdog? Who is the underdog? Why do you think the poet wrote one word beginning with a capital and one beginning with a small letter?
2. What does the speaker admire in Canis Major? Do you think that the actions of Canis Major are really seen or are they imagined?
3. The word "upright" has two meanings. What are the two meanings? How does each make sense in the poem?
4. What does the speaker intend to do "tonight"? How do you think that will make the speaker feel? Are there any things in the world of nature that make you feel better or stand taller?

- **forefeet** (FOR feet) front feet or paws
- **romp** (ROMP) play in a lively way; run and race

349

SAY IT WITH FLOWERS

by Toshio Mori

▶ In business, a person sometimes has to make decisions that do not feel right. It is hard to stand tall when that happens. How do the different characters in this story try to do the right thing? Who stands the tallest?

He was an odd one to come to the shop and ask Mr. Sasaki for a job, but at the time I kept my mouth shut. There was something about this young man's appearance that did not go with a job as a clerk in a flower shop. I was a delivery boy for Mr. Sasaki then. I had seen clerks come and go. You could never tell about a new one. To be on the safe side, I said nothing. We were glad to have an extra hand because the busy season was coming around.

Mr. Sasaki probably remembered last year's rush when Tommy, Mr. Sasaki, and I had to do everything and had so many things to do at one time. He wanted to be ready this time.

"Another clerk and we'll be all set for any kind of business," he used to tell us.

When Teruo came around looking for a job, he got it, and Morning Glory Flower Shop was all set for the year.

When Teruo reported for work the following morning, Mr. Sasaki left him in Tommy's hands. Tommy had been our number-one clerk for a long time.

"Tommy, teach him all you can,"

Mr. Sasaki said. "Teruo's going to be with us from now on."

"Sure," Tommy said.

"Tommy's a good florist. You watch and listen to him," the boss told the young man.

"All right, Mr. Sasaki," the young man said. He turned to us and said, "My name is Teruo." We shook hands.

We got to know one another pretty well after that. He was a quiet fellow with very few words for anybody, but his smile charmed a person. We soon learned that he knew nothing about the florist business. He could identify a rose when he saw one, and gardenias and carnations too. Other flowers and supplies were new to him.

"You fellows teach me something about this business and I'll be grateful. I want to start from the bottom," Teruo said.

Tommy and I nodded. We were pretty sure by then he was all right. Tommy eagerly went about showing Teruo the florist game. Every morning for several days Tommy repeated the prices of the

---

● hand (HAND) hired worker

flowers for him. He told Teruo what to do on telephone orders, how to keep the greens fresh, and how to make bouquets, corsages, and sprays. "You need a little more time to learn how to make big pieces," Tommy said. "That'll come later."

In a couple of weeks, Teruo was just as good a clerk as we had had in a long time. He was curious and willing to work. It was about this time our boss decided to move the date of his yearly business trip ahead. He was satisfied with Teruo, and he knew we could get along without him for a while. He went off and left Tommy in full charge.

During Mr. Sasaki's absence, I was often in the shop helping Tommy and Teruo with the customers and the orders. One day, Teruo learned that I once worked in the nursery and had experience in flower growing.

"How do you tell when a flower is fresh or old?" he asked me. "I can't tell one from the other. All I do is follow your instructions and sell the ones you tell me to sell first, but I can't tell one from the other."

I laughed. "You don't need to know that, Teruo," I told him. "When the customers ask you whether the flowers are fresh, say 'Yes, our flowers are always fresh.'"

Teruo picked up a vase of carnations. "These flowers came in four or five days ago, didn't they?" he asked me.

- greens (GREENZ) **green leaves and branches used along with flowers**
- **corsage** (kor SAZH) **flowers to be worn on the shoulder, waist, or wrist**
- spray (SPRAY) **group of flowers and leaves put together to be in a vase**
- **nursery** (NUR suh ree) **place for growing young plants**
- **experience** (ek SPEER ee uns) **knowledge that comes from having done something often or well**
- instructions (in STRUK shunz) **information about what to do**

"You're right. Five days ago," I said.

"How long would they keep if a customer bought them today?" Teruo asked.

"I guess in this weather they'll hold a day or two," I said.

"Then they're old," Teruo almost gasped. "Why, we have fresh ones that last a week or so in the shop."

"Sure, Teruo. Why should you worry about that?" Tommy said. "You talk right to the customers, and they'll believe you. 'Our flowers are always fresh.'"

Teruo looked at us calmly. "That's a hard thing to say when you know it isn't true."

"You've got to get it over with sooner or later," I told him. "Everybody has to do it. You too, unless you want to lose your job."

"I don't think I can say it convincingly again," Teruo said. "I must've said yes forty times already when I didn't know any better. It'll be harder next time."

"You've said it forty times already, so why can't you say yes forty million times more? What's the difference? Remember, Teruo, it's your business to live," Tommy said.

"I don't like it," Teruo said.

"Do we like it? Do you think we're any different from you?" Tommy asked Teruo. "You're just a green kid. You don't know any better, so I won't get sore, but you got to play the game when you're in it. You understand, don't you?"

Teruo nodded. For a moment he stood and looked strangely at us. Then he went away to water the plants.

In the weeks that followed, we watched Teruo develop into an expert clerk except for one thing. If a customer forgot to ask about the condition of the flowers, Teruo did splendidly. But if someone should mention the freshness of the flowers, he wilted right in front of the customers. He would stand speechless without a reply. Sometimes, looking embarrassedly at us, he would take the customers to the fresh flowers in the rear and complete the sales.

"Don't do that any more, Teruo," Tommy warned him one afternoon after watching him repeatedly sell the fresh ones. "You know we got plenty of the old stuff in the front. We can't throw all that stuff away. First thing you know, the boss will start losing money, and we'll all be thrown out."

"I wish I could sell like you," Teruo said. "Whenever they ask me, 'Is this fresh?' 'How long will it keep?' I lose all sense about selling the old stuff and begin to think of the difference between the fresh and the old stuff. Then the trouble begins."

"Remember, the boss has to make money so he can keep the shop going,"

- green (GREEN) new; not knowing what to do
- **develop** (di VEL up) grow into the thing one can be
- embarrassedly (em BAR ust lee) in a way that shows one is not comfortable and even ashamed
- repeatedly (ri PEET id lee) over and over again

Tommy told him. "When he returns next week, you better not let him see you touch the fresh flowers in the rear."

On the day Mr. Sasaki came back to the shop, we saw something unusual. For the first time, I watched Teruo sell some old stuff to a customer. I heard the man plainly ask him if the flowers would keep. And very clearly I heard Teruo reply, "Yes, sir. These flowers'll keep good."

I looked at Tommy, and he winked back. When Teruo came back to make the flowers into a bouquet, he looked as if he had a snail in his mouth. Mr. Sasaki came back to the rear and watched him. When Teruo went up front to complete the sale, Mr. Sasaki looked at Tommy and nodded approvingly.

When I went out to the truck, Teruo followed me. "Those flowers I sold won't last longer than tomorrow. I feel rotten. The people'll get to know my word pretty soon."

"Forget it," I said. "Quit worrying. What's the matter with you?"

Then one early morning it happened. While Teruo was selling the fresh flowers in the back to a customer, Mr. Sasaki came in quietly and watched. The boss didn't say anything at the time. All day Teruo looked sick. He didn't know whether to explain to the boss or shut up.

While Teruo was out to lunch, Mr. Sasaki called us aside. "How long has this been going on?" he asked us. He was pretty sore.

"He's been doing it off and on. We told him to quit it," Tommy said. "He says he feels rotten selling old flowers."

"Old flowers!" snorted Mr. Sasaki. "I'll tell him plenty when he comes back. Old flowers! They're not old in a flower shop."

"He feels guilty fooling the customers," Tommy explained.

The boss laughed. "That's no reason in a business."

When Teruo came back, he knew what was up. He looked at us for a moment and then went about cleaning the stems of the old flowers.

"Teruo," Mr. Sasaki called.

Teruo approached us as if ready for an attack.

"You've been selling fresh flowers and leaving the old ones to go to waste. I can't afford that, Teruo," Mr. Sasaki said. "Why don't you do as you're told? We all sell the flowers in the front. I tell you they're not old in a flower shop. Why can't you sell them?"

"I don't like it, Mr. Sasaki," Teruo said. "When the people ask me if they're fresh, I hate to answer. I feel rotten after selling the old ones."

"Look here, Teruo," Mr. Sasaki said. "I don't want to fire you. You're a good boy, and I know you need a job. But you've got to be a good clerk here or you're going out. Do you get me?"

- unusual (un YOO zhoo ul) **not common or usual**
- approvingly (uh PROOV ing lee) **in a manner that says a person likes something and thinks it is correct**

"I get you," Teruo said.

In the morning we were all at the shop early. I had an eight o'clock delivery, and the others had to rush with a big order.

Teruo was there early. "Hello," he greeted us cheerfully as we came in. He was unusually high-spirited.

He was there before us and had already filled out the eight o'clock package for me. He was almost through with the big piece when Tommy came in. When Mr. Sasaki arrived, Teruo waved his hand and cheerfully went about gathering the flowers for the big piece. As he moved here and there, he seemed as if he had forgotten our presence. He looked at each vase, sized up the flowers, and then tilted his head at the next one. He did this as if he were the boss and the last word in the shop. That was all right, but when a customer came in, he swiftly waited on him as if he owned all the flowers in the world. When the man asked Teruo if he was getting fresh flowers, Teruo without batting an eye took the customer into the rear and showed and sold the fresh ones. He did it with so much grace, dignity, and swiftness that we stood around like his fools. Mr. Sasaki went on with his work as if nothing had happened.

Along toward noon, Teruo waited on his second customer. He ran to greet an old lady who wanted a cheap bouquet for a dinner table. This time, he not only went back to the rear for the fresh ones but added three or four extras. To make it more irritating for the boss, who was watching every move, Teruo used extra ferns. Tommy and I watched the boss fuming inside of his office.

- high-spirited (HY SPIR i tid) very joyful; in a good mood
- **dignity** (DIG ni tee) a feeling that shows self-respect
- irritating (IR i tayt ing) annoying; making impatient
- fume (FYOOM) feel and show anger

When the old lady went out of the shop, Mr. Sasaki came out furious. "You're a fool. You have no business sense. What are you doing here?" he said to Teruo. "Are you crazy?"

Teruo looked cheerful. "I'm not crazy, Mr. Sasaki," he said. "And I'm not dumb. I just like to do it that way, that's all."

The boss turned to Tommy and me. "That boy's a fool," he said.

Teruo laughed and walked off to the front with a broom. Mr. Sasaki shook his head. "What's the matter with him? I can't understand him," he said.

While the boss was out to lunch, Teruo went on a mad spree. He waited on three customers at one time, ignoring our presence. It was amazing how he did it. He hurriedly took one customer's order and had him write a birthday greeting for it. He jumped to the second customer's side and persuaded her to buy Columbia roses because they were the freshest. Then he leapt to the side of the third customer.

"I want to buy that orchid in the window," she said.

"Do you have to have an orchid, madam?" Teruo asked the lady.

"No," she said. "But I want something nice for tonight's dance, and I think the orchid will match my dress. Why do you ask?"

"If I were you, I wouldn't buy that orchid," he told her. "It won't keep. I could sell it to you and make a profit, but I don't want to do that and spoil your evening. Come to the back, and I'll show you some of the nicest gardenias. They're fresh today."

He came to the rear with the lady. We watched him pick out three of the biggest gardenias and make them into a corsage. When the lady went out with her package, a little boy came in and wanted an inexpensive bouquet for his mother's birthday. Teruo waited on the boy. We saw him pick out a dozen of the expensive roses and give them to the kid.

Tommy nudged me. "If he was the boss, he couldn't do those things," he said.

"In the first place," I said, "I don't think he could be a boss."

When Mr. Sasaki returned, Teruo was waiting on a young lady.

"Did Teruo eat yet?" Mr. Sasaki asked Tommy.

"No, he won't go. He says he's not hungry today," Tommy said.

We watched Teruo talking to the young lady. The boss shook his head. Then Teruo came back to the rear and picked out a dozen of the very fresh white roses and took them out to the lady.

"Aren't they lovely?" we heard her exclaim.

- persuade (pur SWAYD) **talk someone into doing something**
- orchid (OR kid) **kind of flower that is fairly expensive**
- inexpensive (in iks PEN siv) **not costing very much; cheap**
- nudge (NUJ) **poke or push lightly**

We watched him come back, take down a box, place several greens and ferns, place the roses neatly inside, sprinkle a few drops of water, and then give it to her. We watched him thank her, and we noticed her smile and thanks. The girl walked out.

Mr. Sasaki ran excitedly to the front. "Teruo! She forgot to pay!"

Teruo stopped the boss on the way out. "Wait, Mr. Sasaki," he said. "I gave them to her."

"What!" the boss cried.

"She came in just to look around and see the flowers. She likes pretty roses. Don't you think she's wonderful?"

"What's the matter with you?" the boss said. "Are you crazy? What did she buy?"

"Nothing, I tell you," Teruo said. "I gave them to her because she admired them. She's pretty enough to deserve beautiful things, and I liked her."

"You're fired! Get out!" Mr. Sasaki spluttered. "Don't come back to the store again."

"And I gave her fresh ones, too," Teruo said.

Mr. Sasaki rolled out several bills from his wallet. "Here's your wages for this week. Now get out," he said.

"I don't want it," Teruo said. "You keep it and buy some more flowers."

"Here, take it. Get out," Mr. Sasaki said.

Teruo took the money and placed it in the cash register. He rang up a sale. "All right, I'll go now. I feel fine. I'm happy. Thanks to you." He waved his hand to Mr. Sasaki. "No hard feelings."

On the way out, Teruo remembered us. He looked back. "Good-bye. Good luck," he said cheerfully to Tommy and me.

He walked out of the shop with his shoulders straight, head high, and whistling. He did not come back to see us again.

• **wages** (WAY jiz) **money that a person earns**

ALL THINGS CONSIDERED

1. Mr. Sasaki hires Teruo because (a) he's planning to fire his delivery boy. (b) he needs another worker. (c) Tommy said he should.

2. Teruo (a) knows the florist business well. (b) isn't interested in the business. (c) learns the business from Tommy.

3. After Teruo is there for a while, he seems to be (a) doing a good job. (b) upsetting the customers. (c) trying to get Tommy's job.

4. The first problem comes when Teruo learns (a) he is not supposed to sell the freshest flowers. (b) customers do not like him. (c) Tommy and Mr. Sasaki want to do all the selling.

5. Teruo's problem begins at a time when Mr. Sasaki is (a) home sick. (b) away on business. (c) watching him work.

6. After Teruo is told how to sell the flowers, he (a) is no longer a good clerk. (b) tells the customers not to buy in that store. (c) finds it hard to say the flowers are fresh.

7. The freshest flowers are kept in (a) the truck. (b) the front of the store. (c) the back of the store.

8. When Teruo sells the flowers in the front, (a) his face shows he is unhappy. (b) the customers ask for the flowers in the back. (c) Mr. Sasaki gets angry.

9. On his last day, Teruo (a) calls Mr. Sasaki nasty names. (b) tells the boss he is going to quit. (c) gives customers more than they pay for.

10. When Mr. Sasaki pays him, Teruo (a) tells him it is not enough money. (b) does not keep the money. (c) gives the money to the customers.

THINKING IT THROUGH

1. What would happen if the store did not sell the older flowers? Do you think that Mr. Sasaki is a good businessman? Why or why not?

2. Teruo says, "The people'll get to know my word pretty soon." What does he mean by that? How does that statement help explain why he acts the way he does?

3. Do you side with Teruo or Mr. Sasaki in the matter of selling older flowers first? In what ways might each of them have a good argument?

4. What would you do if asked on a job to do something you thought was wrong? How wrong must something be for you to quit your job? Are there any other things you would have to think about before quitting?

357

Building From Details: Review

I. On a separate sheet of paper, answer the questions below. Write your answer to each of the *five w's* in a complete sentence.

1. Who is this story about?
2. Where does the story take place?
3. When does the story take place—long ago; in modern days?
4. What is the main problem in the story?
5. Why? Make up a why question and answer it.

II. Were you able to *visualize* the *setting* of the story? On a separate sheet of paper, make a drawing or a map of the shop.

Relationships: Review

Here are some *causes* and *effects.* On a separate sheet of paper, match the causes in Column A with the effects in Column B.

A	B
1. Mr. Sasaki expects to need extra help in the shop.	a. Tommy is left in charge.
2. Mr. Sasaki goes away on business.	b. Teruo brings a customer to the back.
3. Teruo learns that the older flowers are sold first.	c. Mr. Sasaki hires Teruo.
4. A customer asks about the freshness of the flowers.	d. Teruo is shocked and angry.

Composition

Follow your teacher's instructions before completing *one* of these writing assignments.

1. What would you need to open a flower shop? List some of the equipment you would need. Choose three of the items and write a sentence next to each explaining why you would need it.
2. What do you think Teruo will do next? Write a paragraph that tells what kind of job he will look for and why.

358

VOCABULARY AND SKILL REVIEW ───────────

Before completing the exercises that follow, you may wish to review the **bold-faced** words on pages 340–356.

I. On your paper, mark each sentence *correct* or *incorrect.* If it is *incorrect,* rewrite the sentence to make it correct.
  1. The proud man has a lot of *dignity.*
  2. They needed soil for the *nursery.*
  3. He was new at the job so he had lots of *experience.*
  4. They *trudged* quickly and lightly through the grass.
  5. A *narrator* tells a story.
  6. An animal's *forefeet* are those nearest its tail.
  7. The puppies like to *romp* in the yard.
  8. We hoped the seeds would all *develop* into plants.

II. Match the terms in Column A with their definitions in Column B. If you wish to review the meaning of any word in Column A, refer to the Glossary of Terms (pages 394–396).

A	**B**
1. haiku	a. form a picture in your mind
2. cause	b. who, what, when, where, why
3. effect	c. poem with seventeen syllables
4. five w's	d. something that happens because of something else
5. visualize	e. something that makes something else happen

III. Write each of the following sentences on your paper. Underline the <u>cause</u> once and the <u>effect</u> twice. Sometimes the cause and the effect are in separate sentences.
  1. Since there were no wars to fight, Basho was sent to serve a lord.
  2. I'll give you my money, Mr. Sanderson. You give me the shoes.
  3. We were glad to have an extra hand because the busy season was coming around.
  4. To make it more irritating for the boss, Teruo used extra ferns in the bouquet.
  5. I gave the roses to her because she admired them.

THE PRINCESS AND THE NIGHTINGALE

by W. Somerset Maugham

▶ Part of standing tall is learning to love without making a prisoner of the thing you love. After following some bad advice, the young princess in this story learns a most important lesson about love.

The King of Siam had eight daughters. He called them January, February, March (though of course in Siamese) till he came to the youngest, who was called August. Then another daughter was born and he named her September.

The King had a habit which I think might be usefully imitated in this country. Instead of receiving presents on his birthday, he gave them, and it looked as though he liked it. He often used to say he was sorry he had been born on only one day and so had only one birthday in the year. In this way he managed in course of time to give away all his wedding presents and all his old crowns which had gone out of fashion. One year, on his birthday, not having anything else handy, he gave each of his daughters a beautiful, green parrot in a beautiful, golden cage. There were nine of them, and on each cage was written the name of the month which was the name of the princess it belonged to. The nine princesses were very proud of their parrots, and they spent an hour every day teaching them to talk. Presently all the parrots could say "God Save the King"—in Siamese, which is very difficult—and some of them could say "Pretty Polly" in no less than seven Oriental languages.

One day, when the Princess September went to say good morning to her parrot, she found it lying dead at the bottom of its golden cage. She burst into a flood of tears, and nothing that her Maids of Honor could say comforted her. She cried so much that the Maids of Honor, not knowing what to do, told the queen. The queen said it

- Siam (sy AM) country in Asia that is now called Thailand
- **presently** (PREZ unt lee) before long; soon

was stuff and nonsense and the child had better go to bed without any supper.

The Maids of Honor wanted to go to a party, so they put the Princess September to bed as quickly as they could and left her by herself. And while she lay in her bed, crying still, she saw a little bird hop into her room. She sat up and the little bird began to sing. He sang a beautiful song about the lake in the king's garden and the willow trees that looked at themselves in the still water and the gold-fish that glided in and out of the branches that were reflected in it. When he had finished, the Princess was not crying any more, and she quite forgot that she had had no supper.

"That was a very nice song," she said.

The little bird gave her a bow, for artists naturally have good manners, and they like to be appreciated.

"Would you care to have me instead of your parrot?" said the little bird. "It's true that I'm not as pretty to look at, but on the other hand I have a much better voice."

The Princess September clapped her hands with delight. Then the little bird hopped on to the end of her bed and sang her to sleep.

When she awoke next day, the little bird was still sitting there, and as she opened her eyes he said, "Good morning." The Maids of Honor brought in her breakfast, and he ate rice out of her hand, and he had his bath in her saucer. He drank out of it, too. The Maids of

361

Honor said they didn't think it was very polite to drink one's bath water, but the Princess September said that was the artistic temperament. When he had finished his breakfast, he began to sing again so beautifully that the Maids of Honor were quite surprised, for they had never heard anything like it. The Princess September was very proud and happy.

"Now I want to show you to my eight sisters," said the princess.

She stretched out the first finger of her right hand so that it served as a perch, and the little bird flew down and sat on it. Then, followed by her Maids of Honor, she went through the palace and called on each of the princesses in turn, starting with January and going all the way down to August. And for each of the princesses the little bird sang a different song. But the parrots could only say "God save the King" and "Pretty Polly." At last she showed the little bird to the king and queen. They were surprised and delighted.

"I knew I was right to send you to bed without any supper," said the queen.

"This bird sings much better than the parrots," said the king.

"I should have thought you got quite tired of hearing people say 'God save the King,'" said the queen. "I can't think why those girls wanted to teach their parrots to say it, too."

"The sentiment is admirable," said the king, "and I never mind how often I hear it. But I do get tired of hearing those parrots say 'Pretty Polly.'"

"They say it in seven different languages," said the princesses.

"I dare say they do," said the king, "but it reminds me too much of my councilors. They say the same thing in seven different ways, and it never means anything in any way they say it."

The princesses were vexed at this, and the parrots looked very glum indeed. But the Princess September ran through all the rooms of the palace, singing like a lark, while the little bird flew round and round her, singing like a nightingale, which indeed it was.

Things went on like this for several days. The eight princesses

- temperament (TEM pur munt) **someone's natural way of thinking, feeling, and acting**
- perch (PURCH) **pole or stick for a bird to sit on**
- **sentiment** (SEN tuh munt) **thought**
- admirable (AD mur uh bul) **to be admired; good**
- vexed (VEKST) **annoyed**

put their heads together. They went to September and sat down in a circle round her, hiding their feet as it is proper for Siamese princesses to do.

"My poor September," they said, "we are so sorry about the death of your beautiful parrot. It must be dreadful for you not to have a pet bird as we have. So we have put all our pocket money together, and we are going to buy you a lovely, green-and-yellow parrot."

"Thank you for nothing," said September. This was not very polite of her, but princesses are sometimes a little short with one another. "I have a pet bird which sings the most charming songs to me, and I don't know what on earth I should do with a green-and-yellow parrot."

January sniffed, then February sniffed, then March sniffed. In fact, all the princesses sniffed. When they had finished, September asked them:

"Why do you sniff? Have you all got colds?"

'Well, my dear," they said, "it's absurd to talk of *your* bird when the little fellow flies in and out just as he likes."

They looked round the room and raised their eyebrows so high that their foreheads almost disappeared.

"You'll get dreadful wrinkles," said September.

"Do you mind our asking where your bird is now?" they said.

"He's gone to pay a visit to his father-in-law," said the Princess September.

"And what makes you think he'll come back?" asked the other princesses.

"He always does come back," said September.

"Well, my dear," said the eight princesses, "if you'll take our advice, you won't run any risks like that. If he comes back—and mind you, if he does, you'll be lucky—pop him into the cage and keep him there. That's the only way you can be sure of him."

"But I like to have him fly about the room," said the Princess September.

"Safety first," said her sisters.

They got up and walked out of the room, shaking their heads,

- short (SHORT) **rude; not polite**
- **absurd** (ab SURD) **foolish**

363

and they left September very uneasy. It seemed to her that her little bird was away a long time. Something might have happened to him. What with hawks and people with snares you never knew what trouble he might get into. Besides, he might forget her, or he might take a fancy to somebody else. That would be dreadful. Oh, she wished he were safely back again and in the golden cage which stood there empty and ready.

Suddenly September heard a tweet-tweet just behind her ear, and she saw the little bird sitting on her shoulder. He had come in so quietly and alighted so softly that she had not heard.

"I wondered what on earth had become of you," said the young princess.

"I thought you'd wonder that," said the little bird. "The fact is, I very nearly didn't come back tonight at all. My father-in-law was giving a party, and they all wanted me to stay, but I thought you'd be anxious."

This was a very unfortunate remark for the little bird to make. September felt her heart go thump, thump against her chest. She made up her mind to take no more risks. She put up her hand and took hold of the bird. This he was quite used to. She liked feeling his heart go pit-a-pat, so fast, in the hollow of her hand. I think he liked the soft warmth of her little hand. So the bird suspected nothing. He was so surprised when she carried him over to the cage, popped him in, and shut the door on him, that for a moment he could think of nothing to say. But in a minute or two he hopped up on the ivory perch and said, "What's the joke?"

"There's no joke," said September. "Some of mamma's cats are prowling about tonight. I think you're much safer in there."

"I can't think why the queen wants to have all those cats," said the little bird rather crossly.

"Well, you see, they're very special cats," said the princess. "They have blue eyes and no tails, and they're a specialty of the royal family."

- uneasy (un EE zee) **not comfortable; bothered**
- snare (SNAIR) **trap**
- **fancy** (FAN see) **liking**
- alight (uh LYT) **come down; land**
- suspect (suh SPEKT) **think something is wrong**
- prowl (PROWL) **wander about to hunt**

"But why did you put me in this cage without saying anything about it?" said the little bird. "I don't think it's the sort of place I like."

"I shouldn't have slept a wink all night if I hadn't known you were safe."

"Well, just for this once I don't mind," said the little bird, "so long as you let me out in the morning."

He ate a very good supper and then began to sing. But in the middle of his song he stopped. "I don't know what is the matter with me," he said, "but I don't feel like singing tonight."

"Very well," said September, "go to sleep instead."

So he put his head under his wing, and in a moment he was fast asleep. September went to sleep, too. But when the dawn broke, she was awakened by the little bird calling her at the top of his voice.

"Wake up, wake up," he cried. "Open the door of this cage and let me out. I want to have a good fly while the dew is still on the ground."

"You're much better off where you are," said September. "You have a beautiful, golden cage."

"Let me out, let me out," said the little bird.

"You'll have three meals a day served by the Maids of Honor. You'll have nothing to worry you from morning till night, and you can sing to your heart's content."

"Let me out, let me out," said the little bird. And he tried to slip through the bars of the cage, but of course he couldn't. He beat against the little door, but of course he couldn't open it.

Then the eight princesses came in, and they looked at him. They told September she was very wise to take their advice. They said he would soon get used to the cage, and in a few days he would quite forget that he had ever been free. The little bird said nothing at all while they were there, but as soon as they were gone he began to cry again.

"Let me out, let me out."

"Don't be such an old silly," said September. "I've only put you in the cage because I'm so fond of you. I know what's good for you much better than you do yourself. Sing me a little song, and I'll give you a piece of brown sugar."

• content (kun TENT) **happy**

365

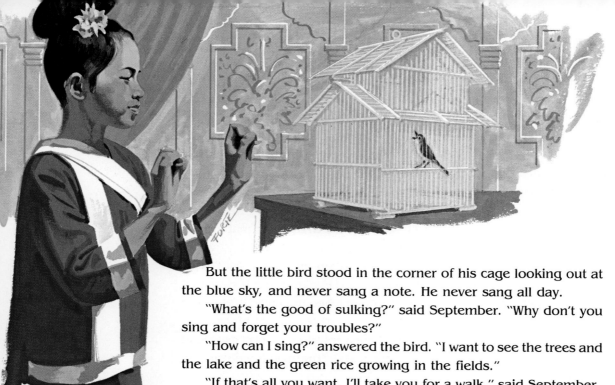

But the little bird stood in the corner of his cage looking out at the blue sky, and never sang a note. He never sang all day.

"What's the good of sulking?" said September. "Why don't you sing and forget your troubles?"

"How can I sing?" answered the bird. "I want to see the trees and the lake and the green rice growing in the fields."

"If that's all you want, I'll take you for a walk," said September.

She picked up the cage and went out, and she walked down to the lake round which grew the willow trees, and she stood at the edge of the rice fields that stretched as far as the eye could see.

"I'll take you out every day," she said. "I love you, and I only want to make you happy."

"It's not the same thing," said the little bird. "The rice fields and the lake and the willow trees look quite different when you see them through the bars of a cage."

So she brought him home again, and she gave him his supper. But he wouldn't eat a thing. The princess was a little anxious at this, and she asked her sisters what they thought about it.

"You must be firm," they said.

"But if he won't eat, he'll die," she answered.

"That would be very ungrateful of him," they said. "He must know that you're only thinking of his own good. If he's obstinate and dies, it'll serve him right, and you'll be well rid of him."

September didn't see how that was going to do *her* very much good, but they were eight to one and all older than she was, so she said nothing.

- sulk (SULK) **be silent and in a bad mood**
- obstinate (OB stuh nit) **stubborn; not willing to change**

366

"Perhaps he'll have got used to his cage by tomorrow," she said.

And next day, when she awoke, she cried out good morning in a cheerful voice. She got no answer. She jumped out of bed and ran to the cage. She gave a startled cry, for there the little bird lay, at the bottom, on his side, with his eyes closed. He looked as if he were dead. She opened the door and, putting her hand in, lifted him out. She gave a sob of relief, for she felt that his little heart was still beating.

"Wake up, wake up, little bird," she said.

She began to cry, and her tears fell on the little bird. He opened his eyes, and he felt that the bars of the cage were no longer round him.

"I cannot sing unless I'm free, and if I cannot sing I'll die," he said.

The princess gave a great sob. "Then take your freedom," she said. "I shut you in a golden cage because I loved you and I wanted to have you all to myself. But I never knew it would kill you. Go. Fly away among the trees that are round the lake and fly over the green rice fields. I love you enough to let you be happy in your own way."

She threw open the window and gently placed the little bird on the sill. He shook himself a little.

"Come and go as you will, little bird,," she said. "I will never put you in a cage any more."

"I shall come because I love you, little princess," said the bird. "And I shall sing you the loveliest songs I know. I shall go far away, but I shall always come back, and I shall never forget you."

He gave himself another shake. "Good gracious me, how stiff I am!" he said.

Then he opened his wings and flew right away into the blue. But the little princess burst into tears, for it is very difficult to put the happiness of some one you love before your own. With her little bird far out of sight she suddenly felt very lonely.

When her sisters knew what had happened, they mocked her and said that the little bird would never return. But he did at last. And he sat on September's shoulder and ate out of her hand and sang her the beautiful songs he had learned while he was flying up and down the fair places of the world.

• **mock** (MOK) make fun of, often by imitating; tease

ALL THINGS CONSIDERED _____

1. The princesses receive parrots as gifts for (a) the King's birthday. (b) their birthdays. (c) New Year's Day.

2. The youngest princess is named (a) January. (b) August. (c) September.

3. All the parrots learn to (a) sing about trees and lakes. (b) say "God Save the King." (c) fly free and return.

4. One day, the Princess September finds her parrot has (a) flown away. (b) died. (c) been stolen.

5. A nightingale (a) hops into her room. (b) is presented to her by the Maids of Honor. (c) eats the King's goldfish.

6. When she shows the nightingale to her sisters, they are (a) glad to see she has a new pet. (b) probably jealous. (c) surprised that she likes it.

7. The eight princesses warn her that the nightingale will (a) stop singing. (b) make her sick. (c) not come back.

8. The princess (a) puts her nightingale in a cage. (b) tells her sisters they are wrong. (c) asks for the King's advice.

9. The nightingale (a) is glad to be safe from the cat. (b) stops singing because it is unhappy. (c) escapes from the cage.

10. The princess learns that (a) her sisters were right. (b) parrots are better pets than nightingales (c) people must let the ones they love be happy in their own way.

THINKING IT THROUGH _____

1. Could this story be true? Find two things in the story to support your answer.

2. Siam is a real country. It is now called Thailand. Why do you think the author sets the story in Siam instead of in England, which was his own country? Why do you think that he didn't make up a name for the country?

3. The author uses humor in telling the story. Find some examples of humor in "The Princess and the Nightingale." How does it help the story?

4. The story is told very simply, but it has an important theme. What is that theme? Do you agree or disagree with it?

Literary Skills: Review

I. Choose the best ending for each statement.

1. The *author's purpose* in telling this story is to (a) amuse you. (b) give his idea about love. (c) explain how to take care of pet birds.
2. The *topic* of this story is (a) love. (b) life in the palace of Siam. (c) birds.
3. The *theme* of this story is (a) all children should have a pet. (b) let the ones you love be happy in their own way. (c) older sisters know best.
4. The story is told from the *point of view* of (a) the princess. (b) the King. (c) a third person.
5. "They raised their eyebrows so high that their foreheads almost disappeared" is an example of (a) a metaphor. (b) exaggeration. (c) rising action.

II. On a separate sheet of paper, answer the following questions about "The Princess and the Nightingale."

1. What is the *setting* of the story?
2. Could the story begin "Once upon a time"? Why or why not?
3. What *conflict* does the princess have with herself? What conflict does the princess have with her sisters?
4. What do you think is the *climax* of the story?
5. What happens at the *conclusion*?

Composition

Follow your teacher's instructions before completing *one* of these writing assignments.

1. Change the conclusion of the story. Take the last paragraph and rewrite it so that the story has a different ending.
2. Imagine that you are either the King or one of the sisters. Write a paragraph that tells what you think about how the princess treats her nightingale.

369

IF I CAN STOP ONE HEART FROM BREAKING

by Emily Dickinson

If I can stop one heart from breaking
I shall not live in vain.
If I can ease one life the aching
Or cool one pain

Or help one fainting robin
Unto his nest again
I shall not live in vain.

WAYS OF KNOWING

1. What does the speaker of the poem believe would make her life worth living? Do you think most people would or would not agree?

2. The poet uses very simple rhymes in this poem. Which lines rhyme with each other? Which line does not rhyme with any of the others? Did you notice the rhymes the first time you read the poem? Do you think that the poem is written the way someone might actually speak?

3. As you read this poem, did you visualize? Tell about the things you pictured. Was the action of someone putting a robin back in its nest the clearest picture? Could the action be a metaphor for something else? (See page 248.) Explain.

• in vain (in VAYN) without purpose or success

THE FIFTY-FIRST DRAGON

by Heywood Broun

▶ Most people can stand tall on their own. But some people need a little help. What happens when the help is no longer there?

Of all the pupils at the knight school Gawaine le Cœur-Hardy was among the least promising. He was tall and sturdy. But his instructors soon discovered that he lacked spirit. He would hide in the woods when the jousting class was called, although his companions and teachers shouted to him to come out and break his neck like a man. Even when they told him that the lances were padded, the horses no more than ponies, and the field unusually soft for late autumn, Gawaine refused to grow enthusiastic. The Headmaster and the Assistant Professor were discussing the case one spring afternoon. The Assistant Professor could see no remedy but expelling him.

"No," said the Headmaster, as he looked out at the purple hills which ringed the school, "I think I'll train him to slay dragons."

"He might be killed," objected the Assistant Professor.

"So he might," replied the Headmaster, but he added, "we must consider the greater good. We are responsible for forming this lad's character."

"Are the dragons particularly bad this year?" asked the Assistant Professor.

"I've never known them worse," replied the Headmaster. "Up in the hills to the south last week they killed a number of peasants, two cows, and a prize pig. And if this dry spell holds there's no telling when they may start a forest fire simply by breathing."

"Would any refund on the tuition be necessary in case of an accident?"

"No," the principal answered, "that's all covered in the contract. But as a matter of fact he won't be killed. Before I send him up in the hills I'm going to give him a magic word."

- jousting (JOUST ing) **fighting on horseback with swords, lances, or other hand weapons**
- lance (LANS) **long weapon, like a spear**
- headmaster (HED MAS tur) **principal of a school**
- character (KAR ik tur) **good qualities like courage and honesty**
- tuition (too ISH un) **money paid for schooling**

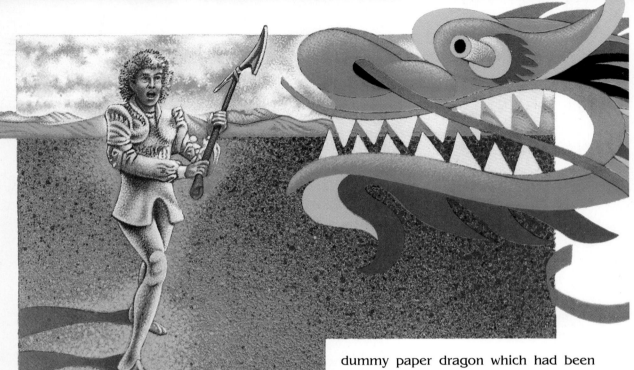

"That's a good idea," said the Professor. "Sometimes they work wonders."

From that day on Gawaine specialized in dragons. In the morning there were long lectures on the history, anatomy, manners, and customs of dragons. Gawaine did not do well in these studies. He had a marvelous gift for forgetting things. In the afternoon he looked better. He would go down to the South Meadow and practice with a battle-ax. In this exercise he was truly impressive, for he had enormous strength as well as speed and grace. He even seemed to look fierce. It was a thrilling sight to see Gawaine charging across the field toward the dummy paper dragon which had been set up for his practice. As he ran he would wave his ax and shout. It never took him more than one stroke to behead the dummy dragon.

Gradually his task was made more difficult. Paper gave way to papier-mâché and finally to wood. But even the toughest of these dummy dragons had no terrors for Gawaine. One sweep of the ax always did the job.

The Headmaster decided by the end of June that it was time for the test. Only the night before, a dragon had come close to the school grounds and had eaten some of the lettuce from the garden. The faculty decided that Gawaine

- specialize (SPESH uh lyz) **learn to be very good at one thing**
- fierce (FEERS) **wild, violent**
- papier-mâché (PAY pur muh SHAY) **shredded paper mixed with water and paste and molded into shapes**
- **faculty** (FAK ul tee) **the teachers in a school**

372

was ready. They gave him a diploma and a new battle-ax and the Headmaster called him to a private conference.

"Sit down," said the Headmaster.

Gawaine hesitated.

"You have received your degree," said the Headmaster; "you are no longer a boy. You are a man. Tomorrow you will go out into the world, the great world of achievement."

"Here you have learned the theories of life," continued the Headmaster; "but after all, life is not a matter of theories. Life is a matter of facts. It calls on the young and the old alike to face these facts, even though they are hard and sometimes unpleasant. Your problem, for example, is to slay dragons."

"They say that those dragons down in the south wood are five hundred feet long," said Gawaine.

"Stuff and nonsense!" said the Headmaster. "The curate saw one last week from the top of Arthur's Hill. The dragon was sunning himself down in the valley. The curate didn't have an opportunity to look at him very long because he felt it was his duty to hurry back to make a report to me. He said the monster, or shall I say, the big lizard?—wasn't an inch over two hundred feet. But the size has

nothing at all to do with it. You'll find the big ones even easier than the little ones. They're far slower on their feet and less aggressive, I'm told. Besides, before you go I'm going to equip you in such fashion that you need have no fear of all the dragons in the world."

"I'd like an enchanted cap," said Gawaine.

"What's that?" answered the Headmaster.

"A cap to make me disappear," explained Gawaine.

The Headmaster laughed. "You mustn't believe all those stories," he said. "There isn't any such thing. A cap to make you disappear, indeed! What would you do with it? You haven't even appeared yet. Why, my boy, you could walk from here to London, and nobody would so much as look at you. You're nobody. You couldn't be more invisible than that."

Gawaine seemed dangerously close to whimpering. The Headmaster reassured him: "Don't worry; I'll give you something much better than an enchanted cap. I'm going to give you a magic word. All you have to do is repeat this magic word once and no dragon can possibly harm a hair of your head. You can cut off his head at your leisure."

- diploma (di PLOH muh) **paper that a school gives to say a person has completed the studies**
- theory (THEE ree) **group of ideas that tries to explain something**
- curate (KYOOR it) **assistant minister**
- aggressive (uh GRES iv) **liking to fight**
- enchanted (en CHANT id) **having a magic power**
- reassure (ree uh SHOOR) **help someone believe in himself or herself**

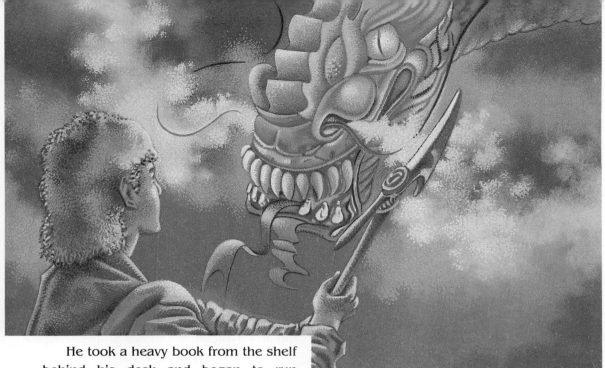

He took a heavy book from the shelf behind his desk and began to run through it. "Sometimes," he said, "the charm is a whole sentence. I think a single word would be best for dragons."

"A short word," suggested Gawaine.

"It can't be too short or it wouldn't be powerful. There isn't as much hurry as all that. Here's a splendid magic word: 'Rumplesnitz.' Do you think you can learn that?"

Gawaine tried and in an hour or so he seemed to have the word well in hand. Again and again he interrupted the lesson to inquire, "And if I say 'Rumplesnitz' the dragon can't possibly hurt me?" And always the Headmaster replied, "If you only say 'Rumplesnitz,' you are perfectly safe."

Toward morning Gawaine seemed to accept his career. At daybreak the Head-master saw him to the edge of the forest and pointed him to the direction in which he should proceed. About a mile away to the southwest a cloud of steam hung over an open meadow in the woods. The Headmaster assured Gawaine that under the steam he would find a dragon. Gawaine went forward slowly. He wondered whether it would be best to approach the dragon on the run as he did in his practice in the South Meadow or to walk slowly toward him, shouting "Rumplesnitz" all the way.

The problem was decided for him. No sooner had he come to the fringe of the meadow than the dragon spied him and began to charge. It was a large dragon

- charm (CHARM) magic thing that helps a person
- inquire (in KWYR) ask
- **fringe** (FRINJ) edge

374

and yet it seemed very aggressive in spite of the Headmaster's statement. As the dragon charged, it released huge clouds of hissing steam through its nostrils. It was almost as if a gigantic teapot had gone mad. The dragon came forward so fast and Gawaine was so frightened that he had time to say "Rumplesnitz" only once. As he said it, he swung his battle-ax and off popped the head of the dragon. Gawaine had to admit that it was even easier to kill a real dragon than it was to kill a wooden one if only you said "Rumplesnitz."

Gawaine brought the ears home and a small section of the tail. His schoolmates and the faculty made much of him, but the Headmaster wisely kept him from being spoiled by insisting that he go on with his work. Every clear day Gawaine rose at dawn and went out to kill dragons. The Headmaster kept him at home when it rained, because he said the woods were damp and unhealthy at such times. Few good days passed in which Gawaine failed to get a dragon. On one particularly fortunate day he killed three, a husband and wife and a visiting relative. Gradually he developed a technique. Pupils who sometimes watched him from the hilltops a long way off said that he often allowed the dragon to come within a few feet before he said "Rumplesnitz." Occasionally he did stunts. Once when an important party from London was watching him he went

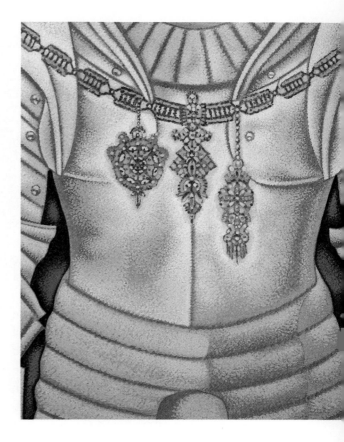

into action with his right hand tied behind his back. The dragon's head came off just as easily.

As Gawaine's record of killings mounted higher, the Headmaster found it impossible to keep him completely in hand. He fell into the habit of stealing out at night to the village. It was after such a long night that he rose a little before dawn one fine August morning and started out after his fiftieth dragon. His head was heavy and his mind slow. He was heavy in other ways as well, for he wore his medals, ribbons and all, when

• technique (tek NEEK) **style or way of doing something**
• **mount** (MOUNT) rise; increase; go up

he went out dragon hunting. The decorations began on his chest and ran all the way down to his abdomen. They must have weighed at least eight pounds.

Gawaine found a dragon in the same meadow where he had killed the first one. It was a fair-sized dragon, but an old one. Its face was wrinkled. Gawaine thought he had never seen so hideous a face. Much to the lad's disgust, the monster refused to charge and Gawaine had to walk toward him. He whistled as he went. The dragon, of course, had heard of Gawaine. Even when the lad raised his battle-ax the dragon made no move. It had been informed that this hunter was protected by an enchantment. It waited, hoping something would turn up. Gawaine raised the battle-ax and suddenly lowered it again. He had grown very pale and he trembled violently. The dragon suspected a trick. "What's the matter?" it asked.

"I've forgotten the magic word," said Gawaine.

"What a pity," said the dragon. "So that was the secret. It doesn't seem quite sporting to me, all this magic stuff, you know. But after all, that's a matter of opinion."

Gawaine was so helpless with terror that the dragon's confidence rose. It could not help showing off a bit.

"Could I possibly be of any assistance?" it asked. "What's the first letter of the magic word?"

"It begins with an 'r,'" said Gawaine weakly.

"Let's see," wondered the dragon, "that doesn't tell us much, does it?"

Gawaine shook his head.

"Well, then," said the dragon, "we had better get down to business. Will you surrender?"

- **hideous** (HID ee us) **very ugly**
- enchantment (en CHANT munt) **something that has a magic power**
- sporting (SPORT ing) **fair**

Gawaine mustered up enough courage to speak.

"What will you do if I surrender?" he asked.

"Why, I'll eat you," said the dragon.

"And if I don't surrender?"

"I'll eat you just the same."

"Then it doesn't make any difference, does it?" moaned Gawaine.

"It does to me," said the dragon with a smile. "I'd rather you didn't surrender. You'd taste much better if you didn't."

With the last word, the dragon drew back his head and struck. In that second there flashed into the mind of Gawaine the magic word "Rumplesnitz," but there was no time to say it. There was time only to strike and, without a word, Gawaine met the dragon with a full swing. He put all his back and shoulders into it. The head of the dragon flew away almost a hundred yards and landed in a thicket.

Gawaine did not remain frightened very long after the death of the dragon. His mood was one of wonder. He was puzzled. Again and again he thought to himself, "I didn't say 'Rumplesnitz'!" He was sure of that. Yet there was no question that he had killed the dragon. In fact, he had never killed one so utterly.

All the way back to the knight school he kept seeking an explanation for what had occurred. He went to the Head-

master immediately and after closing the door told him what had happened. "I didn't say 'Rumplesnitz,'" he explained.

The Headmaster laughed. "I'm glad you've found out," he said. "It makes you ever so much more of a hero. Don't you see that? Now you know that it was you who killed all those dragons and not that foolish little word 'Rumplesnitz.'"

Gawaine frowned. "Then it wasn't a magic word after all?" he asked.

"Of course not," said the Headmaster. "You ought to be too old for such foolishness. There isn't any such thing as a magic word."

"But you told me it was magic," protested Gawaine.

"It wasn't magic," answered the Headmaster, "but it was much more wonderful than that. The word gave you confidence. It took away your fears. If I hadn't told you that you might have been killed the very first time. It was your battle-ax that did the trick."

Gawaine surprised the Headmaster. He was obviously distressed by the explanation. He interrupted the Headmaster with, "If I hadn't of hit 'em all mighty hard and fast any one of 'em might have crushed me like a, like a——" He fumbled for a word.

"Egg shell," suggested the Headmaster.

- muster (MUS tur) **call up**
- thicket (THIK it) **group of bushes that grow close to one another**
- mood (MOOD) **state of mind; way one feels and thinks**
- utterly (UT ur lee) **completely**
- obviously (OB vee us lee) **clearly; easily seen**

"Like an egg shell," repeated Gawaine, and he said it many times. All through the evening meal people who sat near him heard him muttering, "Like an egg shell, like an egg shell."

The next day was clear, but Gawaine did not get up at dawn. It was almost noon when the Headmaster found him in bed, with the sheets pulled over his head. The principal called the Assistant Professor, and together they dragged the boy toward the forest.

"He'll be all right as soon as he gets a couple more dragons under his belt," explained the Headmaster.

The Assistant Professor agreed. "It would be a shame to stop such a fine run," he said. "Why, counting that one yesterday, he's killed fifty dragons."

They pushed the boy into the thicket above which hung a cloud of steam. It was quite a small dragon. But Gawaine did not come back that night or the next.

In fact, he never came back. Some weeks afterward brave students and faculty from the school explored the thicket, but they could find nothing to remind them of Gawaine except the metal part of his medals. Even the ribbons had been devoured.

The Headmaster and the Assistant Professor agreed that it would be just as well not to tell the school how Gawaine had achieved his record and still less how he came to die. They held that it might have a bad effect on school spirit. Gawaine has lived in the memory of the school as its greatest hero. No visitor leaves the building today without seeing a great shield which hangs on the wall of the dining hall. Fifty pairs of dragons' ears are mounted on the shield. Underneath in gold letters is "Gawaine le Cœur-Hardy," followed by the simple inscription, "He killed fifty dragons." The record has never been equaled.

- run (RUN) **the same thing happening over and over without being interrupted**
- **devour** (di VOUR) **eat up**
- inscription (in SKRIP shun) **something written**

This story has been simplified for seventh-grade students.

ALL THINGS CONSIDERED ——————————

1. At first Gawaine (a) brags about fighting dragons. (b) does anything his teachers tell him to do. (c) hides in the woods during jousting class.

2. The Headmaster decides to (a) teach him to fight dragons. (b) ask him to leave school. (c) speak to his parents.

3. Gawaine gets special lessons in (a) riding horseback. (b) wearing medals. (c) fighting dragons.

4. After the lessons Gawaine (a) feels brave. (b) is still afraid. (c) teaches the other students.

5. Gawaine believes that Rumplesnitz is (a) the name of the first dragon. (b) the name of the last dragon. (c) a magic word.

6. The first dragon that Gawaine meets (a) is killed quickly. (b) does not want to fight. (c) is very tame.

7. The real reason that Gawaine can kill dragons is that he (a) wears an enchanted cap. (b) is good at using a battle-ax. (c) has help from the other students.

8. When he meets the fiftieth dragon, Gawaine (a) decides not to use the magic word. (b) forgets the magic word. (c) is too tired to fight.

9. The Headmaster tells him that (a) the magic word still works. (b) he needs a new magic word. (c) the magic word really isn't magic.

10. Gawaine dies because he (a) meets too many dragons at once. (b) stops believing in himself. (c) loses his battle-ax.

THINKING IT THROUGH ——————————

1. Do you know people who have something they wear or carry for luck? What kinds of things are used for good luck? How much of luck is real and how much is imagined?

2. Do you think it was fair for the Headmaster to give Gawaine a magic word? Do you think it was right to tell Gawaine the truth at the end? How did the magic word help Gawaine?

3. What is the theme of the story? What do you think was the author's purpose in writing it? Did he make it funny in places? Does the humor help or hurt the story?

4. Do dragons really exist? Do you think a story like this could be true—but without the dragons? Explain.

Vocabulary and Sentence Meaning: Review

I. Read the following sentences. Tell who or what is referred to by the *pronouns* in *italics*. The page numbers will help you find the sentences in the story.

1. The Assistant Professor could see no remedy but expelling *him*. (page 371)

2. "I've never known *them* worse. (page 371)

3. *It* calls on the young and old alike to face these facts. (page 373)

4. "What would you do with *it?*" (page 373)

5. *Its* face was wrinkled. (page 376)

II. Here are some words with *multiple meanings*. If you only know one meaning for a word, look up its other meanings. Use each one in two of the sentences below. Do your work on a separate sheet of paper.

                character   run   spy

1. The _____ was looking for secret information.

2. Gawaine is the main _____ in this story.

3. The horse liked to _____ in the grass.

4. From the top of a hill, she could _____ a ship on the sea.

5. He had a _____ of good luck.

6. Hard work and study help to build _____ .

Composition

Follow your teacher's instructions before completing *one* of these writing assignments.

1. Use three of the following words in six sentences. Try to use each word twice—with a different meaning each time.

            back   case   charm   record   ring

2. Do you think that Gawaine did or did not stand tall? Write a paragraph telling why you think so.

VOCABULARY AND SKILL REVIEW ────────

Before completing the exercises that follow, you may wish to review the **bold-faced** words on pages 360–378.

I. On a separate sheet of paper, write the term from the list that means the same, or nearly the same, as the term in *italics*.

absurd	devour	faculty	fancy	presently
hideous	mock	mount	fringe	sentiment

1. The dragon threatened to *eat up* the army in one bite.
2. The giant liked to *tease* the peasants.
3. I like the pleasant *thought* in that birthday card.
4. A very *ugly* monster lived in the valley.
5. We watch the people *go up* the stairs.
6. They had a little cottage at the *edge* of the woods.
7. I think it is *foolish* to wear prunes in your hair.
8. *Soon* everyone will return home.
9. The *teachers* voted to have a party.
10. The dog seems to have taken a *liking* to the pillow.

II. Each of the terms below describes one of the sentences that follow. Match the letter of the term with the number of the sentence. If you wish to review the meaning of a term, refer to the Glossary of Terms (pages 394–396).

a. pronoun reference
b. multiple meaning
c. exaggeration
d. dialogue

1. The dragon breathed so hard that the town blew away.
2. She took a fancy to the fancy scarf.
3. "The dragon is destroying the town," said the Headmaster.
4. Gawaine thought that he was brave.

THE KNIGHTS OF THE SILVER SHIELD

by Raymond MacDonald Alden

▶ It is hard to stand tall when you seem to have lost your best chance to prove you are brave. But there are other ways to stand tall, as young Roland learns.

There was once a splendid castle in a forest, with great stone walls and a high gateway, and towers that rose away above the tallest trees. The forest was dark and dangerous. Many cruel giants lived in it. But in the castle was a company of knights, who were kept there by the king of the country, to help travelers who might be in the forest, and to fight with the giants.

Each of these knights wore a beautiful suit of armor and carried a long spear, while over his helmet there floated a great red plume that could be seen a long way off by anyone in distress. But the most wonderful thing about the knights' armor was their shields. They were not like those of other knights. They had been made by a great magician who had lived in the castle many years before. They were made of silver, and sometimes shone in the sunlight with dazzling brightness. But at other times the surface of the shields would be clouded as though by a mist. One could not see his face reflected there.

Now, when each young knight received his spurs and his armor, a new shield was also given him from among those that the magician had made. When the shield was new, its surface was always cloudy and dull. But as the knight began to do service against the giants, or went on expeditions to help poor travelers in the forest,

- plume (PLOOM) large, fancy feather
- dazzling (DAZ ling) shining brightly
- expedition (ek spi DISH un) trip made for a purpose

his shield grew brighter and brighter, so that he could see his face clearly reflected in it. But if he proved to be a lazy or cowardly knight, and let the giants get the better of him, or did not care what became of the travelers, then the shield grew more and more cloudy, until the knight became ashamed to carry it.

But this was not all. When any one of the knights fought a particularly hard battle, and won the victory, or when he went on some hard errand for the lord of the castle, and was successful, not only did his silver shield grow brighter, but when one looked into the center of it he could see something like a golden star shining in its very heart. This was the greatest honor that a knight could achieve. The other knights always spoke of such a one as having "won his star." It was usually not till he was pretty old and tried as a soldier that he could win it. At the time when this story begins, the lord of the castle himself was the only one of the knights whose shield bore the golden star.

There came a time when the worst of the giants in the forest gathered themselves together to have a battle against the knights. They made a camp in a dark hollow not far from the castle, and gathered all their best warriors together. All the knights made ready to fight them. The windows of the castle were closed and barred. The air was full of the noise of armor. And the knights were so excited that they could scarcely rest or eat.

Now there was a young knight in the castle, named Sir Roland, who was among those most eager for the battle. He was a splendid warrior, with eyes that shone like stars whenever there was anything to do in the way of knightly deeds. And although he was still quite young, his shield had begun to shine enough to show plainly that he had done bravely in some of his errands through the forest. This battle, he thought, would be the great opportunity of his life. On the morning of the day when they were to go forth to it, all the knights assembled in the great hall of the castle to receive the commands of their leaders. Sir Roland hoped that he would be put in the most

- bore (BOR) **carried**
- hollow (HOL oh) **valley**
- barred (BARD) **having wooden or metal bars across**
- knightly (NYT lee) **brave and courteous, as is proper for a knight**
- deed (DEED) **something that is done; act or action**

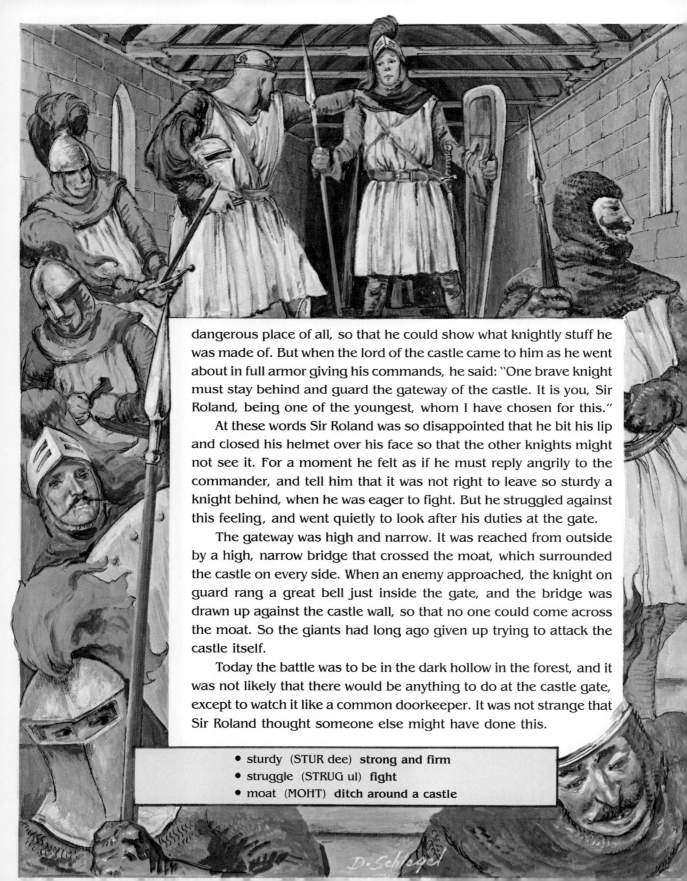

dangerous place of all, so that he could show what knightly stuff he was made of. But when the lord of the castle came to him as he went about in full armor giving his commands, he said: "One brave knight must stay behind and guard the gateway of the castle. It is you, Sir Roland, being one of the youngest, whom I have chosen for this."

At these words Sir Roland was so disappointed that he bit his lip and closed his helmet over his face so that the other knights might not see it. For a moment he felt as if he must reply angrily to the commander, and tell him that it was not right to leave so sturdy a knight behind, when he was eager to fight. But he struggled against this feeling, and went quietly to look after his duties at the gate.

The gateway was high and narrow. It was reached from outside by a high, narrow bridge that crossed the moat, which surrounded the castle on every side. When an enemy approached, the knight on guard rang a great bell just inside the gate, and the bridge was drawn up against the castle wall, so that no one could come across the moat. So the giants had long ago given up trying to attack the castle itself.

Today the battle was to be in the dark hollow in the forest, and it was not likely that there would be anything to do at the castle gate, except to watch it like a common doorkeeper. It was not strange that Sir Roland thought someone else might have done this.

- sturdy (STUR dee) strong and firm
- struggle (STRUG ul) fight
- moat (MOHT) ditch around a castle

Presently all the other knights marched out in their flashing armor, their red plumes waving over their heads, and their spears in their hands. The lord of the castle stopped only to tell Sir Roland to keep guard over the gate until they had all returned and to let no one enter. Then they went into the shadows of the forest, and were soon lost to sight.

Sir Roland stood looking after them long after they had gone, thinking how happy he would be if he were on the way to the battle like them. But after a little he put this out of his mind, and tried to think of pleasanter things. It was a long time before anything happened or any word came from the battle.

At last Sir Roland saw one of the knights come limping down the path to the castle, and he went out on the bridge to meet him. Now this knight was not a brave one, and he had been frightened away as soon as he was wounded.

"I have been hurt," he said, "so that I cannot fight any more. But I could watch the gate for you, if you would like to go back in my place."

At first Sir Roland's heart leaped with joy, but then he remembered what the commander had told him, and he said:

"I should like to go, but a knight belongs where his commander has put him. My place is here at the gate, and I cannot open it even for you. Your place is at the battle."

The knight was ashamed when he heard this, and he presently turned about and went into the forest again.

So Sir Roland kept guard silently for another hour. Then there came an old beggar woman down the path to the castle. She asked Sir Roland if she might come in and have some food. He told her that no one could enter the castle that day, but that he would send a servant out to her with food, and that she might sit and rest as long as she would.

"I have been past the hollow in the forest where the battle is going on," said the old woman, while she was waiting.

"And how do you think it is going?" asked Sir Roland.

"Badly for the knights, I am afraid," said the old woman. "The giants are fighting as they have never fought before. I should think you had better go and help your friends."

"I should like to, indeed," said Sir Roland. "But I am set to guard the gateway of the castle, and cannot leave."

"One fresh knight would make a great difference when they are

all weary from fighting," said the old woman. "I should think that, while there are no enemies about, you would be much more useful there."

"You may well think so," said Sir Roland, "and so may I. But it is neither you nor I that is commander here."

"I suppose," said the old woman then, "that you are one of the kind of knights who like to keep out of fighting. You are lucky to have so good an excuse for staying at home." And she laughed a thin and taunting laugh.

Then Sir Roland was very angry. He thought that if it were only a man instead of a woman, he would show him whether he liked fighting or no. But he shut his lips and set his teeth hard together. As the servant came just then with the food he had sent for, he gave it to the old woman quickly and shut the gate so that she might not talk to him any more.

It was not very long before he heard someone calling outside. Sir Roland opened the gate, and saw standing at the other end of the drawbridge a little old man in a long cloak. "Why are you knocking here?" he said. "The castle is closed today."

"Are you Sir Roland?" said the little old man.

"Yes," said Sir Roland.

"Then you ought not to be staying here when your commander and his knights are having so hard a struggle with the giants. You have the chance to make yourself the greatest knight in this kingdom. Listen to me! I have brought you a magic sword."

As he said this, the old man drew from under his coat a wonderful sword that flashed in the sunlight as if it were covered with diamonds. "This is the sword of all swords," he said, "and it is for you, if you will leave your idling here by the castle gate and carry it to the battle. Nothing can stand before it. When you lift it the giants will fall back, your master will be saved, and you will be crowned the victorious knight—the one who will soon take his commander's place as lord of the castle."

Now Sir Roland believed that it was a magician who was speaking to him, for it certainly appeared to be a magic sword. It seemed

- taunting (TAWNT ing) teasing; making fun of
- cloak (KLOHK) cape
- idling (EYE dul ing) standing around with nothing to do

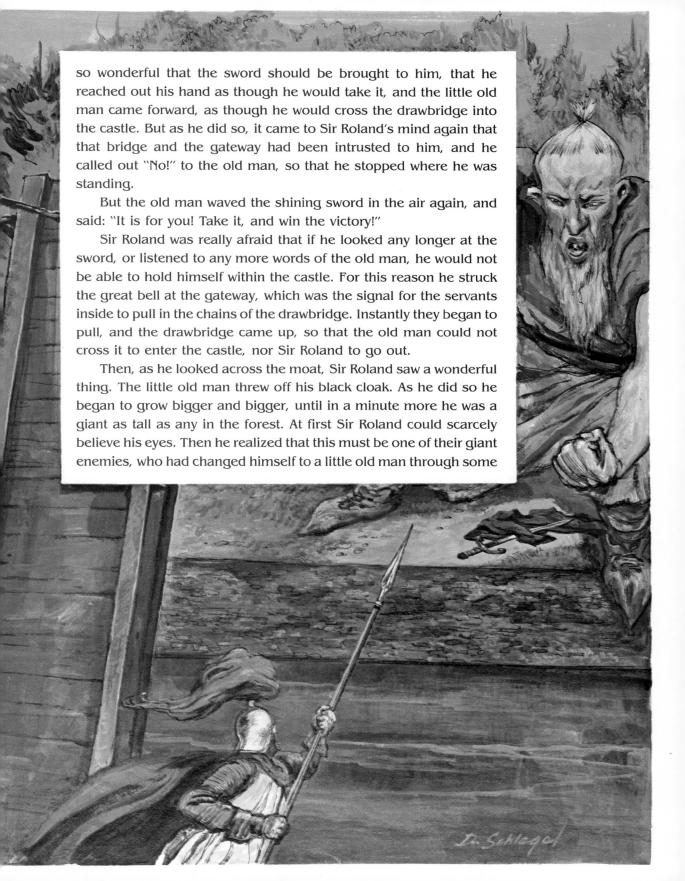

so wonderful that the sword should be brought to him, that he reached out his hand as though he would take it, and the little old man came forward, as though he would cross the drawbridge into the castle. But as he did so, it came to Sir Roland's mind again that that bridge and the gateway had been intrusted to him, and he called out "No!" to the old man, so that he stopped where he was standing.

But the old man waved the shining sword in the air again, and said: "It is for you! Take it, and win the victory!"

Sir Roland was really afraid that if he looked any longer at the sword, or listened to any more words of the old man, he would not be able to hold himself within the castle. For this reason he struck the great bell at the gateway, which was the signal for the servants inside to pull in the chains of the drawbridge. Instantly they began to pull, and the drawbridge came up, so that the old man could not cross it to enter the castle, nor Sir Roland to go out.

Then, as he looked across the moat, Sir Roland saw a wonderful thing. The little old man threw off his black cloak. As he did so he began to grow bigger and bigger, until in a minute more he was a giant as tall as any in the forest. At first Sir Roland could scarcely believe his eyes. Then he realized that this must be one of their giant enemies, who had changed himself to a little old man through some magic power, that he might make his way into the castle while all the knights were away. Sir Roland shuddered to think what might have happened if he had taken the sword and left the gate unguarded. The giant shook his fist across the moat that lay between them. Then, knowing that he could do nothing more, he went angrily back into the forest.

Sir Roland now resolved not to open the gate again and to pay no attention to any other visitor. But it was not long before he heard a sound that made him spring forward in joy. It was the bugle of the lord of the castle. There came sounding after it the bugles of many of the knights that were with him, pealing so joyfully that Sir Roland was sure they were safe and happy. As they came nearer, he could hear their shouts of victory. So he gave the signal to let down the drawbridge again and went out to meet them. They were dusty and bloodstained and weary, but they had won the battle with the giants. It had been such a great victory that there had never been a happier homecoming.

Sir Roland greeted them all as they passed in over the bridge. Then, when he had closed the gate and fastened it, he followed them into the great hall of the castle. The lord of the castle took his place on the highest seat, with the other knights about him. Sir Roland came forward with the key of the gate, to give his report of what he had done in the place to which the commander had appointed him. The lord of the castle bowed to him as a sign for him to begin. Just as he opened his mouth to speak, one of the knights cried out:

"The shield! The shield! Sir Roland's shield!"

Every one turned and looked at the shield that Sir Roland carried on his left arm. He himself could see only the top of it and did not know what they could mean. But what they saw was the golden star of knighthood, shining brightly from the center of Sir Roland's shield. There had never been such amazement in the castle before.

Sir Roland knelt before the lord of the castle to receive his commands. He still did not know why every one was looking at him so excitedly.

- shudder (SHUD ur) **shake with horror or fear**
- unguarded (un GARD id) **not watched or guarded**
- resolve (ri ZOLV) **make up one's mind; decide**
- peal (PEEL) **ring**

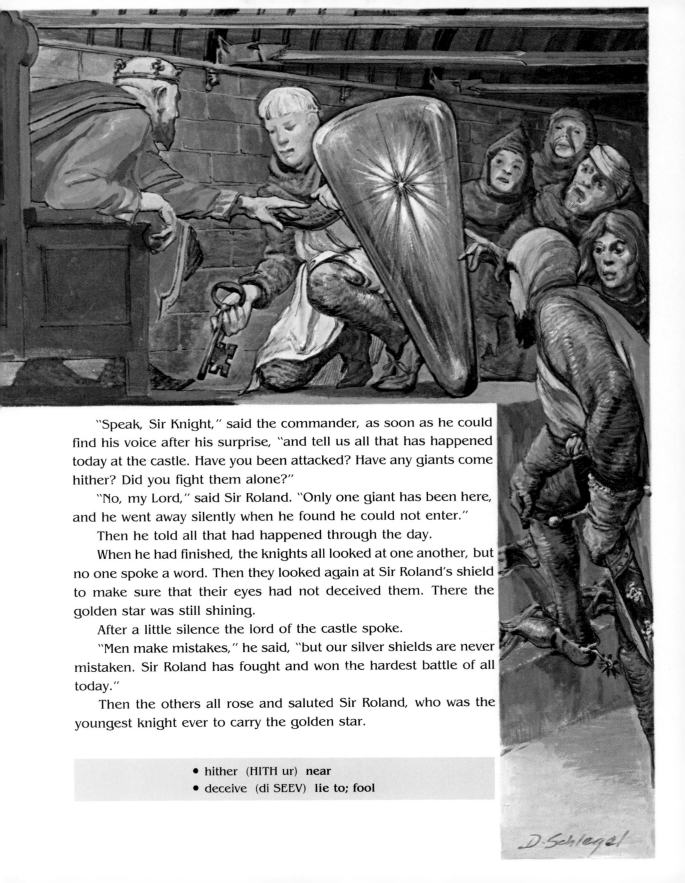

"Speak, Sir Knight," said the commander, as soon as he could find his voice after his surprise, "and tell us all that has happened today at the castle. Have you been attacked? Have any giants come hither? Did you fight them alone?"

"No, my Lord," said Sir Roland. "Only one giant has been here, and he went away silently when he found he could not enter."

Then he told all that had happened through the day.

When he had finished, the knights all looked at one another, but no one spoke a word. Then they looked again at Sir Roland's shield to make sure that their eyes had not deceived them. There the golden star was still shining.

After a little silence the lord of the castle spoke.

"Men make mistakes," he said, "but our silver shields are never mistaken. Sir Roland has fought and won the hardest battle of all today."

Then the others all rose and saluted Sir Roland, who was the youngest knight ever to carry the golden star.

- hither (HITH ur) **near**
- deceive (di SEEV) **lie to; fool**

ALL THINGS CONSIDERED ────────────────

1. The worst enemies of the knights were (a) other knights. (b) giants. (c) magicians.

2. The shields (a) were made of diamonds. (b) had to be won in a battle against the enemy. (c) shone with a golden star when the knights did brave deeds.

3. Sir Roland wants to (a) prove he is brave in battle. (b) be allowed to guard the castle. (c) fight the enemy by himself.

4. The commander tells Sir Roland that it is his job to (a) polish the shields. (b) guard the castle. (c) fight in the battle.

5. A knight limps over to Roland and asks him to (a) change places with him. (b) give him some food. (c) use a special sword.

6. Sir Roland believes that he should (a) go help the other knights. (b) open the drawbridge. (c) follow his commander's orders.

7. The second person who comes to the castle is (a) a wounded knight. (b) an old beggar woman. (c) an old man in a cloak.

8. After a third visitor is turned away, Sir Roland discovers that (a) the visitor is a giant. (b) all the knights are already in the castle. (c) the knights have lost the battle.

9. If Sir Roland had taken the magic sword, the knights would probably have (a) won the battle faster. (b) lost to their enemies. (c) won their shields.

10. There is a star in Sir Roland's shield because he (a) took the magic sword. (b) was loyal and brave. (c) killed the enemy.

THINKING IT THROUGH ────────────────

1. What is the theme of this story? Do you agree with it? Explain why or why not.

2. Could this story really have happened? Which parts of it could be real? Which parts could not be?

3. The lord of the castle says, "Sir Roland has fought and won the hardest battle of all today." What does he mean by that?

UNIT REVIEW

I. How can a person stand tall? Pick your favorite of all the characters you met in this unit. Then write an essay—several paragraphs giving your ideas—about why that character stands tall. Use the following plan to write your essay.

Paragraph 1. Tell who the character is and in what story you met him or her. Then say why you think the character you chose stands tall.

Paragraph 2. Tell some of the things that did go wrong or could have gone wrong for the character. Add ways that the character managed to stand tall anyway.

Paragraph 3. Mention some of the ways readers can learn how to stand tall from the story. Give some real-life examples.

Paragraph 4. Write about the most important thing you think you learned from the story.

II. Make up a story about yourself in which you show yourself standing tall. Although you can, you do not actually have to write the story. You can simply plan it by answering the following questions. Or, if you wish, answer these same questions about a story in this book. Do not choose the same story you chose for your essay.

1. Who are the characters?
2. What is the setting?
3. In one or two sentences, what is the plot?
4. What is the topic?
5. What is the theme?
6. What is the main conflict?
7. What are some important details?
8. What happens at the conclusion?

SPEAKING UP

There are times when everything in the world is new and beautiful again. In this poem, Langston Hughes captures the feeling of those times.

This poem is a good one to practice reading aloud. Notice how certain lines are repeated. You may want to say them a little differently each time you read them. Notice the last four lines of the poem. Make sure you read them in a way that expresses the quiet happiness of the feeling.

IN TIME OF SILVER RAIN

by Langston Hughes

In time of silver rain
The earth
Puts forth new life again,
Green grasses grow
And flowers lift their heads,
And over all the plain
The wonder spreads
   Of life,
   Of life,
   Of life!

In time of silver rain
The butterflies
Lift silken wings
To catch a rainbow cry,
And trees put forth
New leaves to sing
In joy beneath the sky
As down the roadway
Passing boys and girls
Go singing, too,
In time of silver rain
When spring
   And life
   Are new.

WRITING YOUR OWN STORY

When you look at a picture of a faraway place, do you wonder about the people, the place, and the action? Make up a story about this picture.

1. **Prewriting:** Begin the same way you did for your sketch (page 319). Make notes about the characters, setting, and plot. Arrange your notes in the order you wish to tell the story. Your story should have a beginning, a middle, and an end.
2. **Writing:** Write at least five paragraphs to make a complete story. In the first three or four paragraphs, the action should rise as characters face *conflicts* and these conflicts build to a *climax.* The last paragraph should be a *conclusion.*
3. **Revising:** Reread your story. Does each paragraph read smoothly? Does the order of events make sense? Is your story interesting? After you are satisfied that your story works, check the spelling, punctuation, and word choice. Rewrite your story and be prepared to read it to others.

Glossary of Terms

This glossary defines terms that you have studied. The page references shown with the terms indicate where the terms are first defined and discussed. Turn to those pages if you need to review the lessons.

Antonyms p. 11 *Antonyms* are words with nearly opposite meanings, such as young—old; good—bad; love—hate.

Author's Purpose p. 276 Every author has a purpose, or reason for writing. An author's purpose is usually to explain, to persuade, or to entertain.

Autobiography p. 35 An *autobiography* is a true story of a person's life, and it is written by that person. It usually has a theme. (See also *Biography*.)

Biography p. 94 A *biography* is the story of a real person's life. That person is the *subject* of the biography and may or may not be alive today. A biography may tell about the subject's entire life or just an important part of it. (See also *Autobiography*.)

Cause and Effect pp. 165, 213 A *cause* is an event or idea that leads to a certain result called an *effect*. In a sentence, the cause is sometimes stated first. At other times, the effect is stated first. A cause-and-effect statement often has a clue word such as *so, because, when,* and *since*.

CAUSE	EFFECT
The alarm clock rings,	so you wake up.

Characters pp. 7, 34, 43, 58 *Characters* are the *people* in a story—those who do things and have things happen to them. Some characters are more important to a story than others. They are the *main characters*.

Character Traits p. 34 Qualities that describe the character are called *character traits*. For example, one character may be smart, energetic, and curious. Another may be helpful, friendly, and hard-working. A character's likes and dislikes can also be considered traits.

Climax pp. 112, 146 The *climax* is the high point in the action of a story. (See also *Rising Action* and *Conclusion*.)

Conclusion p. 146 Every story has a beginning, a middle, and an end. The end of a story is often called the *conclusion*. The conclusion may be a surprise to the reader, or it may be expected. (See also *Rising Action* and *Climax*.)

Conflict p. 93 A *conflict* is a kind of fight, contest, or struggle. A plot depends on conflict. There are two main kinds of conflict. One kind is the *conflict with oneself*. The other kind is the *conflict a character has with other characters*. (See also *Plot*.)

Context Clues p. 154 *Context clues* are all the words around an unknown word. Context clues help the reader guess at the meaning of an unknown word.

Dialogue p. 171 Characters talking to one another is called *dialogue*. Quotation marks go around a character's exact words: "We've come for the horse," Ti Malice said.

Fiction p. 139 Stories that are not true are called *fiction*. The characters and events have been made up by the authors. Stories that are fiction are usually called *short stories*. (See also *Nonfiction*.)

Figurative Language p. 248 In *figurative language*, the words do not really mean what they seem to say. One kind of figurative language is called *simile*. Another kind is called *metaphor*. (See also *Simile* and *Metaphor*.)

Five Senses p. 104 If a writer really wants to get across an idea, a good way is to use words that appeal to the senses. The *five senses* are *sight, hearing, smell, taste,* and *touch*.

Five W's p. 22 The *five w's* are important question words. They ask the basic questions a reader must answer in order to understand a story. Remember these five words: *who, what, when, where,* and *why.*

Flashback p. 130 A *flashback* is a look at something that happened earlier in the sequence of story events. A story that contains a flashback begins with later events. Then, the flashback tells the reader about events that happened earlier.

Inference p. 121 An *inference* is a reader's guess about something that isn't stated in a story. The reader uses clues in the story and general knowledge to make an inference. (See also *Predictions.*)

Legends p. 243 *Legends* are stories that have been told over the years. They are often based on truth that has been stretched.

Limerick p. 234 A *limerick* is a five-line poem with a particular rhythm and pattern of rhyme. Practically all limericks are humorous with a comic twist in the last line.

Lyric Poems p. 44 A *lyric poem* expresses an idea or a feeling. The language in a lyric poem is often special in some way. For example, in "You" (p. 12), words are repeated and lined up to make a pattern.

Metaphor p. 248 A *metaphor* compares two things. *Example: Her words are icy fingers taking hold of the old man's heart.* To understand what her words are like, the reader thinks of icy fingers. Unlike a simile, a metaphor does not use the word *like* or *as.* (See also *Simile* and *Figurative Language.*)

Multiple Meanings p. 138 Many words have more than one meaning, or *multiple meanings.* For example, the word *throw* can mean "toss" or "pitch." It can also mean "purposely lose a game."

Myths p. 243 *Myths* are stories from the past. They tell the beliefs of a certain group of people. Myths are a way of explaining events in the world, especially in nature.

Nonfiction p. 139 Stories that are true are called *nonfiction.* Nonfiction is about real people and events. Works of nonfiction include autobiographies, biographies, essays, articles, and diaries. (See also *Fiction.*)

Plot pp. 7, 85 The *plot* is *what happens* in a story. It is the series of events or actions that take place. The plot in most stories can be told in one sentence. In "The Horse of the Sword" the sentence that tells the plot might be: "A boy gets an 'outlaw' horse, tames it, and wins a race." (See also *Sequence, Rising Action, Climax,* and *Conclusion.*)

Predictions p. 255 *Making predictions* means guessing at future events. As you read, you wonder what will happen next. Your guesses are *predictions.* (See also *Inference.*)

Pronouns p. 283 *Pronouns* are words that refer to people and things. They point ahead or back to the people or things that are mentioned elsewhere. *I, you, he, she,* and *it* are a few common pronouns.

Rising Action p. 112 The increasing tension in a story caused by conflicts and events is called *rising action.* Rising action keeps a reader interested in a story. Each new event helps build the story toward a *climax,* or high point in the action. (See also *Climax.*)

Sequence p. 112 *Sequence* is the order of events in the plot of a story. It is what happens first, second, third, and so on. Writers often provide words or groups of words that tell *when* and help the reader follow the sequence. Some examples are *once, at the time, that night, in the early 1950s, one morning,* and *several days later.* (See also *Plot.*)

Setting pp. 7, 178, 191, 200 The *time* and *place* of a story are its setting. In other words, *setting* tells *when* and *where* a story happens. For example, "The Cub" happens in a typical home at the present time.

Simile p. 248 A *simile* compares two things by using the words *like* or *as. Example: The moonlight dances like sparkling elves.* (See also *Metaphor* and *Figurative Language.*)

Stanzas p. 183 *Stanzas* are groups of lines in a poem. Each stanza is a separate part of the poem. For example, the poem "Adventures of Isabel" on pages 182–183 has three stanzas.

Tall Tales p. 180 *Tall tales* are funny, exaggerated stories. Characters in tall tales usually have super strength and perform impossible tasks.

Theme pp. 7, 260 *Theme* is the *basic meaning* of a story or other piece of literature. The theme is what the writer says about the topic. It is the message—the meaning—that the writer hopes to give the reader. (See also *Topic*.)

Topic p. 260 The *topic* is what a story or other piece of literature is *about*. It should not be confused with theme. The topic of "The

Fun They Had" is school in the future. (See also *Theme*.)

Trickster Tales p. 162 *Trickster tales* are stories about characters—human or animal—who live by their quick wits. These tales have been around since the earliest days of storytelling.

Visualizing pp. 68, 101, 191 Writers often use descriptive words and details to give the reader a clear mental picture of the characters, setting, and events in a story. Forming a mental picture is called *visualizing*.

Glossary

ab stract (ab STRAKT) *adj.* not knowable through any of the senses; on the level of ideas

ab surd (ab SURD) *adj.* foolish

ad e quate (AD uh kwit) *adj.* enough; able to be used

ad just (uh JUST) *v.* arrange; put in order

ag o ny (AG uh nee) *n.* great pain

al ter na tive (ol TUR nuh tiv) *n.* something else to choose

an ti sep tic (an tuh SEP tik) *adj.* overly clean and bright

anx ious ly (ANGK shus lee) *adv.* in a worried way

a pol o get i cal ly (uh pol uh JET ik lee) *adv.* in a manner that asks to be excused or forgiven

a ris to crat (uh RIS tuh krat) *n.* upper-class person

as sure (uh SHUR) *v.* make certain

as tound (uh STOUND) *v.* amaze; greatly surprise

at trac tion (uh TRAK shun) *n.* something of special interest

bank rupt (BANGK rupt) *v.* cause to lose all money or wealth

bit ter ly (BIT ur lee) *adv.* with hurt feelings

boast (BOHST) *v.* brag; claim with pride

ca reer (kuh REER) *n.* work a person has chosen to do

charm ing (CHARM ing) *adj.* delightful

clar i ty (KLAR i tee) *n.* clearness

com pete (kum PEET) *v.* enter a contest and try to win

com pli ment (KOM pluh munt) *v.* praise

con ceal (kun SEEL) *v.* hide; keep out of sight

con demn (kun DEM) *v.* consider guilty

con fi dence (KON fi dens) *n.* belief in oneself

con fu sion (kun FYOO zhun) *n.* mixed-up state or condition

con scious ness (KON shus nus) *n.* awareness; knowledge

con stant (KON stunt) *adj.* always the same; not changing

con sult (kun SULT) *v.* seek the advice of

cor sage (kor SAZH) *n.* flowers to be worn on the shoulder, waist, or wrist

coun se lor (KOUN suh lur) *n.* one who gives advice

cramped (KRAMPT) *adj.* crowded; having little space to move

crea ture (KREE chur) *n.* living being

de fect (DEE fekt) *n.* fault; imperfection

de fi ant (di FY unt) *adj.* openly resistant

del i cate (DEL uh kit) *adj.* small and fine

de vel op (di VEL up) *v.* grow into the thing one can be

de vour (di VOUR) *v.* eat up

dig ni ty (DIG ni tee) *n.* a feeling that shows self-respect

dis pute (dis PYOOT) *n.* argument

dis tinct (dis TINKT) *adj.* clear; unmistakable

dread ful (DRED ful) *adj.* awful; terrible

du pli cate (DOO pli kayt) *v.* repeat; do the same thing

du ti ful ly (DOO ti fuh lee) *adv.* doing something you think you should do; obediently

en chant ed (en CHANT id) *adj.* under a charm

en dur ance (en DUR uns) *n.* power to keep going

es tab lish (eh STAB lish) *v.* set up; build

ev i dence (EV i duns) *n.* facts needed to solve a case

ex pe ri ence (ek SPEER ee uns) *n.* knowledge that comes from having done something often or well

fac ul ty (FAK ul tee) *n.* the teachers in a school

fan cy (FAN see) *n.* liking

fan ta sy (FAN tuh see) *n.* daydream; imaginary happening

fast (FAST) *adv.* firmly; loyally

fate (FAYT) *n.* something that is going to happen without anyone being able to change it; destiny; fortune

fa vor (FAY vur) *v.* give special treatment

fee ble (FEE bul) *adj.* weak; not strong

fierce (FEERS) *adj.* wild; savage; violent

flat ter er (FLAT ur ur) *n.* one who praises another too much

fol ly (FOL ee) *n.* foolishness

fore feet (FOR feet) *n.* front feet or paws

for lorn (for LORN) *adj.* abandoned; miserable

fringe (FRINJ) *n.* edge

gal lant (GAL unt) *adj.* brave; ready for action

gen u ine (JEN yoo in) *adj.* real; true

goal (GOHL) *n.* something one tries to reach; aim

hast i ly (HAYS ti lee) *adv.* in a hurried way

hes i ta tion (hez i TAY shun) *n.* a short delay; a pause

hid e ous (HID ee us) *adj.* very ugly

hu man oid (HYOO mun oid) *n.* like a human

il lit er a cy (il LIT ur uh see) *n.* lack of ability to read or write

in cred i ble (in KRED uh bul) *adj.* unbelievable

in her it ance (in HER uh tuns) *n.* money and belongings that are passed down from parent to child

in teg ri ty (in TEG ri tee) *n.* honesty; uprightness; wholeness of being

i so la tion (eye suh LAY shun) *n.* being alone; away from others

league (LEEG) *n.* group of teams that play against each other

lone (LOHN) *adj.* single

mare (MAIR) *n.* female horse

merg ing (MURJ ing) *v.* blending; combining

mi rac u lous ly (mi RAK yuh lus lee) *adv.* amazingly; seeming to be caused by a miracle

mi ser ly (MY zur lee) *adj.* stingy

mis sion (MISH un) *n.* job or task a person is sent to do

mock (MOK) *v.* make fun of, often by imitating; tease

mount (MOUNT) *v.* rise; increase; go up

mourn ful (MORN ful) *adj.* sorrowful; sad

my thol o gy (mi THOL uh jee) *n.* collection of myths

nar ra tor (NAR rayt ur) *n.* person who tells a story

nui sance (NOO suns) *n.* bother

nurs er y (NUR suh ree) *n.* place for growing young plants

397

o pin ion (uh PIN yun) *n.* what a person thinks

op po nent (uh POH nunt) *n.* person on the other side; person one is trying to beat

o rig i nal (uh RIJ uh nul) *adj.* first; earliest

out wit (out WIT) *v.* act in a more clever way than someone else

pas sion (PASH un) *n.* strong feeling

pas sion ate (PASH un it) *adj.* full of strong feeling

per cent age (pur SEN tij) *n.* part of a whole; part of 100

pierc ing (PEERS ing) *adj.* sharp

plaque (PLAK) *n.* flat piece of wood or metal with something written on it, usually given to honor someone

poised (POYZD) *adj.* balanced and ready to move

pos sess (puh ZES) *v.* have

pres ent ly (PREZ unt lee) *adv.* before long; soon

proc ess (PRAS es) *n.* way of doing something

proc la ma tion (prok luh MAY shun) *n.* public announcement of something important

prop o si tion (prop uh ZISH un) *n.* offer

pro vi sions (pruh VIZH unz) *n.* food and other items

quiv er (KWIV ur) *n.* case for holding arrows

quiv er ing (KWIV ur ing) *adj.* shaking; trembling

ra vine (ruh VEEN) *n.* deep valley

re sent ful (ri ZENT ful) *adj.* annoyed; angry

re sist (ri ZIST) *v.* oppose; be successful in avoiding

re spect (ri SPEKT) *v.* look up to; admire

rheu ma tism (ROO muh tiz um) *n.* disease of the joints that brings pain and stiffness

romp (ROMP) *v.* play in a lively way; run and race

scorn (SKORN) *v.* look down upon

self-re li ant (SELF ri LY unt) *adj.* able to get along alone; depending on oneself

sen ti ment (SEN tuh munt) *n.* thought

shield (SHEELD) *n.* something used for protection

sigh (SY) *v.* take a long breath

slung (SLUNG) *v.* past tense of *sling;* threw

soar (SAWR) *v.* fly upward

so lar (SOH lur) *adj.* having to do with the sun

sol emn (SOL um) *adj.* serious and sad

sou ve nir (SOO vuh neer) *n.* item kept as a reminder

spir it ed (SPIR i tid) *adj.* lively

stride (STRYD) *n.* long step; way of walking

tack le (TAK ul) *v.* try to do

ten sion (TEN shun) *n.* strain; feeling of worry

tex ture (TEKS chur) *n.* smoothness or hardness

tour ist (TOOR ist) *n.* person who travels for enjoyment

tra di tion (truh DISH un) *n.* the way things have always been done

trag ic (TRAJ ik) *adj.* very sad or harmful

trek (TREK) *n.* difficult journey

trudge (TRUJ) *v.* walk in a heavy way

twist er (TWIS tur) *n.* rough windstorm; cyclone or tornado

un der dog (UN dur DOG) *n.* person who is not thought of as a winner; a person not favored to succeed

un e mo tion al (un ih MOH shun ul) *adj.* without feeling

u nique (yoo NEEK) *adj.* one of a kind; having no like

un pleas ant (un PLEZ unt) *adj.* not pleasing; annoying

vague ly (VAYG lee) *adv.* not clearly

var y (VAYR ee) *v.* change back and forth

venge ance (VEN juns) *n.* revenge

vi tal (VY tul) *adj.* necessary for life; very important

Index of Authors and Titles

Page numbers in **bold-faced** type indicate profiles (short biographies).

Acrobats, The / 122
Adventures of Isabel / 182
Advice to Travelers / 69
AESOP / 9, 162
ALDEN, RAYMOND MACDONALD /
Alice in Wonderland / 224
ANGELOU, MAYA / **35,** 36
ANONYMOUS / 234, 235, 244
Arithmetic / 223
ASIMOV, ISAAC / **277,** 278
Atalanta / 141

Base Stealer, The / 102
BAUGHMAN, MICHAEL / 107
Bear Hunt, The (excerpt) / 106
Bear in Reverse, A / 234
BELLOC, HILAIRE / 208
Black Pearl of Kowloon, The / 214
Boo on Hockey Fights / 157
Bouki Rents a Horse / 167
BRADBURY, RAY / 341
BROUN, HEYWOOD / 371
BUAKEN, MANUEL / 76
BUCKLEY, F. R. / 48

Canis Major / 349
CARLSON, NATALIE SAVAGE / 26
CARROLL, LEWIS / 224
Cat's in the Cradle / 24
CHAPIN, HARRY / 24
CHAPIN, SANDY / 24
Clever Manka / 172
Come Skating / 122
Comeback, The / 86
COSBY, BILL / 263
Courageous Dodger, The / 124
COURLANDER, HAROLD / 167
CROUTCH, LESLIE / 268
Cub, The / 2

DEVANEY, JOHN / 94
DICKINSON, EMILY / 370

Different Ones, The / 289
Donkey Who Did Not Want to Be
    Himself, The / 9

Echo and Narcissus / 256
Emerald-Blue, The / 114
EMERSON, RALPH WALDO / 330
End of My Long Night, The / 13
ESKIN, EDEN FORCE / 141

FARBER, NORMA / 242
Fifty-First Dragon, The / 371
Flea and a Fly in Flight, A / 234
Football Game, A / 103
FRANCIS, ROBERT / 102
FROST, ROBERT / 262, 349
Fun They Had, The / 278

GIBSON, WALKER / 69
GIOVANNI, NIKKI / 12, 337
Glorious Whitewasher, The / 148
Gold-Mounted Guns / 48
Greatest Woman Athlete, The / 94

Hatch, The / 242
HEINZ, W. C. / 131
HOPPE, ARTHUR W. / 210
Horse of the Sword, The / 76
House Fear / 262
HUGHES, LANGSTON / 392

If I Can Stop One Heart from Breaking /
    370
In Time of Silver Rain / 392
Is There Life on Other Planets? / 317
Izzy-Wuzzy / 237

KELLER, HELEN / 13
King and His Counselors, The / 162
KLEIHAUER, LOIS DYKEMAN / 2
Knights of the Silver Shield, The / 382

La Llorona / 244
LADER, MARTIN / 124
LANE, MARION / 317
Lifeboat in Space / 322
Lineage / 331
LIVINGSTON, MYRA COHN / 235

Magic Shop, The / 305
MARRIOTT, ALICE / 249
Matilda / 208
MATSUO BASHO / **339,** 340
MAUGHAM, W. SOMERSET / 360
MERRIAM, EVE / 44
MORI, TOSHIO / 350
Mother in Mannville, A / 60
MYERS, WALTER DEAN / 214

NASH, OGDEN / 182
Nation's Strength, A / 330
Ninth Street Bridge / 263
No Medals for Mary / 332
Not Me / 262

O'JOHN, CALVIN / 72
One of Our Future Poets,
    You Might Say / 202
One Throw / 131
O'REILLY, EDWARD / 184

PEACOCK, MALINDA / 249
Pecos Bill / 184
PHELPS, ETHEL JOHNSTON / 172
Phizzog / 45
Playmate / 268
POWNALL, EVE / 332
Princess and the Nightingale, The /
    360
Put Your Brains in Your Pocket / 210

Racing a Champion / 107

RAWLINGS, MARJORIE KINNAN / **59,**
    60

SANDBURG, CARL / 45, 223
SAROYAN, WILLIAM / **201,** 202
Say It with Flowers / 350
SERLING, ROD / 289
SILVERSTEIN, SHEL / 122, 262
Speckled Hen's Egg, The / 26
STAMM, CLAUS / 192
Stars and Planets / 285
STILLEY, FRANK / 285

Tall-Tale Sampler / 180
Taste of Life, A / 36
TAYLOR, MILDRED D. / **113,** 114
This Day Is Over / 72
Three Haiku / 340
Three Strong Women / 192
Thumbprint / 44
Thunders, The / 249
TOLSTOY, LEO / 105, 106
Tooter Tutor, A / 234
Transparent Ghost, The / 235
TWAIN, MARK / **147,** 148

VAN ECK, ALICE / 103
VAN STEENWYK, ELIZABETH / 86

WALKER, MARGARET / 331
WOLF, WARNER / 157
WELLS, CAROLYN / 234
WELLS, H. G. / **304,** 305
WHITE, ANNE TERRY / 256
WILLIAMS, GURNEY, III / 322
Willie and Millie / 235
Wings of Summer / 341
Winter / 337
Word Play / 222

You / 12

ACKNOWLEDGMENTS

We thank the following authors, agents, and publishers for their permission to reprint copyrighted material.

FORREST J ACKERMAN—for "Playmate" by Leslie Croutch. Copyright 1951 by Greenleaf Publishing Company. Adapted and reprinted by arrangement with Forrest J Ackerman, 2495 Glendower Avenue, Hollywood, CA 90027.

APPLETON-CENTURY-CROFTS—for "Pecos Bill," adapted from "The Saga of Pecos Bill" by Edward O'Reilly. First appeared in *The Century Magazine*, October 1923. Reprinted by permission of Appleton-Century-Crofts.

ATHENEUM PUBLISHERS—for "Wailed a Ghost in a Graveyard at Kew," limerick from *A Lollygag of Limericks* by Myra Cohn Livingston. Copyright © 1978 by Myra Cohn Livingston. (A Margaret K. McElderry book.) Reprinted by permission of Atheneum Publishers.

THE BOBBS-MERRILL COMPANY, INC.—for "The Knights of the Silver Shield," adapted from *Why the Chimes Rang and Other Stories* by Raymond Macdonald Alden. Copyright 1906, 1908, 1924, 1945 by The Bobbs-Merrill Company, Inc. Used by courtesy of the publishers, The Bobbs-Merrill Company, Inc.

CURTIS BROWN, LTD.—for "Gold-Mounted Guns" by F. R. Buckley. Copyright © 1922, 1949 by F. R. Buckley. Adapted and reprinted by permission of Curtis Brown, Ltd.

SANDY CHAPIN—for "Cat's in the Cradle." Music by Harry Chapin, lyrics by Sandy Chapin. Reprinted by permission of Sandy Chapin for the Estate of Harry Chapin.

DON CONGDON ASSOCIATES, INC.—for "Wings of Summer" from the Reader's Theater adaptation of *Dandelion Wine* by Ray Bradbury. Reprinted by permission of Don Congdon Associates, Inc. Copyright © 1953 by Ray Bradbury, renewed 1981.

BILL COOPER ASSOCIATES AGENCY, INC.—for "The Fifty-First Dragon" by Heywood Broun, adapted from *The Collected Edition of Heywood Broun.* Copyright 1921, 1941 by Heywood Hale Broun. Used by permission.

BILL COSBY—for "Ninth Street Bridge" by Bill Cosby. Copyright © 1961 by Manger Music. Reprinted by permission of the author and his agent, Norman Brokaw of William Morris Agency, Inc.

GUY DANIELS—for translation of excerpt from "The Bear Hunt" by Leo Tolstoy. From *Ivan the Fool and Other Tales of Leo Tolstoy,* selected and translated by Guy Daniels. Copyright © 1966 by Guy Daniels. Reprinted by permission of the author's representative, Gunther Stuhlmann. All rights reserved.

DODD, MEAD & COMPANY, INC.—for except from "The Quitter" from *The Collected Poems of Robert Service.* Reprinted by permission of Dodd, Mead & Company, Inc.

DOUBLEDAY & COMPANY, INC.—for "This Day is Over" by Calvin O'John from *Whispering Wind,* edited by Terry Allen. Copyright © 1972 by The Institute of American Indian Arts.—for "The End of My Long Night," adapted from *The Story of My Life* by Helen Keller. Copyright © 1902, 1903, 1905 by Helen Keller.—for "The Princess and the Nightingale," adapted from Chapter 32 of *The Gentleman in the Parlour* by W. Somerset Maugham. Copyright © 1929, 1930 by W. Somerset Maugham. Above selections reprinted by permission of Doubleday & Company, Inc.—for "The Fun They Had" from *Earth Is Room Enough* by Isaac Asimov. Copyright © 1957 by Isaac Asimov. Reprinted by permission of Doubleday & Company, Inc. and NEA Service, Inc.

E. P. DUTTON, INC.—for "The Emerald-Blue" from *Let the Circle Be Unbroken* by Mildred D. Taylor. Copyright © 1981 by Mildred D. Taylor. Reprinted by permission of the publisher, Dial Books for Young Readers, a Division of E. P. Dutton, Inc.

THOMAS FARBER—for "The Hatch" by Norma Farber. Copyright by the Estate of Norma Farber. Used by permission of Thomas Farber.

THE FEMINIST PRESS—for Ethel Johnston Phelp's retelling of "Clever Manka," adapted from *Tatterhood and Other Tales,* edited by Ethel Johnston Phelps. Copyright © 1978 by The Feminist Press. Reprinted by permission of The Feminist Press.

HARCOURT BRACE JOVANOVICH, INC.—for "Phizzog" by Carl Sandburg from *Good Morning, America.* Copyright 1928, 1956 by Carl Sandburg.—for "Arithmetic" by Carl Sandburg from *The Complete Poems of Carl*

Sandburg. Copyright 1950 by Carl Sandburg; renewed 1978 by Margaret Sandburg, Helga Sandburg Crile and Janet Sandburg.—for "Bouki Rents a Horse," adapted from *The Piece of Fire and Other Haitian Tales* by Harold Courlander. Copyright © 1964 by Harold Courlander.—for "One of Our Future Poets, You Might Say," adapted from *My Name is Aram* by William Saroyan. Copyright © 1940, 1968 by William Saroyan. All selections reprinted by permission of Harcourt Brace Jovanovich, Inc.

HARPER & ROW, PUBLISHERS, INC.—for "The Speckled Hen's Egg," abridged and adapted from *The Talking Cat: And Other Stories of French Canada* by Natalie Savage Carlson. Copyright © 1952 by Natalie Savage Carlson.—for text of "Come Skating" from *A Light in the Attic: Poems and Drawings of Shel Silverstein.* Copyright © 1981 by Snake Eye Music, Inc.—for text of "The Acrobats" from *Where the Sidewalk Ends: The Poems and Drawings of Shel Silverstein.* Copyright © 1974 by Snake Eye Music, Inc.—for "The Thunders" as told to Alice Marriott by Malinda Peacock. Adapted from "The Sky Beings: Thunder and His Helpers" from *American Indian Mythology* by Alice Marriott and Carol K. Rachlin. Published by Thomas Y. Crowell. Copyright © 1968 by Alice Marriott and Carol K. Rachlin. Reprinted by permission of Harper & Row, Publishers, Inc.

HASTINGS HOUSE, PUBLISHERS, INC.—for "Before Starting" from *Come As You Are* by Walker Gibson. Copyright © 1958 by Walker Gibson. Reprinted as "Advice to Travelers" courtesy of Hastings House, Publishers, Inc.

W. C. HEINZ—for "One Throw" by W. C. Heinz. Copyright 1950 by Collier Publishing. Copyright © 1978 by W. C. Heinz. Reprinted by permission of William Morris Agency, Inc. on behalf of the author.

HOLT, RINEHART AND WINSTON, PUBLISHERS—for "House Fear" from *The Poetry of Robert Frost,* edited by Edward Connery Lathem. Copyright 1916, © 1969 by Holt, Rinehart and Winston. Copyright 1944 by Robert Frost.—for "Canis Major" from *The Poetry of Robert Frost,* edited by Edward Connery Lathem. Copyright 1928, © 1969 by Holt, Rinehart and Winston. Copyright 1956 by Robert Frost. Reprinted by permission of Holt, Rinehart and Winston, Publishers.

ARTHUR W. HOPPE—for "Put Your Brains in Your Pocket," adapted from *Computers, Computers, Computers* by Arthur W. Hoppe. Copyright © 1974 by Chronicle Publishing Company. Reprinted by permission of the author.

INSTRUCTOR—for "A Football Game" by Alice Van Eck. Reprinted from *Instructor,* November 1960. Copyright © 1960 by The Instructor Publications, Inc. Used by permission.

INTERNATIONAL CREATIVE MANAGEMENT, INC.—for "The Different Ones," adapted from Rod Serling's *Night Gallery 2.* Copyright © 1972 by Rod Serling. Reprinted by permission of International Creative Management, Inc.

LOIS DYKEMAN KLEIHAUER—for "The Cub" by Lois Dykeman Kleihauer. Adapted and reprinted by permission of the author and her agent, John K. Payne Literary Agency, Inc., 175 Fifth Avenue, Room 1101, New York, New York, 10010.

ALFRED A. KNOPF, INC.—for "In Time of Silver Rain" by Langston Hughes. Copyright 1938 and renewed 1966 by Langston Hughes. From *Selected Poems of Langston Hughes.* Reprinted by permission of Alfred A. Knopf, Inc.

LITTLE, BROWN AND COMPANY—for "The Adventures of Isabel" from *I Wouldn't Have Missed It* by Ogden Nash. Copyright 1936 by Ogden Nash. Reprinted by permission of Little, Brown and Company.

McGRAW-HILL BOOK COMPANY—for "Boo on Hockey Fights," excerpt (p. 94) from *Gimme a Break* by Warner Wolf. Copyright © 1983 by Warner Wolf. Reprinted by permission of McGraw-Hill Book Company.

MELBOURNE UNIVERSITY PRESS—for "No Medals for Mary," adapted from *Mary of Maranoa* by Eve Pownall. Reprinted by permission of Melbourne University Press.

EVE MERRIAM—for "Thumbprint" from *It Doesn't Always Have to Rhyme* by Eve Merriam. Copyright © 1964 by Eve Merriam. Reprinted by permission of the author.

STEVEN MORI—for "Say It with Flowers" by Toshio Mori. Adapted and reprinted by permission of Steven Mori.

WILLIAM MORROW & COMPANY—for "You Came, Too" from *Black Feeling, Black Talk, Black Judgment* by Nikki Giovanni. Copyright © 1972 by Nikki Giovanni. Reprinted as "You" by permission of William Morrow & Company.—for "Winter" from *Cotton Candy on a Rainy Day* by Nikki Giovanni. Copyright © 1978 by Nikki Giovanni. Reprinted by permission of William Morrow & Company, Inc.

402

PETER PAUPER PRESS—for "Three Haiku" by Matsuo Basho, from *Haiku Harvest,* translated by Peter Beilenson and Harry Behn. Copyright © 1962 by Peter Pauper Press. Reprinted by permission of Peter Pauper Press.
PLAYS, INC.—for "Is There Life on Other Planets?" by Marion Lane. Adapted by permission from *Space and Science Fiction Plays for Young People,* edited by Sylvia E. Kamerman. Copyright © 1965, 1981, 1983 by Plays, Inc. This play is for reading purposes only; for permission to produce, write to Plays, Inc., 120 Boylston St., Boston, MA 02116.
G. P. PUTNAM'S SONS—for "Stars and Planets," adapted from *The Search* by Frank Stilley. Copyright © 1977 by Frank Stilley.—for "The Greatest Woman Athlete," adapted from *Great Olympic Champions* by John Devaney. Copyright © 1967 by John Devaney. Reprinted by permission of G. P. Putnam's Sons.
RANDOM HOUSE, INC.—for "A Taste of Life," from *I Know Why the Caged Bird Sings* by Maya Angelou. Copyright © 1969 by Maya Angelou. Reprinted by permission of Random House, Inc.—for "The Courageous Dodger" by Martin Lader, adapted by permission of Random House, Inc. from *The Masked Marvels: Baseball's Great Catchers* by Phyllis Hollander and Zander Hollander. Copyright © 1982 by Associated Features, Inc.
THE RICHMOND ORGANIZATION—-for "Not Me," words and music by Shel Silverstein. Copyright © 1968 by Evil Eye Music, Inc., New York, N.Y. Used by permission of The Richmond Organization.
CHARLES SCRIBNER'S SONS—for adaptation of "A Mother in Mannville" from *When the Whippoorwill* by Marjorie Kinnan Rawlings. Copyright 1940 by Marjorie Kinnan Rawlings. Copyright renewed 1968 by Norton Baskin. Reprinted by permission of Charles Scribner's Sons.
SPORTS ILLUSTRATED—for "Racing a Champion" by Michael Baughman. Adapted and reprinted courtesy of Sports Illustrated. Copyright © 1984 by Time Inc. First Person by Michael Baughman. "The Author Found He Was in Over His Head When He Took On This Oldtimer."
VIKING PENGUIN INC.—for "Three Strong Women" by Claus Stamm. Copyright © 1962 by Claus Stamm and Kazue Mizumura. Adapted by permission of Viking Penguin Inc.—for "The Black Pearl of Kowloon," adapted from *The Black Pearl and the Ghost* by Walter Dean Myers. Copyright © 1980 by Walter Dean Myers. Reprinted by permission of Viking Penguin Inc.
WALKER AND COMPANY—for "The Comeback," adapted from *Fly Like an Eagle* by Elizabeth Van Steenwyk. Copyright © 1978. Reprinted by permission of the publisher, Walker and Company.
MARGARET WALKER—for "Lineage" from *For My People* by Margaret Walker. Copyright 1942. Published by Yale University Press. Reprinted by permission of the author.
FRANKLIN WATTS, INC.—for "Lifeboat in Space," adapted from *True Escape and Survival Stories* by Gurney Williams III. Copyright © 1977 by Gurney Williams III. Used by permission of Franklin Watts, Inc.
WESLEYAN UNIVERSITY PRESS—for "The Base Stealer" from *The Orb Weaver* by Robert Francis. Copyright 1948 by Robert Francis. Reprinted by permission of Wesleyan University Press.
WESTERN PUBLISHING COMPANY, INC.—for "Echo and Narcissus," adapted from *Golden Treasury of Myths and Legends* by Anne Terry White. Copyright © 1959 by Western Publishing Company, Inc. Reprinted by permission of Western Publishing Company, Inc.
Every effort has been made to locate Manuel Buaken to obtain permission to adapt his story "The Horse of the Sword." If either the author or heirs are located subsequent to publication, they are hereby entitled to due compensation.
The following selections are in the public domain. Some have been slightly adapted for the modern reader by Globe Book Company: Aesop, "The Donkey Who Did Not Want to Be Himself," "The King and His Counselors"; "A Bear in Reverse," "A Flea and a Fly in Flight," and "Willie and Millie" from *The Golden Treasury of Poetry,* courtesy of Western Publishing Company, Inc.; Hilaire Belloc, "Matilda"; Lewis Carroll, excerpt from *Alice's Adventures in Wonderland;* Emily Dickinson, "If I Can Stop One Heart from Breaking," courtesy of Little, Brown and Company; Ralph Waldo Emerson, "A Nation's Strength"; "Izzy-Wuzzy" from *American Popular Entertainments,* edited by Brooks McNamara, courtesy of the editor; "La Llorona," from "Selected Multi-cultural Instructional Materials," courtesy of Superintendent of Public Instruction, State of Washington; Mark Twain, "The Glorious Whitewasher" from *The Adventures of Tom Sawyer;* H. G. Wells, "The Magic Shop."

403

Acknowledgments

Photo Acknowledgments

Bill Longcore/Photo Researchers: xii; United Press International; 35; UPI/Bettmann Archive: 59; Jean Paul Jallet//Photo Researchers: 74; Photo Researchers: 73; AP/Wide World Photo: 96, 98, 99; E.P. Dutton: 113; Culver Pictures: 147; Frederick Lewis/ Harold M. Lambert: 157; Photo Researchers: 159; Mimi Forsyth/ Monkmeyer Press: 160; Pastoral Scene by Phonard (detail), Haiti Collection of Manu Sassoonian, Art Resource: 167; *Market Place*, Petion Sarain, Museum of Modern Art of Latin America: 168; Brown Brothers: 201; Frederic Lewis/Dean: 239; Steve Maslowski/ Photo Researchers: 240; Bettina Cirone: 277; The Bettmann Archive: 304; Clair-Renard/Photo Researchers: 320; The Granger Collection: 323; NASA: 325; Woodfin Camp (c)1979 David Alan Harvey: 337; Sekai Bunka: 339; Leo de Wys/Tom Zimberoff: 393.

Illustrators

Michael Adams: 37, 41; Bill Angresano: 49, 51, 55, 125, 127; Ted Burwell: 2, 3, 5, 149, 152; Don Dyen: 114, 117, 119; Mel Erikson: 180, 222; Julie Evans: 60, 61, 64, 68, 351, 354, 356; Joseph Forte: 8, 142, 144, 243, 307, 309, 312, 361, 364, 366; Gordon Haas: 211, 327; Ken Hamilton: 15, 16, 17, 19, 108, 109, 245, 285; Kathy Krantz: 87, 89, 91; Anita Lovitt: 10; Eileen McKeating: 257, 258; Neal McPheeters: 26, 28, 29, 31, 184, 186, 188, 191, 342, 345; Linda Miyamoto: 77, 81, 82, 83, 172, 174, 176; Alan Nahigian: 265; Marlies Merk Najaka: 101; Bill Negron: 182; Joanne Pappas: 204, 208, 251, 253; Robin Peterson (tinting): 96, 98, 99; Karen Rolnick: 270, 271, 273; John Sandford: 163; Don Schlegel: 132, 135, 193, 195, 198, 290, 293, 294, 297, 298, 300, 383, 384, 386, 387, 389; Clare Sieffert: 279, 281; Gerald Smith: 183, 215, 217, 218, 234, 235, 340, 349; Illustrations by John Teniel: 225, 227, 229, 230, Art Frames: Sylvia Glickman, Teniel Photos courtesy of the New York Public Library, Astor, Lenox & Tilden Foundations; Jean and Mou-Sien Tseng/HK Portfolio: 372, 374, 375, 376; Kimanne Uhler: 333; Kevin Walter: 317.